Some of the most fascinating characters
in modern fiction are playing to win in ...

THE GAMES

SCOTT REYNOLDS, a dissolute and handsome American
track star, competing in the Marathon at the risk of his
life ...

MATHEW KAVERLY, the eccentric American millionaire
and fanatic chairman of the all-powerful Olympic Committee ...

LUBA IVANOVA, the sensuous and beautiful public relations woman who could put any idea across—whether
she did it with her brains or her body ...

SUNNY PINTUBI, an Australian aborigine whose astonishing gift for speed made him a natural for the Marathon
and a target for the ruthless power-brokers ...

HARRY HAYES, the quiet English runner for whom the
race had become a shattering test of loyalty or love ...

"A BOLD AND POWERFUL NOVEL OF THE INTERNATIONAL
DRAMA BEHIND THE OLYMPICS!"
—Literary Guild Preview

ABOUT THE AUTHOR

A man of many parts, HUGH ATKINSON is a world-rated polo player, an amateur jockey, and a writer who has been by turns journalist, scriptwriter and advertising man. Born in Australia, he has resided in Britain, France, Germany, India, Pakistan, Ceylon and assorted South Sea Islands. While at work on *The Games,* he moved to Majorca, where he now lives with his wife, their two small children and a cat, in a converted bakery.

THE GAMES

BY HUGH ATKINSON

RESEARCH AND BACKGROUND
BY PHILLIP KNIGHTLEY

BANTAM BOOKS
TORONTO · NEW YORK · LONDON

*This low-priced Bantam Book
has been completely reset in a type face
designed for easy reading, and was printed
from new plates. It contains the complete
text of the original hard-cover edition.*
NOT ONE WORD HAS BEEN OMITTED.

THE GAMES
*A Bantam Book / published by arrangement with
Simon and Schuster, Inc.*

PRINTING HISTORY
Simon and Schuster edition published April 1968
Literary Guild edition published May 1968
Bantam edition published October 1968

*Bantam Books are published by Bantam Books, Inc., a subsidiary
of Grosset & Dunlap, Inc. Its trade-mark, consisting of the words
"Bantam Books" and the portrayal of a bantam is registered in the
United States Patent Office and in other countries. Marca Registrada.
Bantam Books, Inc., 271 Madison Avenue, New York, N.Y. 10016.*

PRINTED IN THE UNITED STATES OF AMERICA

To MIKE

Contents

THE GAMES

PART ONE

THE PLAY

The United States of America

1

IT WAS after midnight now, and still they came and went. The antique chest inside the door and the rack above it were piled high with coats and scarves. Winter had come early to Washington. In the big room, darkened, couples clung together joined pelvis to pelvis, dancing barefooted on the carpet. A champagne bucket rolled on the floor. Rock music beat loudly.

In another room Bob Schultz looked into his glass and wondered why he did not go home. The groups were small now, cozy with each other; Bob wasn't connected anywhere. Little Harvey Tonkin was asleep or pretending, his head in the lap of a girl, a hand on her tucked-up knee.

Bob Schultz felt the sour, rising burn of envy in his stomach. It was always this way, too. You drank too much too fast to get the ease that came naturally to the others. You got it and prepared to be as easy as hell and next drink it changed into melancholy. Robert Schultz, State Department Santa Anna Bureau, Inter-Americas sector. Robert Schultz, man to watch—as much in demand here as ants at a picnic. Well, this was the last of it. The last of Harvey. He'd go short of champagne in Bombay. Bob Schultz began to feel bad for Harvey Tonkin, had a sudden realization how he would miss him when the little man had gone to his new appointment as Vice Consul in Bombay.

Scott Reynolds came in from the light with a short, plump girl. Finding Schultz still backed gloomily on the wall, he pushed the girl down on his knee. "Keep this warm for me. His name's Bob," he told the girl.

"You a friend of Scott's?"

"You could say that."

"I only met him tonight. My brother knows him, he's at Yale. Scott's a big track star, isn't he?"

"You could say that too."

"I think he's dreamy."

They were sitting like that, the girl on his knee, both of them upright and stiff, when Scott came back with a bottle of Scotch.

Usually, Bob Schultz drank warily. Tonight it was different. He and Harvey had been friends a long time. They had roomed together at Yale. Poor boy Schultz, rich boy Tonkin. There had not been much time in his life to nourish friendships. He had always been going somewhere, aiming, pushing, grinding. He had ground out his athletic scholarship, made the football squad, made a touchdown when it mattered, against Notre Dame. He had ground out the degree which had taken him into the State Department. He had ground out the vacations, working at anything for money, helping Papa Schultz in the bakery. He had majored in German, using the advantage of having come by the tongue in the home. His eye had been on Bonn. When he had been posted to Inter-Americas he got over his disappointment. Two years later he had ground through Spanish and Portuguese and was beginning to be noticed in his department. Harvey, for his own inexplicable reasons, had always stayed in touch.

Later, much later, Schultz was frankly drunk. The apartment had almost emptied. Reynolds was there because he was staying overnight. Schultz was there because the decision to go, or to stay—any decision—had been paralyzed by his tiredness and the drink. Harvey's girl was asleep on the couch. The little man had climbed under the shower fully dressed and had been helped into pajamas and a gown. Plates painted with egg yolk and scrapped with bacon littered the buffet table. Harvey was doggedly drinking coffee, sipping champagne occasionally.

"Let's pack it up," Reynolds suggested to Schultz. "It's way past sack time."

"You pack it up. You're the one in training."

"Who's drinking? Not me, old buddy. Come on. We've got to get Harvey in the sack."

In his blurred condition Schultz had been feeling a lot of love for Harvey. He had often patronized him. It balanced the awe he would never admit. Money apart, he knew himself to be Harvey Tonkin's superior and had often felt the need to remind himself of it. Now he wanted the little man back in his life. He focused on Reynolds. The sentiment that washed him needed an alkaline balance. He decided that he'd never like Scott.

4

"We *worked* in my day. No playing around. We worked our butts off. You didn't get Olympic selection handing around the big smile."

Scott began, "Some got it—"

"My day, you worked your butt off. On the Olympic team you'd be proud."

"So I'm proud," Reynolds said without interest.

Schultz brooded. "Only thing you proud, these lays you get."

"You against lays?"

"What I'm against an Olympic man playing around. Crissake, an opportunity like that. Do something for your country."

"Horseshit," said Scott Reynolds.

Bob Schultz lifted his head. "You said what?"

"Horseshit."

"Horseshit do something for your country? Horseshit the Olympics?"

"In spades," Reynolds said.

Bob Schultz pushed himself up, hunted for a drink, found an untouched glass of champagne. "A thing like that, great ideal like that, you say horseshit. Man, you're a bum. And that's in spades."

Reynolds had paled. "I'm getting pretty sick of this Olympic thing. You State Department people have got to be sanctimonious about something. You don't know what you're talking about. You know what the Olympics are? A scoreboard for the State Department. Ideals, horseshit! It's war in track shoes and everybody makes out except the athletes busting a gut. You know how much they spent on the Games at Tokyo? Six hundred million dollars, boy. You think they get money like that for ideals? Six hundred million dollars— who do you think got it? The politicians, the contractors, the officials, the chambers of commerce, or some boy jumping over a bar? Don't snow me. I've met these old athletes walking on their heels with a gold-plated slug at home in a box. You don't eat medals, boy. All I want out of a medal is a pro football contract and then you can have mine to throw passes if you haven't lost your arm."

There was a pale light in the window. It sobered Schultz. The trees on the sidewalk opposite the old brownstone looked sad and graven, tatty with thinned torn leaves. Bob stood at the window feeling for something to say. He couldn't find the energy.

Reynolds said abruptly, "I'm going to the can."

5

Harvey could not comfort his girl.

"Dry your eyes, will you?"

"What'll become of me?" she moaned.

"Here, look. I've got something for you." He remembered that his clothes were in the bedroom. "Here, dry up now. Wait and see what I've got for you."

The girl was sitting up, sobbing on an anticipatory note when Harvey got back to the room.

"What is it?" she asked.

Harvey stretched out an arm with the fist shut. He opened his hand. Keys dangled on a fob.

She dried her eyes. "What is it?"

"The car keys. The MG. It's yours."

The girl's face stopped. And then she threw herself into Harvey's arms, covering his face and head with kisses. Clutched, they fell awkwardly on the couch. They lay there for a moment, then Harvey struggled free, catching the girl's right hand and pushing it away. "Hey. Cut it out," he said. "None of that grab business while the guests are watching."

He found a glass of champagne. The extravagance of his gift had made him emotional. He lifted his glass to Bob Schultz. "This is it, then, old buddy."

"To you, Harve." Schultz coughed on the brandy.

"Been a long time," Harvey said.

"A long time."

"Fair weather, foul weather. In luck and out."

"You'll do great, Harve."

"You'll do great yourself."

Harvey thought. "Got something for you. Hold it."

He came back from the bedroom. "The apartment. From me to you, Buddy. Coming man, you shouldn't be living in a fleabag." Harvey held out his house keys.

When the taxi he had called arrived outside the brownstone, Bob Schultz had established that he would pay Harvey rent, which Harvey had established should be nominal. They had both got choked up. Scott Reynolds had to separate them.

Riding home, his head against the wound-down window for the frosty bite of air, Bob Schultz remembered with alarm that this was a working day.

In bed, Harvey blinked, watching his girl undress, and wished that he had had more keys to give away. He remembered that his apartment had long been promised to a cousin who would be seeing him off at the airport.

"T'hell with it," Harvey decided.

Later the girl was shaking Harvey ineffectually.

"Come on, honey," she pleaded. "You gotta try harder. You can't leave me like this."

"Tried," Harvey mumbled sleepily. "Won't work. Goddam thing won't work."

"Hold still, baby," the girl said, turning in the bed and running her lips down Harvey's chest. "Now hold still. If this don't do the trick then nothing will."

2

IT TOOK Bob Schultz Friday and the weekend to recover. The cleaning woman woke him, looking knowingly at the clothing on the floor. He groaned when he saw the clock. His throat and lungs wheezed and flared from the cigarettes. His tongue scratched in his mouth.

That night after work he collapsed on the bed as soon as he reached home and only much later, feeling better and hungry, he remembered about Harvey Tonkin's apartment. He was unsure whether Harvey's offer had been seriously intended, or if it would be proper to accept it. Harvey's sister resolved his doubts next day. She telephoned to say that she had moved the last of Harvey's things and had informed the janitor that Bob would be coming in. He moved on Sunday.

At the end of a week he was comfortably installed. He had not invited anyone in. The pressure in Santa Anna Bureau left no time for preening. He buckled his watch strap, looking out on the gray, unfriendly morning. He thought again about Scott Reynolds, the words between them. It had stayed with him. As he turned the lock on the pigskin briefcase which had been his parents' Christmas gift, he felt a tremor of nerves. Was this the right time? Should he wait until things got worse in Santa Anna or abandon the idea as eccentric? Standing thinking, he could see George Cole, the Bureau Chief, the handsome white head bent over its long, deliberating pauses. The dismissal, wiping out all the earned advantage. "In this Bureau we deal in facts. Eighty percent of the information that comes into this Bureau is inspired deceit, failed understanding or someone's wishful thinking. We identify these errors and reject them. We determine the hard facts. We check out these facts, we measure them against other hard facts. In this Bureau there is no place for unrealistic enthusiasms."

Inter-American Affairs, in the old block of the New State Department Building on the corner of 21st and Virginia Avenue, had wakened to importance during the Bay of Pigs and the confrontation with Castro and Khrushchev. George Cole had been recalled then from his post as Ambassador to the Argentine to advise his friend the Secretary and had suffered a mild heart attack soon after. Recovered, he had been given the Santa Anna Bureau to fill in the few years before his retirement. Cole's record, his reputation and his severe dignity were daunting to the men who served him.

The overnight reports changed nothing. At midday a thin sun broke through the gray scum of cloud. Schultz pocketed a sandwich and rode down to Lafayette Park.

Watching the walkers in the park, Bob began to relax. You could go over it too often, get mixed up in the subtleties, miss the hard facts George Cole insisted on.

Hard fact one: Time was the essence. "Bueno's a good President. If we can buy him time," Cole had said, "he will make Santa Anna one of the most stable pro-American democracies in Latin America."

Hard fact two: Tin prices were down, and according to the economists' report, would stay down.

Hard fact three: The tin mines, backbone of the economy, were in a bad way and would stay like that unless there was massive capitalization to modernize the mining system, replace the rolling stock and build a deepwater harbor.

Hard fact four: The mine owners were in an uproar about Bueno's intention to nationalize the mines.

Hard fact five: Castroite subversion was mounting daily.

Hard fact six: Bueno's political rival, Pisarro, was getting ready to move.

Santa Anna Bureau shared a conference room with the Bureau for Chile. It was big enough for a long table and twelve chairs. Schultz, the political expert, the economics expert, the records chief, the military expert, and the visiting attaché from the Santa Anna Embassy arranged themselves and waited for George Cole. His secretary had prepared the Chief's place with files and drawn his chair back.

A minute after two thirty, Cole entered, wished the meeting a good afternoon and took his glasses from their case. He opened the top file and then sat head bent, deliberating.

"You have all read the overnight reports?"

They nodded, said yes.

"Well, gentlemen. This is the crunch. That report of an arms discovery means Santa Anna will blow within weeks unless we can prop Bueno effectively and swiftly. How do we do it? How do we get the money to him? Suggestions?"

Around the conference table the experts made their points, casting around for an answer. There were plenty of sources for the financial aid which Santa Anna needed, but any overt influx of money, whether it came from the United States, Russia, China, or anywhere else, would be the excuse that Pisarro was waiting for to launch a revolution and overthrow the government. Santa Anna would be lost to the West as Cuba had been.

Down the table in the junior position as the Chief of Bureau's aide, Bob Schultz made notes. He was still without a decision. His idea was wildly outside normal reference. If it was dismissed he would be a laughingstock for years. He felt wilted even thinking about it. No one remarked on his silence, for it was customary for Schultz not to furnish an opinion until the Bureau Chief asked for it. In lulls like this, when the ideas ran dry, George Cole would say, "Well, Bob. Have you got anything?"

It came on cue: "Well, Bob, have you got anything?"

As he listened, Schultz had felt his confidence mount. Now it melted, leaving him empty. He began to say "No, sir," heard himself cough. "Yes. I think I might have."

They turned with surprise to look.

Bob could not get started. He coughed again. "The problem . . . essentially . . . the problem is getting the money in?"

Cole said, "Yes. Essentially."

"I think there could be a way. It's a bit uncertain. I mean, if it could be *arranged* it would be certain."

Now that he had begun, it seemed monstrous. Schultz could hardly bring up the words. "We could get the Olympics for Santa Anna."

The silence was complete. The attaché leaned forward gaping. Cole stared at his aide.

It was the military expert who finally spoke. "We—could —do—what?"

Weakly, Schultz said, "We could try to get Santa Anna the Olympics."

The economist flushed. "Godamighty. You being funny here?"

Cole bent his head.

Schultz said, "I told you it would take getting used to." He had done it now. There was no way to go but forward. "The Olympics have never been to Latin America since they were revived. I've been reading up on the Olympics. Doing a lot of reading . . ." He caught his voice as it began to trail. "I've got some facts here. Some hard facts," he said, directing himself to Cole's bent head.

Nobody answered.

Schultz felt a pulse of anger rising. It armed him. "We've been talking here about getting the money in. Everyone agrees about that. Now before you laugh this off, consider it. Do you know how much the Japanese spent on the Tokyo Games? Six hundred million dollars. This is a matter of record. Checked out. I checked it with the Japanese Embassy."

"So what?" the military expert asked.

"The Japanese built five separate villages to house the athletes and visitors. They built a lake that took six years to construct. They built a vast new road and rail network between the Games sites and the city. I've got a handout here from the Japanese Trade Commissioner. I will quote it. Quote: 'The Olympic Games have precipitated almost the complete rebuilding of Tokyo.' Listen to this, Joe: 'A complete deep-water harbor was built at fantastic cost. Ten million dollars' worth of cameras, transistors and tape recorders bought by the visitors.' Unquote. Here is another piece, from *Fortune* magazine. Quote: 'There is no doubt that the Olympic Games will put Japan Airlines on the map. Their share of international passenger travel is climbing steadily. Indirectly the Games started a fad round the world for Japanese food. Japanese trade in hundreds of products benefited directly. Perhaps most important of all, Japan and the Japanese have won back much of the world's goodwill which they had forfeited during the war. The sale of Japanese motor vehicles has boomed around the world.' Unquote."

"What was that figure?" the political expert asked. "What they spent?"

"Six hundred million dollars. The point is that the Japanese made the Olympics an excuse to rebuild. If Santa Anna got the Olympics it would unite the country. It would put the entire Latin-American hemisphere behind Bueno."

"Oh, come on," the military expert said, "that's stretching it a bit, isn't it?"

Schultz had warmed up now. "I don't think so. The prestige that goes with staging the Games is an international issue. I might be guessing a bit here, sir, but if the balloon went up for Santa Anna it would take everything else off the front pages in Latin America."

The attaché said, very tentatively, "I don't know that I

wouldn't agree with that. There's a lot of pride down there. A lot of inferiority feeling. A thing like that, the Olympics—a world focus, I mean—it would stir up a lot of excitement."

Because nobody knew what to say they waited for George Cole.

He played with his files. "Imaginative, perhaps. But hardly within the scope of this Bureau."

As far as the meeting was concerned, that was the dismissal.

Schultz said, quickly, "Sir, I would like to quote from the Policy Statement." He did not wait for permission. "The State Department determines Government policy in relation to international problems; formulates measures for promoting friendship with other countries; develops policies and programs for U.S. participation in international organizations." He pushed his papers away. "As far as I can see, sir, there is nothing here outside this Bureau's terms of reference."

It was as far as Schultz had ever presumed with his chief. He waited while Cole considered him. The table waited.

At length Cole said, "I see you've done your homework."

"Sir," Schultz said, "if Santa Anna got the Olympics, Bueno would be free to borrow anywhere. There would be nothing Pisarro could do."

The military expert banged his pencil down. "I think we've wasted enough time on this. Santa Anna would have as much chance as a snowball in hell of getting the Olympic Games."

The Chief of Records interrupted with a rare question. "Who runs these Games? How does this Olympic thing work? Do we run the Games?"

The meeting was distracted again, awaiting a lead from George Cole, the closing of the subject.

He said, "While we are entertaining ourselves with theory, what have you got to say, Joe?"

The political expert made a disinterested face, shifted about on his chair. "That six hundred million dollars Bob said the Japs spent. That gets to me. You know? That's real unpolitical money. It doesn't even come under aid. Or no aid I ever heard about. It's more like business money without the business. Know what I mean? Bueno could call for building tenders, contract payment over five years with interest, stuff like that. If he got his deepwater harbor, got the mines jumping, that would be any man's safe risk. That's the theory, if you want the theory, sir. If the building companies didn't like the terms, we could pick up the contracts. You know, dummy it up."

"Good point," Joe said. "Unpolitical money. Right, left or center, Pisarro couldn't make capital out of that kind of money."

"Who owns these Olympics?" the Records Chief asked again. "Do we own them?"

"Which brings us back to the hard facts," George Cole said. "Is there any realism in this proposal? What machinery governs such a decision? Is this machinery tractable? Would Santa Anna be acceptable? How is such an initiative mounted?"

"I've got some background on that, sir."

Again they turned to look at Bob, their mockery touched by surprise. He was more prepared than his stumbling, unlikely suggestion had indicated. Because George Cole remained with his head bent, Bob continued.

"The Games are run by the International Olympic Committee. The Committee consists of around sixty-nine members from fifty-four countries. These members are not elected, but appointed by the existing members. Every four years the International Committee meets to select the next Olympic city. Applications are made on a standard form and are usually submitted by the Mayor of the city making the application."

George Cole interrupted. "What does the application form require?"

"General questions, sir. What stadiums are available? What stadiums does the applicant city propose to build? How much does the city propose to spend? What accommodations will be available for visitors? Are there any laws, customs, regulations, which would make it difficult for any member country to compete? Will entry to the host country be free to all national Olympic associations? Things like that, sir."

They thought for a minute and then the economics man said, "OK. So the application is filed. Then what?"

"The applicant country makes a presentation at the IOC congress. A sales pitch. They lobby. Cocktail parties, lunches, direct approaches, vote swapping, all that. In the final session the IOC votes in secret."

George Cole put his elbows on the table and asked Bob directly, "From what you know, from what little you know, how realistic would Santa Anna's chances be? We want something hard here."

"Sir, the Olympics have never been outside the Western world until Tokyo. There's a lot of feeling about that. I've got a statement here made by the IOC Chancellor on this point."

Cole said, "Go ahead."

"The Chancellor said, quote: 'The Games have survived two world wars and there are only three organizations that can boast of that—the Red Cross, the Vatican and the Olympics. I regret to say that in my judgment certain national Olympic committees are subscribing to the interests of national glory. Political pressures have seen the Games go repeatedly to the West. This must stop. It is important to encourage the Olympic ideal in the underdeveloped countries, in South America for instance.' Unquote."

"You sure picked your clippings," Joe said.

"That clip is from CIA Research."

The military expert got up and walked a circle, stamping his foot. "Pins and needles. Look, if we're taking this seriously, how about timing? Nobody has said anything about timing."

"I started with that," Bob Schultz said. "The IOC will be voting on applications six months from now. They are meeting in Bombay. The last congress was held in Hamburg."

The military expert punched his leg. "You're making a real play here, aren't you?"

Cole turned his actor's profile to consider the window. "It does appear to have interest. It is imaginative. There is a place in diplomacy for imagination, if it checks out against the facts. What is the opinion? Should it be gone into? Joe?"

"I don't know, sir. I suppose we've got nothing to lose. All that building. There could be years in that. We get building crews down there making friends, that's the Good Neighbor bit."

"Greg?"

"As far as I can see it would move the money. If it moves the money I'm for it."

"Harry?"

The military expert was unimpressed. "A thing like this would take a lot of setting up, a lot of manipulating. Even if it could be swung we wouldn't know for six months. That's about the deadline. Pisarro will have moved by then."

"Just a minute," the political expert said. He looked eager. "Suppose this proposition interests Bueno? You know, so that he can see light up ahead. He could take the heat off the tin. If we sold him on this, all the unpolitical money, he could give Pisarro anything he wants for six months—any damned thing he asked for."

Cole recased his glasses and put the long cigarette holder in his inside pocket. He turned to the window again, scratching a fingernail on the table. Bob Schultz's hands gripped his knees. He had got this far. They had not laughed him out. For minutes it seemed that Cole had forgotten them. And then he turned briskly and closed the cover of his files.

"We will go further into this. Bob, I want a detailed history of the past IOC congress. I want dossiers, as far as possible, on the top people. Greg, you set up a ways-and-means committee on the money. Joe, let us have a political appraisal from you. Until further notice these matters will be treated as priority. If you have other pressing business, delegate it. We will meet again"—he checked his diary—"on the seventeenth, one week from today. Until then I would like daily progress reports. Verbal will suffice."

Cole stood up. "That's it, then. Thank you, gentlemen."

When the door had closed they all turned to Schultz again, examining him as though he were new. Bob was easing the grip on his knees.

The political expert said, looking quizzical, "Jesus, boy. You've started something here."

3

LATER in the week, after hearing the verbal progress reports, George Cole instructed Schultz to have CIA represented at the meeting on the seventeenth by a man of their own. When the Bureau heads were seated, Cole's secretary introduced the CIA representative round the table. Lance Dobson, a big young man with a factory-made gloss about him. He had been answering questions, mostly put to him by George Cole. Dobson did not seem to need the stack of reference material before him. He had his facts memorized.

"The Agency only really got interested," Dobson said, "in July 1951, when the U.S.S.R. was admitted to Olympic membership. CIA Plans had prepared an estimate of the political advantage membership would mean to the Russians. CIA Plans concentrated mostly on the meaning this would have for the uncommitted countries. An unsophisticated African, for example, measures superiority in physical terms. If Russians can run faster, jump higher, shoot better than Americans, then his way of life, his political system, must be superior. I have here a CIA projection, made at that time, based on known standards. This projection, unfortunately, was misleading. In calculating the Gold Medals the Russians might hope to win, it did not account properly for gymnastics, a little-known Western sport at that time. The Russians won every Gold Medal in the gymnastic events at their first Games. Their total score was an upset, dangerously close to our own. Is there anything here you would like me to elaborate on?" Dobson was speaking to George Cole's bent white head.

"I don't believe so. What other interest has CIA in the Olympics?"

"Defections, of course. Seven Hungarians defected during the 1956 Games in Melbourne, Australia. We had pre-advice about that. It made valuable propaganda material."

"What else?" asked Cole.

"The structure of Olympic management has been under Russian attack on the grounds that the Games are a Western monopoly. In 1959, they tabled a workable scheme for "democratizing the Olympics," as they call it. The Russians want the IOC enlarged to two hundred members. These members they want elected, instead of appointed as at present. They want the index of games enlarged to include thirty-five new events they have listed. Most of these sports they suggest are hardly played in the Western world. If the Russians succeed in this democratization program they will not only dominate the Gold Medals but they will have the voting support in the IOC to take the Games out of the West."

"What are their chances?" Joe asked.

"So far, we have been able to keep these proposals out of discussion time."

"We?"

"The International Olympic Committee," Dobson corrected.

George Cole said, "We thank you, Mr. Dobson. You have given us more than enough to go on with." He pressed his buzzer. "Miss Brasher, would you see Mr. Dobson out? Thank you."

In the morning session the experts tabled their reports. "The hard facts of practicability," Cole called them. The money could be moved in. The economic expert outlined three plans, each to cover an eventuality shadowed in the political expert's appraisal.

During the hour with the CIA man Bob Schultz had been in agitation. He did not know how topical Dobson's information would be. He felt he had the clincher. CIA Research had got it for him from National Olympic Headquarters in New York. It was his. He was the one who should break it.

Cole asked the meeting, "Any questions or viewpoints, gentlemen?"

They said no.

"Very well. Let us hear from you then, Bob."

"It isn't generally known, but these are the applicant cities for the Olympic venue: Detroit, Accra, Lyons—"

"Lyons, where?" asked Joe.

"Lyons, France. And *Prague*," Schultz said, and waited.

"Prague?" the economist wondered. "That's something Dobson didn't know."

George Cole's head had come straight up on Prague. "Are you sure of this?"

"I am now, sir. That is why I didn't put it in my verbal reports. I waited until today for substantiation." Schultz felt a flicker in his stomach. He had kept the Prague information back deliberately. To time and control it for the best effect. "This application from Prague changes everything, sir." He had to show his excitement. "This could be the edge we need. The Russian bloc will mount a massive effort behind the Prague application. Prague is a city with a lot to offer. It would be a great showcase for Communist Europe."

The Bureau Chief was suddenly cold. "Communist Europe is not the concern of this Bureau."

"Granted, sir. But from what I know, this Prague application will split the voting. If the Russian bloc can't win with Prague they will go all out to stop Detroit and Lyons, to win against the West."

The political expert turned in his chair. He indicated Schultz with a turn of his head. "He's betting on a compromise. East and West stalemate and Accra gets the Games."

"East and West stalemate and Santa Anna gets the Games," Schultz said.

The fuse he had lit a week ago burned bright and hot now. He had come this far on Cole's tolerance. On the man's preparedness to examine any hypothesis against the facts of reality. Now that he had the Prague application, Schultz wondered how his proposal had ever been seriously considered without it.

"Let us hear that dossier on Kaverly," Cole said.

Schultz read: "Matthew Curtis Kaverly, President of the International Olympic Committee. Born Chicago, Illinois, 1901. Both parents United States nationals. 6 feet. 203 pounds. Male Caucasian. Lives in New Mexico. Unmarried. Lives with spinster sister and staff of four. Director and major stockholder, Kaverly Canneries Inc. Holds stocks and government bonds, cash deposits, to an estimated 15 to 20 million dollars. Republican. Chairman, 1942–45, All-Services Supply Coordinating Committee, Washington, D.C. Main interest: Presidency International Olympic Committee, Mon Repos, Lausanne, Switzerland, since 1949. Gold Medal winner, Olympic Hammer Throw, 1920. Founded Kaverly Canneries 1921 with bank loan guaranteed by then president, Chicago Chamber of Commerce. PERSONAL: Does not smoke or drink. No evidence of sexual license or deviation. Is an amateur meteorologist. Lives austerely, travels widely, usually on IOC business. Politically reliable but naïve. Fanatical defender of amateurism in sport indicates failure of realism. Is expected to retain IOC presidency in foreseeable future."

Cole said, "While it occurs to me, gentlemen, Records will classify all paper from now on."

The Records Chief nodded.

"Sorry, Bob. Go on with the dossiers."

"Dr. Hans Stein," Schultz read, "IOC Chancellor. . . ."

Later Miss Brasher knocked and entered with coffee. She drew the curtains, switched on lights, put George Cole's heart pills at his elbow. Outside the October afternoon had faded unseasonably early.

4

COMING IN over the desert, the mesquite patches making shadows on the dunes, Bob Schultz saw the distant flash of the airfield, a glinting ribbon stretching into the distance. The shrill green of watered lawns and golf courses looked like eruptions as the pale monotony of dunes and desert came up under the aircraft's tilted wing. Rooftops and insect cars spun beneath as the aircraft banked tighter.

He had risen early that morning, bracing himself against the growing Washington cold. Now, with the hot dry desert air on his skin, he needed to pause, make a considered adjustment to his flight out of winter. He checked his coat and attaché case and signaled a cab.

The used-car lot had a sign. It read, FAIRDEAL FRASER. Fairdeal himself was sitting at a desk in a shack, reading a magazine. Schultz bought a 1961 Ford station wagon for $280, with a free tankful of gas. He was careful about the car. He did not want any unplanned breakdown. He drove back to the airport, following the signs. The Ford was sound, it handled well. Schultz got his case and topcoat and put them on the seat beside him. He checked the time. It was four forty-five. Sundown would be around six thirty. If he spent an hour in a newsreel, forty-five minutes on the road, an hour there for food and a drink, another hour on the desert, he would reach Kaverly's home about eight thirty. He studied the route on a map he had got from Fairdeal Fraser.

Schultz played the car radio and fixed his thoughts on the meeting ahead. There was an air of fake dramatics about the project. They had looked for other ways. The more they had learned about the old man, the more necessary it had become to meet him, feel him out, measure him for friend or foe.

He pulled into a gas station and asked for an oil and battery check. He wanted no trouble with his headlights.

Standing next to the attendant bent under the hood, he said, "You wouldn't want to get lost in this country. Off the highway, I mean."

"That's right." The attendant wiped the dipstick. "She'll take a quart, I reckon."

"No trouble getting a tow truck, I suppose, if there was trouble off the highway?"

"Are you kidding? We work the highway. We're not about to work the desert."

A mile into the desert and the roar of the trailer trucks was already just a distant buzz, the headlights of the speeding traffic a glare on the hard black line of the horizon in the rear-vision mirror. Schultz slowed to pull off the road, wincing at the jarring corrugations that found every squeak and failure in the station wagon's body. He got out to empty his bladder, the silence beating on his eardrums. The hot urine made a tearing sound on the crusted sand he could not see. He stood, looking and listening.

Back in the car Schultz began to nerve himself for what would happen ahead. This wasn't a matter of George Cole's hard facts. He would have to sense his way with the old man. He would have to play it by ear and there would be no second prize. His job was to estimate how Kaverly would use his influence at the Bombay voting, so they could plan their strategy accordingly.

Schultz was checking the trip meter against the map on his knee when he saw the turning. His attention had been drawn by a frame board set on a white metal post. Up close, the board and its message were above the arc of his headlights. He took a flashlight from his case and got out. He tilted the flashlight and moved the thin beam from word to word like a finger: IT IS DANGEROUS TO GO ANY FARTHER ALONG THIS ROAD.

The clouds thinned and a moon hung suddenly behind

their veils. The desert around him lit and silvered. Schultz felt for a cigarette and tried the lighter on the dashboard. He discovered with pleasure that it worked. It couldn't be much longer now.

One minute there was nothing but silvery glimpses of desert in the moonlight; then the road dropped beneath him. Ahead, long, low buildings with lit windows appeared, and behind and around the buildings an estate of trees; fixed as though by searchlights in an intense, searing white illumination. The sight was so unexpected, so demanding, that involuntarily Schultz pushed for the brake pedal and cut the engine. Now that he could hear, a music unbelievable in that place rose from the desert. It seemed as if there were hundreds of thousands of birds bubbling their throats in an orchestration as orderly as a score. Schultz was struck still, half in and half out of the car. Because it could not be believed he waited for the sound to stop or translate itself into something recognizable with which the desert had tricked him. There was no change. The world was filled with birdcalls, their different voices blended and harmonized like instruments. On a lonely passage as counterpoint rose the unmistakable, desolate cry of sea gulls. Sea gulls in the desert. In full cry, the bird music stopped. The silence pressed back, a weight and a force on his eardrums. Shaken, because there could be no explanation, Schultz stepped back into the car and slammed the door on the desert. He turned the ignition key and moved carefully forward toward the white light. The moon rode through the clouds. A quarter mile from the estate Schultz pulled over and shut off the engine. He took the flashlight and a small adjustable wrench from his case and pressed the hood release. On the fuel line, near the carburetor, he unscrewed the locknut. Gas spilled on his hands. From an inside pocket he took a tiny can which CIA had provided. He lifted the lid and shone the flashlight on the oily sludge inside. Schultz pinched his fingers and forced the sludge into the fuel line where it entered the carburetor. Then he tightened back the locknut. The engine only ran a few minutes before it began to miss. Schultz raced the engine. It began to miss badly. He closed the door and engaged first gear. The Ford jerked along. He trod hard on the accelerator, slipping the clutch. The Ford jerked another hundred yards, picked up, again began to choke and jerk. Then it cut out. He put the flashlight and the wrench back in the attaché case and got out to hurl the can of sludge into the desert. Then he began to walk toward the estate and the searing white light.

His shoes and the cuffs of his trousers were white with dust long before he got to the asphalt that led to the house under the mountain. Wrought-iron gates at the end of the asphalt were set in the surrounding wall. Outside the wall, square with its edge, a circle of yellow concrete painted with a black cross was suddenly noticeable. In an opened hangar beyond the yellow circle, blades tipped toward him, Schultz saw a helicopter.

The figure in the doorway was small enough to need to look up at Schultz. The face was sun-dried and sun-blacked, thin and deeply creased, the eyes squinted permanently. He could have been a weathered forty, or sixty.

The man asked, looking over Bob's shoulders, "You alone, son?"

"Very much," Bob said cheerfully. "I had some car trouble. Dirt in the fuel line, I think. It was quite a relief to see the lights."

The man sucked at his tooth stumps. "This road don't go anywhere but here."

"I must have taken a wrong turn."

"What yer aim ter do now, son?"

Bob said, uncertainly under the man's squinted eyes, "Well, I saw the lights. I thought that perhaps I might get help."

"You see that signboard? Clear back there where you took this side road?"

"No, I saw no signboard."

"They come clear on," the man said, shaking his head. "A board like that, twice as large as life, and they come clear on." He studied the sky. The moon was clear of cloud again.

"It ain't about ter rain. Them machines can figure it out twenty ways, but I say it ain't. I'm set in me mind about that."

Something buzzed near the man's head. Still watching the sky and sniffing at the air, he leaned back inside the door. Schultz heard a crackled voice.

"Young fella," the little man said. "Car's busted back near the draw."

The voice crackled again.

The little man lifted his lip off the gapped, broken teeth. He squinted at Schultz. "Nice-lookin' young fella. College boy, I reckon." He listened again.

"Moon's ridin' high. Hard and clear as a silver dollar. It ain't about ter rain. Come in, son," he said.

Schultz bent and beat the white dust off his trouser bottoms.

There was only time for impressions. His guide had crossed a wide entrance hall, turned a corner and was gone while Schultz was still stepping inside. He was aware of the splashed color of Indian rugs, statuary, marble tiles, and dark rooms that spread on split levels, a few steps above or below him. The other man paid Schultz no further attention. He moved quickly, sidling slightly, his right shoulder carried high against the ear, the arm crooked and stiffened. The blade of the shoulder worked at the faded denim. It was not a mannerism. At some time the bones must have been broken and mended without proper setting.

They turned to follow a corridor, wide and floored with rubber. It ended in a pair of solid double doors. Karl pressed a button and the doors parted and slid into the walls.

The room opened was huge and long, low and white. A buzzing sound and an agitated clacking filled it. Karl turned to Schultz, his lip lifted off his teeth in a silent parody of his wet snigger. He pointed. Among tables at the end of the big room, Schultz saw a heavy back in denims, leaning over a bench. The clacking noise stopped and then started again. It drew his eyes to a setting in the corner. A bank of teleprinters curled paper tongues into metal boxes. On polished tables, set like desks in the room, glass-covered instruments drew moving patterns. Schultz was held by a haunt of recognition. In the room's ruled edges, the clinical white concrete, the dead, windowless walls, it came to him. He was in a command post, an operations room.

At the bench the old man turned. He looked older than in his photographs, and more tired. A boyish abundance of hair, chestnut and curling, drew notice to the folding jowls and the deep lines around the mouth, eyes and nose. It was a hound's face, vaguely woebegone.

"Bring the young man in. Shut the door."

"This here's Mathew C. Kaverly. What's yer name again, son?"

"Robert Schultz. How do you do, sir?"

Kaverly shook hands and turned his back again, watching his instrument. "You should know better, young fella, than to drive about the desert at night."

In the denims, looking more like a laborer than a world figure and a millionaire, the shirt-sleeves rolled on thick forearms, the old man's normality reassured Schultz.

"I'm sorry to be a nuisance," Schultz said. Both the old man and Karl were intent on the machine.

The teleprinters had stopped. There was only a low buzz

21

now. The bench Kaverly leaned on appeared to be a cabinet for the instrument he studied. A keyboard like a typewriter's was let into the cabinet. Behind it, under glass, a moving head typed a pattern of X's, loops and circles on pink paper.

"Ha!" Kaverly said, and straightened. Without looking he reached and took the houseman by his scrawny neck, pushed his face hard down to the pattern growing on the pink paper. "See!" he gloated. "Now, what do you say?"

Karl flapped in the grip, the misshapen shoulder working against his right ear, his eyes squinted at the instrument. "Dang it ter hell. Do you hear? Dang it ter hell."

Kaverly's hound face was concentrated on the man under his arm. "Say it will rain."

"It ain't about ter rain."

Schultz stared at them. His mind went back to Kaverly's dossier: "Does not drink or smoke. Is an amateur meteorologist." The pattern being drawn by the machine was a weather map.

Kaverly lumbered away, making notes on other instruments. Karl watched him viciously, rubbing hard at his neck, his lip high off his teeth. Then he began to sidle backwards toward the closed door, his bad shoulder jerking.

"Who got caught in L.A.?" he shouted at Kaverly's wide back. "Chopper on the ground fogged in tight. Clear day, he said, sun'll ride high, pilot couldn't tell him. Sittin' on the ground in a fogged-up chopper like a buzzard with a busted wing."

The houseman went down in a squat and flapped his elbows. The seamed, sun-dried, sun-blacked face and the accident of the crooked shoulder made the imitation gruesome.

The old man spun, congestion flaming up his neck. Karl dashed to the door, the flat of his hand on the button. He was gone. The doors met behind him.

Kaverly stood until the red on his neck began to fade.

"Karl is quite a character," he told Schultz in a voice painfully under control. "An old desert rat. Twenty years ago a mine he was working caved in, broke him up. He was buried for ten days without food or water. My sister finds him good company. Do you know anything about meteorology, young fella?"

"Just about enough to recognize a high pressure from a low pressure, sir."

Kaverly moved among his instruments. "One day man will make the weather. That's what we're here for, isn't it? To dominate the environment? I've got everything I need, you

22

know. Recording thermometers, barometers, hydrometers, anemometers, this new visibility and cloud base recorder here, a telescope observatory in the garden to track my hydrogen balloons. We must not be at the mercy of the elements, young fella. I know what to expect wherever I am and make my arrangements accordingly."

He tapped the glass case. "This is a data transmission machine. It is linked by landline to a computer in my Chicago office. I type out the data here, you see. The data is programmed in Chicago and the computer feeds back the conclusions."

Because he guessed otherwise Schultz said, "The teleprinters, sir—are they for weather data?"

Kaverly was rolling down his sleeves, buttoning the cuffs on his heavy wrists. "I spend a lot of time here. No newspapers, you know. I get a service from Associated Press. Another machine links me with my business in Chicago. Another is a link with a European interest."

"Would that be Lausanne, Switzerland?"

The old man stopped his fingers on a cuff. It was a watchdog's face he lifted. "Why would it be Lausanne, young fella?"

Schultz smiled winningly. "Mathew C. Kaverly. I've just remembered the name. I was a scholarship athlete at Yale."

Kaverly examined Schultz. He had not bothered before. He returned to buttoning his cuff. "Field man?"

"Quarterback."

"Look more like a field man. What do you do, young fella?"

Schultz was prepared: "A little property dealing."

Kaverly shook his head and hung his jowls. "The fast dollar," he said. "That's the trouble with this country today, young fella. Everyone's out for the fast dollar. Nobody wants to start at the bottom and work up anymore. All got their hands in the pot to grab as much as they can without putting anything back. There's more wishbone than backbone in these United States today. A young fella like you, an athlete, you should be making, not taking."

"You have to start somewhere, sir, build up a stake."

"Hard work and guts are all the stake a man needs. That's how I got started. I didn't have a college education, young fella. I wasn't a scholarship athlete."

"But you were an Olympic Gold Medalist, sir. That's a pretty big thing to be."

The old man spun to face Bob Schultz, almost a jump. It

was the same surprising lightness he had shown when he turned on the houseman. Congestion flamed again on his neck.

"Don't say that to me. Understand? Don't say that to me."

Schultz was stunned. Like the houseman he had the instinct for flight. "I'm sorry. I only meant that—"

"You meant that I used my medal to get started. I know what you meant."

"Please. Believe me. I meant no such thing. I only meant—"

"That medal is private. Understand? I won it against the world's best. For the love of it. Not for the gain. I trained for that medal on top of a day's work that would break the back of most young men today. I was an amateur. We all were. We didn't connive and cheat to degrade an ideal. We loved what we did. We were strong, proud men. They're all trying to degrade us now. The politicians, these athletes on the make. I never used that medal. It's a private thing. Do you think I'd degrade something that is the world's last hope against war? The last free meeting place of the world's young people is on the Olympic field. When they go to fight on the sports field and leave the politicians to blow each other up, that will be the end of war. We can get on with the conquest of space, of the weather, of our own minds and bodies."

The athlete Bob Schultz had been, the Lutheran puritanism in him, kindled on the old man's words. This was the Kaverly he had prepared for.

"You mistook me," Schultz said. "I intended to say that a Gold Medal is an honor, an achievement. I couldn't agree with you more, sir."

Absurdly, Schultz meant it. In that moment he forgot his purpose, the deceit of his presence in this house, the lies he had told, the power and guile at work in Washington to betray this odd old man.

Kaverly sat on the edge of a bench. His face became woebegone again. "You do, do you? You're in the minority, young fella. It's a funny world we live in. There's not much that's clean and decent. Not much left anywhere that money or the politicians have not corrupted."

He looked about the bright white room, its instruments moving and buzzing. "It's different out here," he said in a softer voice. "It's clean out here. When you live with it, fighting it, you need a place to go."

He switched off the transmission terminal and looked again at the weather map. "If it doesn't rain, Karl won't let me forget it. Now, young fella, what are we going to do about you?"

"Perhaps if I could use your telephone. Get a mechanic out?"

Kaverly boomed a laugh. "Out here? At night? Not a chance. Dick—he runs the helicopter—is having a few days off. He's due back in the morning. He'll fix you up, if you haven't broken a part."

"I'm fairly sure of that, sir. The motor just began missing and cut out. But I can't impose on you."

"You haven't much choice. Unless you'd prefer to sleep in the car. You shouldn't be driving these deserts at night, young fella."

Schultz said, "It's awfully good of you."

"No trouble. It's a big house. I usually take a walk about this time and have a hot drink with Miss Kaverly before bed. She'd be glad of a bit of company. Would you like to take a walk?"

Off the rubber-floored corridor Kaverly opened a door which Schultz had not seen. And they were bathed in that searing white light. A plantation of trees and gardens stretched into the boundary of the night.

Kaverly watched him. "Quite a sight, eh?"

"I've never seen anything like it. That light. Where does it come from?"

"That light, all that light, comes from two lamps."

"It couldn't," Schultz said.

"I'll show you directly. One lamp produces 200,000 lumens. A 100-watt bulb produces about 1,700 lumens. So, you see."

"That you do," Schultz said.

Kaverly smiled. "Listen."

There was a box on the wall. Kaverly opened a metal door. He walked into the garden and lifted his jutted eyebrows. Acting, he held up two fingers and put them in his mouth to whistle.

The bird music, the unearthly orchestration which had chilled Schultz out on the desert, rose and filled the garden. It bubbled everywhere. Schultz could not help himself. He almost ran forward, peering into the trees.

He heard Kaverly's boom of a laugh. "There they go! There they are! Up in that tree there. Look!"

Schultz turned, shaking his head; he was laughing too.

"Stereophonic tapes," Kaverly said. "They're piped all over the garden."

"But it's music."

"Yes, it's music. The music of nature. These tapes were made for me in Brazil. Birdsong records are best sellers in Brazil. But I'm probably disturbing Miss Kaverly."

Acting again, he put his fingers in his mouth and blew two notes. The bird music stopped.

"How does it work?"

"Simple electronics. The laws of the universe. Even the stars in their courses obey the same laws as the atoms in the head of a match. You should know that. You're a Yale man."

Schultz said, risking it: "You're a strange man, Mr. Kaverly."

"Perhaps. There are those who say so." He went to another metal box, almost hidden among climbing blossoms on a trellis.

"Watch the fountain," Kaverly said.

An ornamental bowl of chipped granite near them began to glow with light. Spurting, dribbling, a feather of colored water began to grow and jet. It mounted to eye level and fanned into geometric shapes. Circles, cubes, squares, diamonds and rectangles continually redrew their sizes and patterns.

"It looks best with the light out," Kaverly said.

He watched for a few minutes, shut off the fountain and closed the door on the box. The patterns failed and dwindled; the colored jets fell and disappeared into their nozzles.

"Some people watch fish. I tried that. It's supposed to be relaxing. Fish are rather dull creatures. This fountain is programmed. If it ran day and night for a year it wouldn't repeat the same sequence of patterns. We had better join Miss Kaverly. It's past my bedtime."

5

"IT SOUNDS like the comics," the military expert said. "That operations room. That fountain. That bird music. All he needs out there now is Batman."

The economics expert said, "He's a spook. Everything we've got on him adds up the same."

Cole's soft voice froze them. "Bob's report makes it clear that no help of any kind can be expected from Mathew C. Kaverly. An approach to him, however subtle, could be disastrous. For our purposes we must count him a hostile. Now to this reaction from Santa Anna. Bueno's enthusiasm means that this project must be pressed forward. And, gentlemen, it must be pressed forward . . . *successfully.*"

The political expert said, "Well, sir, we've still got this Prague thing going for us."

"Since Bueno has asked for our proposals to finance, I think we should hear the economic adviser on his second thoughts, as he calls them."

"The first proposals were to cover political possibilities. They remain sound. However, presuming an open go, there are more means of handling the finance. But most of them are unworkable for one reason or another."

"You do have a fixed proposal?"

"Yes, sir."

"Since the details are on paper, as you say, let us proceed to the fixed proposal."

"We come back to home base. We've got the Development Loan Fund, to improve underdeveloped countries. We've got the International Bank, the Export and Import Bank, and we've got the Inter-American Development Bank to help the member countries. Inter-American has got funds of a billion dollars. Let's suppose Santa Anna applies for a loan. The application has to be OK'd by the State Department. We see to that. Now Inter-American, by its charter, is authorized to defer payment of capital and interest for a period of six years. Well, that just suits our book fine. There's nothing in Inter-American's charter that sets fixed interest rates. OK, we make it a half percent, deferred."

"Come on," the political expert said. "Inter-American Development is for practical projects. Not for an Olympics."

"Who said anything about the Olympics? This loan would be for a deepwater harbor, new villages, new roads. Who cares if the new villages are Olympic villages first? All that bank wants to be sure about is that it will get its money back in six years. We can guarantee that. From Bueno's end you reverse it. The money is for the Olympics. The construction is incidental."

"I can't see it," the political expert said doggedly. "Inter-American is not going to hand out that kind of money blind. They're going to want to know what's to be done with it, down to the last blueprint. We can't suborn Inter-American Development. The whole thing would blow up in our faces. They can't put out money to build tourist hotels."

The economist saw that Cole was paying careful attention to the political expert's argument.

"I'll tell you a story about that," he said. "A certain country, nameless, got forty million out of Inter-American to buy a fleet for a peasant fishing cooperative. You know what they spent that money on? They bought a used destroyer, two East German gunboats and four fishing dinghies as a gesture. You're a pawnbroker and you lend a guy ten dollars on his wristwatch because he says he's got a sick mother. What are you going to do if he blows it on the racetrack?"

"Is Santa Anna a member of the Inter-American Development Bank?" asked Cole.

"No. There was no point to it. Bueno knew Pisarro wouldn't let him borrow American money."

"And now he can? If it's for the Olympics?"

"If the Olympics are the big prestige thing everyone has been saying they are. If we have been right about the politics. That's not my department."

Schultz said, "It would be in the timing, wouldn't it, sir? The announcement first, the money afterwards."

"Olympics go to Santa Anna, black type," the political expert said. "Santa Anna unites behind Olympic Games, headline and screamer."

Cole's secretary knocked and entered with a tray of coffees. She put Cole's pillbox beside his cup. When she had gone, closing the door firmly, Cole said, "And now, gentlemen. The small matter of getting Santa Anna elected in Bombay."

6

TWICE in the past four weeks George Cole had been suddenly awake, cold with foreboding. He had struggled to get a breath, fear at his throat like fingers as the pain spread in his chest.

After the second alarm George Cole spent the weekend in a clinic. For a routine checkup, he told Mrs. Cole, casual and offhand about it.

On Sunday afternoon the specialist who was also a friend drove in from his country club and conferred with the clinic's doctors and technicians.

"Well, George, you want to know how you stand?"

George Cole steadied himself, put a cigarette in the long holder.

"You've got a bad case of cardiac neurosis."

Cole showed more suspicion than relief. "What do you mean by that—neurosis?"

"It's usual after an attack. It takes time to readjust. An in-

28

digestion pain or a touch of heartburn and you think the balloon's going up. You've mended well, George. To put it plainly, you're suffering more from anxiety than anything I can treat you for. You need to relax more, get out on the golf course, let the young men do the worrying. It's up to you, George. It's simply a matter of how you handle yourself."

The years ahead greatly mattered to George Cole. His daughter was expecting a baby. He and his wife had waited a long time for a grandchild. Riding home that Sunday, light with relief, he determined that he would allow no unnecessary pressure to distress him. Let the young men do the worrying. It was a young man's world.

In the Bureau the Santa Anna operation drove forward. George Cole's unexpected detachment had increased the weight on Bob Schultz. It had been his idea. It was being handed to him as his project. Cole still made the decisions, his attention going unfailingly to flaws in their planning, but at Bureau meetings he increasingly encouraged Schultz to talk. It was noticeable to the others and did not go unresisted. Schultz knew that he was on the firing line.

A statement issued in Lausanne and ignored by the press had been added to the files: "International sport, one of the few fields where all who take part are on equal footing, cannot survive if it is used either as a tool or a weapon for political purposes." The IOC had declared itself opposed "to any interference in sport for political, racial or religious reasons which might prevent the unhindered entry of competitors and officials to member countries." The Pakistani member of the executive committee had moved that political and national coloring, such as the playing of national anthems and the raising of national flags, be eliminated from the Olympic Games.

Dobson, the CIA man, had information to table. "It's not easy to get inside information. The IOC meetings are held behind closed doors. The decisions announced at the press conferences often vary significantly from the IOC bulletins published later. Mathew Kaverly is the only public voice. It was Kaverly who insisted that West and East Germany should compete as one nation. There is no Berlin Wall on the sports field, he said. The same with Korea. As far as Kaverly is concerned the thirty-ninth parallel doesn't exist. I was in that war. I'd like to tell him. At the Olympics in Melbourne, Australia, he barred Nationalist China from parading. They had to ditch their banners and parade under signs saying Formosa. They were pretty sore about that. For years the Russian influence in the IOC has been trying to get South Africa expelled. Kaverly has blocked it. You get all these contradictions. He can face both ways."

Schultz said, "He doesn't face both ways on amateurism."

George Cole said, "What do you have for us on the presentations which were made last time in Hamburg?"

"I've got a rundown on most of it, sir. I've got a copy of the film the Detroit delegation used for its pitch."

Bob Schultz got up. "I'll get the screen and projector."

The film ran for forty-five minutes. It included speeches by General Eisenhower, President Kennedy and Rafer Johnson, the Olympic Decathlon champion. Dobson told them that fifty-eight delegates had gone from Detroit to propose their city. The Egyptian delegation had arrived with a color film prepared by a famous English director. The film was shot in 35-mm. and their portable projector was 16-mm. The Italians and French had quarreled over presentation space. The scale models of the stadiums the Italians proposed to build had overflowed their allotted floor area. The French simultaneous translating equipment had broken down and the Detroit delegation had loaned them theirs.

Partying and lobbying had continued for a week. The French uncased one thousand bottles of champagne and provided liveried French footmen to serve it. The Swedes ran a nonstop smorgasbord with aquavit. The Filipinos offered French champagne. The Detroiters served cocktails backed by a jazz combination playing " 'S Wonderful" as the delegation's theme. The Americans lost by a first-vote margin of sixteen.

Cole polished his glasses and shook his head. "It's a circus."

Dobson had been let go.

"This presentation can't be left to Santa Anna. This is a job for professionals. It's no good our working through the back door if things don't stack up at the front."

Schultz said, "The Detroit presentation was handled by professionals."

"That's what we need. A little Madison Avenue glitter."

"Can we arrange that, sir?"

Cole considered it. "I don't see why not. The best way would be to have a firm propose themselves to the Mayor. I could arrange with Bueno to have the firm accepted. Who would one hire for a job like this?"

Schultz said, "I've thought about this. I think the best thing might be to get advice from Inter-Americas' Public Relations."

Cole said, "It well might be. Public Relations is bound to keep secrets just like us, is it not?"

"Yes. They have a joke about it. They say they're bound to tell them."

Cole pressed his buzzer. "Miss Brasher, I would like you to set up an early appointment with the chief of Inter-Americas' Public Relations. When you have a time let Mr. Schultz know."

"Yes, sir."

The job of preparing the Santa Anna presentation to the IOC in Bombay fell to Prentice and Clark, a coming Madison Avenue PR company. Sam Clark and the director of Inter-Americas' Public Relations had been deskmen together on *Time* magazine.

They met for dinner at "21." Sam Clark waited a decent interval and then began to fish. He had rationed his drinks. He did not want to waste himself, to collect a hangover, unless his companion had something solid.

Over the main course he said absently, "You mentioned you might have something for me."

The Public Relations director paused. It was a rare pleasure to pass on a hot one. He chewed his food, took a drink of wine and sat back.

"Sam, I've got a beauty, but it's a secret."

Clark relaxed. It was going to be a long evening. He ran through his early morning appointments in his head. There was nothing he couldn't postpone or delegate. "Something hot?" he asked, pushing a morsel of food to one side as though it occupied all of his attention.

"Hotter than a pistol."

They both let it go at that. There was time enough.

Sam Clark searched the menu. "The hell with the calories. I'm going to have crêpes suzette."

Clark waited until they had been served with brandy and cigars. "You want to talk about it?"

The director rolled his glass. "It's a one-shot," he said.

Some of Clark's warmth departed. You can do a lot of work and not get much back on a one-shot. The other man knew it. He wasn't going to put it all in Clark's lap at once.

"This is what you might call a long-term one-shot."

Clark looked puzzled. "A long-term one-shot I never heard of. How long a term?"

"Four, maybe five, years."

"Crissake. What kind of product you got?"

"It's not a product."

"What the hell is it, then?"

"It's a country."

"A country?" Clark said, leaning forward and looking upset. "Crissake. You're not giving me one of these African countries where the Cabinet eats the Prime Minister?"

"I'm giving you Santa Anna."

They sat, heads almost touching across the table. The Public Relations director had dropped his voice.

"Santa Anna? Santa Anna's got no tourist trade worth a nickel. Where's the one-shot down there?"

"The Olympics. The Olympic Games. Let's just say Santa Anna *might* get them."

"You're snowing me."

"You want to believe that?"

"Crissake. Where would we start?"

"At the bottom. The International Olympic Committee is meeting in Bombay in about four months from now. Santa Anna is going to have a complete, glossy presentation for that meeting. Films, speeches, brass bands, parties, press, the lot."

"*Four* months? You'd need a regiment on the job to come under the wire in four months."

"You can have a regiment. There's an open-end budget on this. Whatever it costs—spend it."

"What help would I get?"

"All the help you need. I will be your liaison. Any strings you want pulled, you tell me."

"They'd be big strings? Government strings?"

"They'd be big strings."

"Crissake," Clark said. "Let's you and me have another brandy."

When the waiter had warmed new glasses and left the table, the director said, "What's the word, then?"

"It's too big to miss. I might bust a gut, but it's too big to miss. Where do we start? How do we make the contact?"

"That will be set up. What you do is clear the decks. Fly down there in a few days. I'll tell you when from Washington."

Four days after the dinner at "21," Sam Clark was back from Santa Anna. A week after that a sixty-page action outline had been dictated and Clark and Prentice had twice

32

spent the night in their offices. The day after the outline was completed three experts from a research service had been briefed and dispatched to Santa Anna. Rex Prentice had hired a documentary film group out of Hollywood and packed them off with instructions to shoot everything that moved until a script could be written. Pip Harris, an Englishman on the staff who had been account executive for a successful West Indies land development, had flown out to look into Santa Anna's tourist attractions. An ex-*Life* photographer, working as a free lance, joined the documentary film unit to cover Santa Anna for stills. Three staff writers and Luba Ivanova were sent in with the research team.

Luba Ivanova was the only member of Clark's staff who spoke Spanish. The partners had hired her as account executive for a fashion house which had folded after two seasons. Luba had a curious history and a curious need to talk about it. "That Ivanova broad's a foreigner in four languages," Clark used to say.

She had been born in 1938 in Saigon, of a White Russian father and a Spanish mother. She had got Russian from her father, Spanish from her mother, French from the convent where she had been educated, and English from an American technical adviser to the French whom she had married at the age of fifteen. As Luba told it, her life had been hard. "You don't know," she would say, "since a little girl, all the guns banging, always trouble, always not enough to eat."

The American she had married had been thirty years her senior and given to oddity, according to Luba. On her wedding night he had kept her up until morning massaging the gout that troubled him.

She would sadden her eyes, telling the story and wrinkling her nose with disgust. "Think of it. Massaging, massaging. Always like this. Not nice, no? I tell you. We come to America, and that is the end of my husband."

The husband's end had been a beginning for Luba. She had an inescapable presence; the musk of sex was on her like a perfume. Luba had no use or need for discretion herself, and the office soon learned who her newest lover was—and for a few weeks he would be known as "Luba's latest"—until she replaced him.

When Luba flew out with the staff writers Rex Prentice said, "Ten dollars which one comes back as Luba's latest."

"How many you send?"

"Cross, Openshaw and Hall."

Clark said, "You give me fifty to ten, I'll spot you the team."

The Spaniards had climbed to the small plateau on the shoulder of the Emperatriz Mountains and founded the city as a summer refuge from the heat and sickness of San Bernardino on the coast. The Governor had been carried up on a litter, dying of fever, and in the perpetual spring on the plateau he had celebrated the recovery of his health by naming the settlement Santa Anna after the patron saint whose charity he had invoked when the Last Rites were given to him halfway up the mountain.

The plateau sloped toward the Emperatriz peaks, giving the northern end of the city an authority and eminence over the spread of white roofs to the south. The institutions of government, the Presidential Palace and the new American Embassy shared command on the heights. The Avenida de España, with gardens down the center, rose from the gates of the Presidential Palace and ran to the Plaza de la Luna, the Times Square or Piccadilly Circus of the city of Santa Anna. At the Plaza de la Luna the Avenida de España became the Avenida de la Independencia and passed the big Retiro Park, ending at an abrupt fall of cliffs over which the Governor, whose health had been saved, once dispatched four hundred mutinous Indians.

The old city, walled and congested, lay on the left of Retiro Park. This was the center of Santa Anna's night life, a clot of grubby bars and eating places, a good place to walk since the flagged streets were too narrow and twisting to admit motorcars. On Sunday the *paseo* or parade was Santa Anna's best-loved entertainment. Even the families from the heights came to walk in the old city on Sunday, exchanging pleasantries and exhibiting their children and taking wine or coffee with dishes of nuts, olives and dried fish as appetizers. The young boys and girls rolled eyes at each other.

When Sam Clark and Rex Prentice flew in, their high-priced advance troops had had about enough of Santa Anna. The altitude had affected most of them. They had been unprepared for the physiological handicaps of high-pressure activity at eight thousand feet.

The Hotel San Francisco was the best on the heights, a comfortable place of indefinite period set in beautiful gardens. It offered good food and poor service and sixty-eight rooms, forty of which were air-conditioned.

A big room hired for private parties had been reserved by

the partners to confer in. They had got into Santa Anna on the night flight after a late meeting in New York and had summoned a conference for nine o'clock in the morning.

It was now eleven. Rex Prentice slouched sideways in his chair. He kept pushing the wide, horn-rimmed glasses on his nose and looking about him with alarm. Clark rubbed at his crew cut as though the top of his head gave him pain. The experts, fifteen of them, not counting Luba Ivanova, sat smoking, doodling and rearranging their papers.

"Crissake," Clark said, "it can't be that bad."

Ray Cross, his chief writer, lit another Gauloise. "The place has got nothing," he said. "That's its gimmick."

"But this is Latin America. Bongo drums, señoritas, Mardi Gras in the streets."

Nobody answered.

"The bulls. We passed this bullring. There must be something going for us there. Like that bull-running they got in Spain. Where is it they got that bull-running?"

"Pamplona," Prentice told him.

"Yeah, Pamplona. That thing's famous all over. Hemingway wrote about that. The tourists get a big bang out of it."

Prentice said, "All the tourists get out of it is a horn up the arse. Who wants to fly down here to be chased by the bulls?"

Clark was hanging on hard. "There's got to be a Mardi Gras, a fiesta or something. All Latin America's got one."

The headman from the research agency said, "There used to be a Mardi Gras sort of thing but the Church closed it."

"What for?" Clark asked. "Maybe we could get it revived."

"It got out of hand."

"See," Clark told the table, "it got out of hand. There's a lot of spirit down here. Fill us in on this."

"Well, as in general in South America, there's a lot of Indian influence in the social structure. The Indians had a carnival just before the beginning of Lent, to let their hair down before the period of renunciation. The Church recognized it as a feast, an indulgence of appetites to prepare the converts for fasting."

"So what was wrong with that?" asked Clark.

"The Indians took it that it meant they could indulge all their appetites. According to an old record I've got here, 'copulation went unrestrained.' A few years later it had become general for Santa Anna husbands and wives to discard their wedding rings for the night. On order of the Bishop,

35

reinforced by Presidential decree, carnival was abolished. St. Mark's Day, which is celebrated in the rest of Latin America, got abolished down here too."

Clark said, "What in hell happened to St. Mark's Day?"

"I'll read it to you," the research man said. "It's from an old publication. 'These beasts seek Christian blessing for their pagan rituals. The degrading orgy of gambling, drinking, cockfighting, brawling and lewdness on St. Mark's Day was abolished by his Holiness and enforced by arms.'"

"Crissake," Clark said. "The poor bastards have had it all taken away from them."

"That's about it. We are left with Christmas, Easter and November first."

Prentice pushed on his glasses. "Christmas and Easter. That's going to be a real come-on for the wheat farmers out of Idaho. What happens on November first?"

"November first is the Day of the Dead."

"You're putting me on."

"I'm afraid not. You want to hear about it?"

Clark waved.

"November first. A festival day to welcome the returning souls of the dead," the research man read. "In the last weeks of October the stores are stacked with delicacies favored by the dead. At midnight on November first, parents set their tables with candy skulls, coffins, skeletons and chocolate and frosted-sugar bones and other funeral sweets in the memory of the departed souls of children. In the morning the children consume these offerings with wild excitement."

Clark wandered to the window and back. "I need coffee. The Day of the Dead. Crissake. Someone, get a gallon of coffee in here."

Rex Prentice assembled himself and stood up, polishing his glasses. "Somebody has to have something. Something has to go right somewhere."

He turned to the bearded Englishman who had operated successfully in the West Indies. "Pip, how are we for amenities? Service, accommodations, playgrounds, nightclubs?"

"It doesn't look too good, Rex."

"Let's have a quick rundown."

"You're at the airport," the Englishman said.

"OK, I'm at the airport, let's take it from there."

"It's a DC-4 airport. I doubt if it could handle big jets."

"We need a new airport. Note that, Luba. Go on, Pip."

"You get to customs."

Luba said, "Not nice, no? All those dirty fingers in your underwear."

"She's got a point. Put down no customs clearance for visitors, Luba."

"You get a taxi and rattle into town."

"True," Clark said. "I lost a filling coming in last night. We've got to have a new road to that airport."

"You get to your hotel," the Englishman said.

"Not good, eh?"

"Air conditioning isn't general. We need about two thousand more air-conditioned double rooms and about a thousand singles. With bathroom of course."

"How's the service?"

"Very inexpert. Very *mañana*. There are no theaters. So there's no theater problem. There are three good movies showing subtitled Westerns, and more night life than would appear at first, in the old city. That quarter reminds me of the old part of Athens. There's good music, Spanish and native dancing, and the bars are scruffy enough to be interesting. I think we could do a lot with the old city."

"Second that," the ex-*Life* photographer said. "I've got some good coverage on it."

"That's *something* we got going for us," Clark noticed.

They broke for lunch at one and remet at two thirty. The partners ate in their suite. They had confidences to exchange.

After food and a siesta the spirits of the conference improved. The documentary film group reported. The director was cheerful. He told them that he had just shot a film for the Turkish Government. If he could make Turkey look good, he said, he wasn't about to have trouble with Santa Anna. The director was anxious to get away. He had arranged an out-of-season bullfight for the next day's shooting and wanted to inspect the preparations.

"No blood," Prentice instructed him.

The director said he had seen the bull. Any blood about would be from the transfusion needed to get it on its feet.

By the end of the day they had made progress. It had been decided to haul sand from the coast to build a beach on the Retiro Park lake and all hands had agreed with Clark that a fiesta would have to be invented.

In their suite, Clark and Prentice talked over a nightcap.

"It's not as bad as it looks," Clark said. "We get over the hump of the presentation, we've got four years to tidy up."

"You're still betting they get the Games?"

"I'll lay you fifty to one on it."

"Faith, that's what you've got," Prentice said. "Me, I believe in this open-end budget."

HARRY HAYES

United Kingdom

7

WHEN HARRY resigned his apprenticeship old Mrs. Hayes was upset for weeks. The white coat he wore on his rounds was a worry and reminder to her. Harry learned not to wear it in the flat. He kept the white coat at the depot. Because his mother could not understand she could not be comforted. "Your poor dad was dead set on you learnin' a trade, Harry. That boy won't go on the barges, he used to say. That boy's goin' to have a trade."

But she was failing now, her memory often tricked her and the extra money made a great difference. With commissions, Harry's weekly earnings averaged sixteen pounds. He had bought a television set to entertain his mother, and other bits and pieces to please her.

There were four hundred customers on Harry's list. He ran every delivery, jogging from the milk truck to the doors. In the first month he had felt the benefit of the fresh air and exercise. He had not had a cold since he left the printing works. In the mornings he was on the job by five and home most days by two. In the afternoon he worked with the weights Bill Persons had put him on. "All your strength is in your legs," Persons had said. "A man runs with his whole body. You need some weight lifting to put muscle on that chest."

It was after seven now. He had still not finished his weekly accounts. Friday was the long day, collection day, the day to balance the books. He went over the figures yet again, mobilizing his concentration, trying to hold down the numbers that glazed on the pad and escaped into tomorrow. The squeak of the cinders was in his ears; the inky figures were little black men racing between the lines. Harry's fingers shook on the pen. He got up and roamed aimlessly and restlessly about the kitchen, lit the gas and put on the kettle for tea he did not want. If Bill said he was ready he must be ready. It had been the shock of it. He had not run in competition for months. "You run against yourself, against the best that's in you, against God if you're good enough." He had done that. He had forgotten that there are other men, other runners to beat.

"How would you feel about the big one?"

"What big one?"

"The AAA championship. You're running at White City on Saturday."

No warning. Just those cold pale eyes, mocking him.

Every night since then he had run the race in his mind. Asleep and awake, dreaming it, stiff in the bed, his eyes stretched at the dark.

Persons had come to London early in the week, had put Harry on an easy schedule. Last night he had said, "I'll see you at White City."

"But I'll see you tomorrow. I'll be finished by seven."

"Tomorrow you're on your own, lad. Just remember. Jameson is the man to beat. Stay away from the club tomorrow. Watch television with your mother."

The kettle whistled. He heard his mother. "Harry, you makin' a cuppa?" As he put tea in the pot, the unfilled hours between now and tomorrow seemed too long to be lived through.

The hideous old structure had been saved by racing grey-hounds. It had been built in 1908 for the Franco-British Ex-hibition and used in the following war as an ammunition sup-ply depot. The damage done then had been thorough. Fish bred in the dressing-room tunnels which had silted with filth and filled with water. A Japanese garden which had been the Exhibition's pride grew into a Japanese jungle. The owners of the Exhibition placed a claim for a million pounds as their estmate of the ruin done.

In the late 1920's, the novelty of dogs chasing a mechani-cal hare had saved White City's fortunes. The dogs still had the best of it. The greyhound track dominated the enclosure. It was bigger and better-built than the athletic track and field which had become a profitable sideline. The unpainted asbes-tos roof, which had once been gentled by surrounding acres, now jutted starkly against a housing development and the en-croaching BBC and War Office buildings. Two clocks at ei-ther end of the ground were set in corrugated-iron towers, an eyesore of such ramshackle perfection that they might have been deliberately designed for that purpose. Inside the turn-stiles a tarred road ran beneath the stands and circled the ground. Hot dog concessions, Coca-Cola stands, rent-a-pillow kiosks, lavatories and ambulance stations lined the road. The stale taint of old catering and old greyhound urine was too deep ever to be eradicated.

Harry woke late from a nervous sleep. He sharpened his spikes on an oilstone to find work for his hands. He walked from Charing Cross Station to Hyde Park, leaving early to ease the waiting. It was a gray day, with a misting rain and light, gusting wind. The wind was unsettling. It would be hard to run against.

The open space and the massive green trees soothed him. At the round pond he sat on a bench and watched the children sailing their boats. The will that Persons had trained into him rose to his bidding now. He quietened himself. Later he would release the tension, expend it in measured drops.

Jameson was the man to beat, Britain's champion miler. The morning press tipped Brigs, the Thames Valley Flyer, to press the champion hard. Tiller, the American, could be an upset, but his performances had been erratic. Harry Hayes, the Royal Park entrant, was "promising," said the papers.

At White City 20,000 spectators were counted through the turnstiles an hour before the first event scheduled. The weather cleared, but the light wind had settled into strong gusts and prevailed from the south. On the field, the officials were already shaking their heads. Unless the wind blew out, times would be poor.

The spectators climbed the stands, rented pillows, bought Coca-Cola and hot dogs. Club colors flashed on the green. The loudspeakers made a tinny bray, announcing the opening event.

Timing himself according to Bill Persons' instructions, Harry Hayes left the round pond and walked across Hyde Park to the tube. While the concrete stadium was still distant, Harry heard the mob roar. The terrifying, one-throated sound that rocks and breaks like the sea. He tightened his hold on the case containing his track gear, walking on into the roar. "If you can hear the crowd you've lost your concentration," Bill had said. "There's no crowd. There's nothing and nobody except you and the man you must beat." He saw Persons first, before Persons saw him. The familiar stocky figure in the tweed hat was pacing the entrance to the dressing rooms.

Persons looked up and stilled. He said nothing. A long time of looking. Then he smiled. "Have you seen the papers?"

"Some of them."

"Promising Harry Hayes."

"That's what they reckon."

"You'd better get changed. Time marches on."

They walked through the cold bare tunnel, into the noise and the light.

On the edge of the field, Persons put his face up close. "Now! Let it go."

Harry could smell Person's hot breath.

"You're full of it, lad. You're choking on power. Get it into you. Let it go."

Hayes drew a shuddering breath. His heart stretched. Blood pulsed behind his eyes.

"Every step you take, every breath you take, I will be with you. You can be great. You were born for this. Let it go."

A loudspeaker brayed close to them. He saw the officials moving toward them, felt Persons steering his elbow. Then Jameson, the reigning champion, was smiling at him. He heard him say, "Best of luck." Saw him put out his hand, raised his own hand to meet it, felt the pain of the chop with which Persons knocked his arm down. Jameson was walking away, the officials with him, turning to stare over their shoulders.

Bill Persons was hissing at him. "Are you mad? Do you think he's a pal, a teammate? He's a toffee-nosed twat patronizing you because you're working-class. He's going to try to take something away from you. Something you own. Something you need and that is yours. He's going to try to take it away from you."

The officials were ready at the starting blocks.

Persons pushed him. "Run! Run right over the bastards."

The world was empty except for the track. Brown cinders that stretched without boundary. The great coiled spring that pushed in his chest was an almost unbearable hurt. He heard the start being counted. There was no distinction between the bang of the starting pistol and the bang of the spring bursting in his chest. He was running. Up, away and running.

Hayes had drawn the inside lane. Had he been running tactics he either would have to set the pace from the start or would risk being boxed in. But Harry Hayes was not running tactics. He was running as Persons had taught him. Against the protests of his own mind and body.

The Athletic Association official thumbed the stop button

and held up the watch. "Fifty-eight seconds. Into the wind like that."

The loudspeakers brayed. "Time for the first quarter, 58 seconds dead."

In the packed stands the mob voice growled appreciation.

Harry Hayes counted on the time clock in his head. Tiller, the American, was almost under his spikes, a few yards behind Brigs, who was pulled in behind Jameson. Coming into the second quarter, Harry Hayes stepped wide.

In the stands they began to get up. Hayes was going round.

The shorter figure of the American half turned his head, clapped on speed. Outside him, Hayes came up, holding himself there. The American was pushing Brigs now. Brigs moved up on Jameson, the champion. Locked in that position they ran the second quarter.

"Time for the half mile, 1 minute, 58.7 seconds."

Again they were running into that cruel gusting wind.

Harry Hayes, still wide, running extra yards on every quarter, passed Tiller. In his effort, disturbed by the wind, the American began to labor, lost his rhythm. Now it was Brigs, the Thames Valley challenger, whose turn it was to be struck by fear as the long figure came up to haunt him.

The bell rang.

"Time for the third quarter, 3 minutes, 4.8 seconds."

It could scarcely be heard. The White City roof was trembling.

The pain was on Hayes now. Red-hot irons in his chest. Simpson saw the tilted shadow, struggled desperately to throw it off. The champion was running in his own pain, frantically feeling for his last reserves.

"Hayes, Hayes, Hayes, Hayes." One hoarse chant in the stadium.

In millions of homes, before television, they pounded the arms of their chairs.

Using his last drops of energy, Jameson held the long shadow. With the tape in sight of his rolling eyeballs he saw the shadow move up. Hayes was at Jameson's shoulders. Panic clawed the champion. Hayes was in front. Spaced opened between them. Jameson was beaten—broken—his knees buckled as he crossed the broken tape. He was down, writhing epileptically with cramp.

Harry Hayes shuddered in Bill Persons' arms, fighting the vise that squeezed his bursting chest.

"Time for the mile, 4 minutes, 0.8 seconds."

Spectators washed out of the stands on to the track, milling with the officials and police who tried to drive them back.

Harry's ears opened on the excitement. His shoulders straightened in the arm holding him like a lover's. His consciousness was still blurred to the officials who pumped his hand, slapped his back, needing somehow to touch him.

He looked up into Persons' illuminated face. "All . . . all . . . right?"

"You killed them, Harry. You ran right over the bastards."

As he began to heal, come back from the pit, his body shook with wonder.

"Hayes, Hayes, Hayes."

"Hear them, boy? That's for you. That's for us."

Wearily he pushed back the black hair gummed in sweat on his forehead.

It was true, then. He was champion.

"Not now," Persons said, pushing at the reporters. "You will have your chance after he has showered."

Holding Harry, Persons steered their way toward the dressing-room tunnel.

The Sunday press gave the mile unusual coverage. Not only because it had been a "dark horse" win but because of the impossible conditions. There had been a touch of sensation, too. In a statement made in tears when he was recovered enough to speak, Jameson had said, "I never want to go through anything like that again. They can have it. I'm finished. I'm hanging up my spikes."

The game of conjecture played in the papers continued for weeks. By how much would Harry Hayes have broken the four-minute barrier had he not been running against that wind?

In a television interview, Harry Hayes was spoken of as Britain's next Olympic Gold Medalist. . . .

8

BILL PERSONS had insisted on a victory dinner. His excitement had twice turned to savagery during the evening. Persons had almost leaped at the restaurant manager when he doubted if he had a free table. When the wine waiter showed little interest in Persons' peremptory signals, his pale eyes had frozen. The waiter had to rearrange the table settings which had been jarred out of place by the fist Persons had pummeled wildly on the table. Alec McBride, the sports editor whom Persons had invited to the dinner, had put his hand comfortingly on Harry's leg. "Don't worry," he said privately, "that's just Bill. I know him from the old days."

McBride was in his forties, a big man, clumsy in the bone. His nose had been broken at some time and had not properly reset. The bent nose suited the spaniel sadness of his eyes and the gentle voice, traced by the accents of Yorkshire.

Harry Hayes was deeply happy. The other two had much to remember. He was pleased to listen. He sat smiling, impressed by the expensive restaurant, in a sensual peace of physical recovery. McBride asked him no reporters' questions except to say, "What next, Harry? An Olympic medal?"

"What was the name of that little Cockney photographer you always had with you?" Persons asked. "Eddie, was it?"

"Addie. He's still with me."

"That's right, Addie. This Addie," Persons told Harry, "used to hate athletes. He used to say that nobody could write about the bloody gladiators like Alec here. Said he could only do it because he's as bent as the gladiators."

They ordered more wine.

Harry was almost asleep before they noticed and asked for the bill. McBride insisted on a last glass of brandy to toast Harry.

"To the champion."

Harry Hayes felt his stomach lurch. He had not realized it all yet.

"Royal Park wants to give him a party tomorrow," Persons told McBride. "That's if he's awake by five o'clock."

Persons was not far out. Harry Hayes was still asleep next day at twelve o'clock. That morning, careful not to wake him, Mrs. Hayes had been a dozen times to her front door to answer the neighbors asking for Harry. She had sat for hours in the kitchen over the newspapers spread on the table.

The next week was difficult for Harry Hayes. He heard nothing from Bill Persons. He had expected a letter, or a telephone call to the dairy. His mates inspected him as if he were a curiosity. Their faces and voices became deferential when he checked in or out with the milk truck. They treated him with a mixture of awe and reproach that burdened the shyness of his nature.

On the route the men found a reason to be at their doors when it got about that the milkman was Britain's new champion miler. They inspected him with the same abrasive curiosity as his workmates, picking at him with their eyes and conversation for some palpable difference between Harry and themselves. He took no pleasure in it. Twice in the first days after White City the manager of the dairy had pressed him into drinks at his local.

He was worried about Bill Persons. Toward the end of the week he sent a telegram to the farm: WORRIED ABOUT YOU. ANYTHING WRONG? It was two days before he got a reply: BEEN A BIT OFF. OK NOW. WILL BE UP ON SATURDAY.

After the war, when they got him home, it had been a year before Persons stood again in the world he had left in another lifetime.

The hospital had been reluctant to discharge him. He had fought until the doctors gave in. They did not believe that Sergeant Persons would live long enough to spend his back pay or the special disability pension the Ministry had ordered for him.

Bent on the stick he could not stand without, Persons had stood outside the hospital in a world in which he was utterly alone. His father, a widowed doctor, had died in an air raid. A younger brother had been shot down over the Channel, so soon after his father's death that he had never known about it. The hammer that crushed them both spared each the mourning of the other.

Persons had taken rooms close to the hospital. The condition of his discharge had been that he would report back once a week. Alone, as he was accustomed to being alone, he set his will to rebuilding his shattered body. Before that year was out the doctors had changed their minds about Persons.

Incredibly, at the end of a year, the dead man began to run. Beginning with a quarter mile, across the grass of a nearby park, he pushed himself into a shuffle. After each painful victory, spent, racked and retching, he would rise and begin again. In time he could cover a half mile. At the end of nine months he was running a mile.

In the first year, when he had hardly had the strength to walk, Bill Persons read endlessly, constructing—out of medical books, poetry, mysticism and the great rational works— the philosophy that bore him up. In all the words written about him when he began setting athletic records at fifty, there had not been a single mention of his staggering history. It had been his guarded secret. Only Alec McBride shared the knowledge. It had come to him by accident, a remark overheard in the stands, passed between two men who had been

Persons' doctors. Patiently, and in growing wonder, McBride had begun to check back. He was led at last to the hospital, and then to army records. After that he had got drunk, meanly and moodily as he sometimes did. "Mac's attacks of the reds," Addie the photographer called them.

After one of Persons' Marathons, big-boned McBride had stood over him in the emptying dressing room, the sad eyes and crooked nose humped against the cold in his coat collar. Persons had looked up. McBride had just stood there, near enough to touch. Persons had finished dressing and was packing his bag and still the big man stood watching sadly. Persons had turned at last and looked him in the eye.

"I know about you," McBride said.

The pale eyes had widened. "What do you know?"

"All of it. All there is to know. Backwards and forwards from the prison camp."

They had gone to a pub together and Alec McBride never wrote about what he knew.

Dreams had not been uncommon in the repatriation hospital. Many of the patients had nightmares to work out. But these kept coming back. After Harry Hayes's win at White City the dreams had come to Persons and crushed him. Every night, for four nights, he dreamed. He was afraid to sleep after the second night and sat up by the fire in a chair. Even there the dreams came back.

He had been taken at Singapore in February 1942, after the British surrender. The Japanese shipped 1,500 of them to Sandakan, in North Borneo. They landed on July 18 and spent the night in the Catholic school. Next day the prisoners were force-marched to Eight-Mile Camp, an old agricultural station. The Japanese were short of men to guard them and demanded from the British senior officer an undertaking that the prisons would not escape. The senior officer refused. The demand was presented again and refused again. The senior officer was felled by a rifle butt and gored by the boots of the guards. Next day the prisoners were paraded. The senior officer had been hurt, but he struggled up and refused the demand again. The guards felled him again and then pulled him to his feet to be shot under the eyes of his men. Before the order was given the men broke ranks to sign the undertaking.

By September conditions at Eight-Mile Camp were unbearable. The prisoners had yet to learn how much a man can bear. They had begun to starve and the polluted water racked many with dysentery. That month three privates escaped. For a week the Japanese withdrew all rations. In October others of the tormented men made the break for the jungle. The escapers were caught. The Japanese built cages on the parade ground and locked up the captured men. The cages were built so that a man could not sit down or lie in them.

Under the sun the anguish of the caged men maddened their helpless comrades. Attempts were made to reach them with scraps of food and water. The beatings and punishments mounted. Morale began to break in the misery. The dysentery cases started to die.

The senior officer was an old man by the standards of the youths around him. He had been a fit fifty, but the beatings had hurt him inside; he was bent and often coughed blood. He was on one of the tiered platforms that served for beds in the crowded fetid huts when Persons was told to report.

"You don't mind if I don't get down, Sergeant."

"Of course not, sir."

"I've been thinking. The men need something to give their morale a boost. Those poor chaps out there in the cages. You know?"

"It's hard, sir."

"You're a Signals man. An engineer in civvy life, I understand. I've been wondering. Do you think you could scrounge the parts for a wireless set, something to keep us in touch? The natives might help. We still have a little loot. Some money, watches, fountain pens. That kind of trading thing."

It was a slow, tricky business. The first news the prisoners heard on the set Persons had built was a relay from Australia. The *Queen Mary* had docked at Southampton with 15,000 American troops. There was a reference to the sinking of the German pocket battleship *Scharnhorst* in a Norwegian fjord.

On December 20, 1942, following rumors among the natives, the Japanese conducted a surprise search of the camp. It began at first light, while the prisoners were still on their platforms, and continued throughout the day. Among the pathetic caches of food scraps and family snapshots uncovered, was a diary. It spoke of the good news about the *Scharnhorst* and the wireless set which had been scrounged by a sergeant of Signals.

Persons was arrested. After questioning by the army Commandant he was beaten and stood at attention all night outside the guardroom. Next morning he was sentenced to fourteen days in the cage. It rained heavily. At the end of the fourteen days Persons was admitted to hospital delirious with fever. He was then returned for another fourteen days to the cage and questioned again by the Commandant about the existence of the wireless set. In good English the Commandant told him that if he refused to answer he would be handed over to the Kempei Tai, the Japanese security police, who specialized in terror.

After five more days in the cage Persons was bound an driven to Kempei Tai headquarters in Sandakan. With twelve other prisoners, three of them English civilians, he was sat cross-legged in a guardroom. At night they were allowed to lie down. Apart from regular interrogations and visits to the latrine, Bill Persons was kept cross-legged in the guardroom from January 22 to April 24.

In this period, whenever he was strong enough, he was tortured. With a bayonet in his back the guard would prod him to the interrogation room where an interpreter and the Kempei Tai waited. They would produce the diary. Where was the wireless set hidden? The questions and Persons' answers never varied. The torment did. He was beaten with rifle butts until black blood spilled from his mouth and ears. Cigarette ends were held to the soft flesh under his arms. He was beaten with a riding crop.

On April 24 Bill Persons was taken to another building where the Kempei Tai showed a statement obtained from the natives. The statement identified Persons as the prisoner who had traded with them for wireless parts. The Kempei Tai also wanted to know which prisoner had kept the little leather-covered diary. Persons got hold of a guard by the throat. He was clubbed off by rifle butts. After he had been revived he was again burned under the arms and carpet tacks were hammered into the quicks of his thumbs. For assaulting the guard he was punished by having his arms lashed to a beam above his head which suspended him on his knees. A board was placed over his ankles and a Kempei Tai stepped up on each end. After a few minutes of this Persons collapsed unconscious.

When he was able to walk again the Kempei Tai declared him intractable.

He was sentenced to the torture jail in Singapore. Bill Persons survived three years in the torture jail, including twelve months of solitary confinement. Long before the liberation, the Japanese left him, alone in his isolated cell. The peasant guards regarded him with a mixture of fear and superstition. Nothing human could account for his unbroken resistance.

Yet it was his tormentors who had goaded him to his revelation. He had made his peace with death in the beginning, after the first assaults on his flesh. Fear cannot exist without hope. He had clamored for death in his spirit, and his death had been denied him. So he returned, piece by piece, and found inside himself a citadel beyond the blows of the clubs, a place for the mystic and the martyr, reachable by rapture but not by pain, a place for man's limitless possibilities. There he had been content. They had tortured him into the country of unconcern.

When the British reached the infamous jail, Persons was still in solitary confinement. He weighed eighty-four pounds. His knees, elbows and shoulders were open sores. The bones had protruded through the skin. When his rescuers helped him into the light, horrified that the thing in their hands could be a man, Persons had adjusted his frightening eyes to the light and smiled. It was recorded in his papers that he said, "Took you chaps long enough to get here."

Before the fire in his cottage in the fields, Persons dozed, his chin on his chest. He was dreaming: he and Harry Hayes were running at White City. It would be all right now. He kicked the embers, swinging the kettle over the stirring flames. He was thirsty and hungry.

9

SEVENTY YEARS before, when it had been founded on the subscriptions of the local merchants, the Royal Park Athletic Club had had pretensions to equal its name. The district had been upper-middle-class then, gentlemanly, leisured, assured and certain about God and the Empire. The Club had provided for gentlemanly athletics and gentlemanly cricket in season. Decay had begun in the thirties, hard on the Great Depression, and the committee was forced to build a cycling track, to provide for lower-class interests. A wooden one at first, and then as finances improved, a concrete track with banked turns and a loudspeaker system. The Club's old guard struggled on until the postwar Welfare State raised boxed and ugly Council flats on the sites of many old mansions. In one disastrous year, a football field and a children's paddling pool were added to the Club's leafy acres. Industrial workers began to join the Club from the dormitory suburb a few miles down the hill, where Council flats piled everywhere and cut-price shops went in and out of business. The accents in the dressing rooms changed, but the older members fought on. Signs saying THIS IS NO PLACE TO WASH BOOTS went up over the basins. The new members put up signs of their own: FREE WARM BATHS FOR OLD-AGE PENSIONERS; APPLY TO SUPERINTENDENT.

Harry Hayes was not champion then. When he joined Royal Park a year before, walking up the hill from the industrial suburb, little remained of the onetime gentility. The tradition of running as a summer sport disappeared with the solstice. A new breed of year-long athlete moved in.

Then, the track suit was new. So was the stopwatch: it was a Gruman, the best, and he had saved for it. Conscious of the new track suit, the stopwatch held in his hand, full of a small boy's pleasure in the swaggering equipment, he had been driving himself over the track. In his imagination spectators packed the stands. He was running a race. His heart swelled. His breath sobbed and made spittle. He summoned his will, driving himself past the other runners in training who watched him go in surprise. He ran three miles before exhaustion stopped him, lost to everything but himself. Wobbling off the track on legs suddenly jellied, he lay on his back in the grass. His hand was clamped on the stopwatch he had forgotten. The clawed fingers would not open. Sitting up, grunting at the pain, his mouth gaped for breath, he saw the legs of the man who stood over him.

"Here. Give me your hand."

The man squatted and took Harry's hand between his own, working on it with strong, squat fingers.

"You want to run, do you?" asked the stranger, working on the hand.

"Reckon I do," Harry gasped.

"You call that running? You were stamping holes in the ground. A runner moves over the ground, not through it. Have you ever seen a gazelle run? That's the way to move. You stretch and you fly."

The stranger looked up. In the seamed, tanned face his eyes were frightening: they were pale, a transparent blue, as cold as marbles.

"I'm Bill Persons."

"Seems to me there used to be a Marathon runner named that."

"One and the same."

Persons had helped Harry up. "What's that for?"

"It's a stopwatch."

"I can see that, lad. What's it for?"

"Well, I run against it. In trainin'.'"

"I'll bet you do. Those bloody watches."

The transparent eyes began to burn. Persons raised his voice. "You don't run against a bloody stopwatch, do you hear? A runner runs against himself, against the best that's in him. Not against a dead thing of wheels and pulleys. That's the way to be great, running against yourself. Against all the rotten mess in the world. Against God if you're good enough."

Harry stared up at him. He could not understand. "Yeah? How do yer know how you're goin', then?"

Persons knocked hard on Harry's forehead with his knuckles. "That's how you know, in there. Nature has built a stopwatch into all of us. Nature has built everything into us—if we knew how to dig and get it out. Get rid of the bloody thing. You've got a better watch inside you. Here, I'll do it for you." He picked up the Gruman and threw it with savage force out of sight over the plane trees.

Persons left him like that, gaping after the departed stopwatch. Harry changed into flannels and the blazer with the red, white and blue badge of the Club on the breast pocket, and searched for his watch. He did not find it.

The next day, Harry went to the Club library and looked through the old record books. He found what he wanted. There was enough of it. At the incredible age of fifty-two, Bill Persons had run races that shook the athletic world. He had taken on the strongest and most talented young men in Britain and in race after race had left them prostrate. He had established a United Kingdom record for the Marathon. He had broken the sixty-mile record. He had become the third Briton to run a hundred miles, setting a new time for the distance. In five years he had run twelve thousand miles in training.

In the changing room, a few days later, Harry Hayes put on the new track suit and made up his mind to run three miles again. He had not worked out a training schedule for himself yet. He was a new member.

He did not know how to pace himself. He just went out and ran. At the end of the second mile the going got hard. His chest began to cramp and flame. His heart hammered

52

and his strength began to spill. There was fog over his eyes, and in all the world nothing so imperative as rest. To be still. To not move. To lie and pant in the healing oxygen. He thought he heard his name then and turned his head fractionally. In track gear, Bill Persons was running at his shoulder.

"It hurts, does it? You want to drop, do you, like those nancy-boy runners at Oxbridge? Let's see what you're made of."

Persons moved a little to the front. He ran looking back. Harry stumbled after him, until at last he was down, his legs in the cinders, his upper body writhing in the grass. A thin bile hung in ropes on his chin. The blood draining from his gorged muscles racked him with pain. He had a moment's terror that these were death throes, then he drowned in the pain.

It was an hour before Hayes found the power to rise. Persons helped him off the track to the clubhouse, fed him glucose-and-water while he stretched on a bench. When he was better, had put his feet on the floor, Persons smiled at him. Painfully, Harry smiled back. Then, almost frightened, he felt laughter rising in him. When Persons began to laugh, a wild laugh with his head back, Harry's own laughter burst and engulfed him. Tears streamed from his eyes. Their maniac laughter brought wondering heads out of the shower cubicles.

"Now you know," Persons said. "Now you have been there. If you want to be great, that is what you will live with. Think about it."

He was gone before Harry could reply.

The day after he had run himself into collapse, Harry Hayes was drawn back to the Club. He was too sore to run. He stood in the field and watched the others, looking continually toward the clubhouse in hope of the sight of Bill Persons. He had no way to understand what had happened to him. His flesh recoiled from the memory of the pain that had struck him when he went down in the cinders. But then there had been that strange after-feeling. The laughter that had gushed out, as though something dumb and shackled inside him had been suddenly made free.

Harry waited until the secretary locked up. Persons did not appear.

He went to the Club again the next day, and the day after that, and at last he asked for Persons. Most of the members had heard of him but did not know that he had visited Royal Park. A cross-country runner said he could not have done, that Bill Persons was dead. On the third day, meeting Harry in the locker room, the secretary said, "Oh, Hayes. I've found Bill Persons for you. He's staying with George Mitchell."

In the telephone box opposite the ticket office at the railway station Harry Hayes looked up Mitchell's number in the book. Mitchell was on the Club committee. He began to dial the number, then stopped. He couldn't think what he would say; he did not know what he wanted from the other man. He stood outside the box, unable to leave, caught among the commuters hurrying through. Then he pushed his way back to the box, put in the coins and dialed the number.

"Just a minute," a woman's voice answered. "I'll call him."

"Persons speaking." The voice was hopelessly strange.

"This is Harry Hayes."

"Who?"

"Harry Hayes." He waited. "Harry Hayes from the Club."

Again there was a ghastly silence. "The boy with the watch?"

"Yeah," Harry said miserably. "That's me."

"Did you find it?"

"I didn't look for it," Harry said, flushing.

"Hmm. You didn't, eh! Well, what can I do for you?"

Doggedly Harry said, "I thought we might have a talk. You know, you might be able to give me a tip. If you could spare the time."

He had to wait for Persons again.

"Where are you speaking from?"

"The railway station."

"Well, Harry, I haven't much time, as it happens. I'm going home tonight."

"I'm sorry." Harry worked to find other words. "It just crossed me mind. I was here at the phone box."

"Do you drink beer, Harry?"

"Well, yeah, sometimes. Not much. You know, I'm in trainin'."

"A few beers don't hurt. It's the nicotine that kicks the heart. What's your pub?"

Harry did not have one. "There's the Golden Lion."

"Where is it?"

"At the foot of the hill. Near the station."

"I will meet you there in ten minutes. All right?"

"Yeah. That would be great. I mean, thanks."

Persons accepted the beer Harry ordered for him, leaned on the bar, and turned his worrying eyes on the young man.

"Now, then. Tell me. Why do you want to run?"

"Well, you know, it's just that I've got this feelin'—" Nothing from the other man, just his waiting. "It makes you feel good. You're doin' somethin'. It's like you're usin' yourself properly."

The waiting, the expressionless eyes staring into his.

"It's what you *should* do, sort of. You feel different. Properly alive. I don't want to be half alive like me dad was, always coughing up his heart with the cigarettes. And then, it's somethin' you do by yourself. It's like bein' independent. You get this feelin' like there's nothin' or nobody can mess yer about anymore."

Bill Persons smiled, the changing, joyous smile he had given in the clubhouse. "Tell me all of it," he said. "Think back. When did you first want to run?"

It was a long time ago; Harry's father was still alive. They lived in three rooms in Islington; his father worked a barge on the Thames. There was little money but the family managed. In that district they all managed as best they could. The school was old and broken. In the winter a film of moisture shone on the classroom walls. In the summer a musk of old stones and rotted woodwork exuded in the sunshine. The playground was asphalt and potholed. When it rained, puddles lay for days. There were no playing fields, no bicycles or scooters at Christmas. The boys played cricket in the streets with a packing case or a petrol tin for the wicket, kicked balls, picked sides for running games. Round the Block was popular. They would start out, up to twenty of them, and run round and round the block until they dropped or dropped out. Last one in was King of the Castle. The boys on the block were proud of Harry. When they played against boys from other streets Harry was always King of the Castle. He had not had much feeling about it. It was something he could do and was glad for. He was not much good at anything else.

He was twelve when it happened. On an Easter holiday the Quakers from a settlement which had opened for good works in the district took the children from Harry's class for a day in the country. They had ridden out of London on a special bus, scrubbed by their mothers, dressed in their best and exhorted to behave themselves. Shouting and waving, they had hung from the bus windows, pointing out the sights for each other.

In Sussex, on a river with ducks, in a reserve with swings and a seesaw, the Quakers had spread blankets for a picnic.

A stall in the reserve, made from an old railway carriage, served meat pies, toffee apples and orange and lemon cordials from big glass globes with taps. Harry had not seen the country before. Real-life cows and sheep were a wonder to most of the children.

The sun shone. It was strange and beautiful. The ducks dived and paddled on the river. Harry felt a need to get away, to not have to share it with the others. He walked backward, watching the Quakers, until the old railway carriage stood between him and his party. Then he made off, climbing a fence, and when he was safe had followed the course of the river.

At a place in the reeds he lay on his stomach and strained his eyes at the water, looking for fish. He dipped a hand and with spread fingers felt the river moving. He stood up. Without thinking, he leaped. Then, in a rush, he was off. Along the river's rough bank, jumping at obstacles, he ran as free as the blowing of the wind. There was no effort. No sense of being driven by his stick-thin legs or arms. He was suspended. The river's bank, the logs, grass tussocks, trees, were running backwards beneath him. It was unlike anything the boy had ever known. He could run like that forever. Across continents, jungles, mountains, the ocean. When at last he threw himself down, panting into the earth that was dungy with the smell of animals and the sap of grass, he had felt no tiredness, was unaware of his thin chest's heaving. He only knew a happiness deeper and higher and wider than anything he could have imagined.

Harry told this to Bill Persons, using different words. It tumbled out once he started. Again Persons smiled. He had already missed his train. He took Harry to a small restaurant near the pub and ordered wine. It was the first time Harry had drunk wine in a restaurant.

"When did you join Royal Park? Tell me about that."

And Harry told him, the black hair heavy with grease flopping on his forehead. It was easier now, after the beer and the wine, in the excitement of a good restaurant.

Len Sparks, the Marathon captain, had introduced Harry to Royal Park. Sparks was a civil servant in his thirties, an Oxford Blue. It was the winter Harry Hayes had turned nineteen. He and his mother had moved from the old rooms in Islington to be near the Government Printery where Harry had got an apprenticeship.

That night he left the bus he had caught from the technical

college and was walking through Royal Park, over the hill from the big houses and trees to the Council flats and disposal stores which had so isolated the smart suburb. Harry was carrying the case he used for his textbooks and sandwiches. It was cold. Other pedestrians passed, their ears shrugged into their coat collars. On the top of the hill Harry heard someone behind him running. A man in a white shirt and track shorts, his breath smoking, approached and passed. Harry Hayes had quickened his step, rising on the balls of his feet. He tightened his grip on the case and began to jog. The white shirt bobbed away in front of him. Harry had begun to step out, drawing up his elbows. His lungs began to fill with the cold bright air. His chin came up; he was conscious of a high clear sky and stars. He began to stretch, moving faster. The tails of his raincoat flogged at his heels. In front the white shirt kept its distance. Harry began to lift. He flung the case away.

The man in the white shirt looked back with surprise at the loud slap of leather on concrete. He slowed, moving over as Harry came on, almost stopped as the flying raincoat went past. He expected to hear a shout of "Stop thief!" he explained afterwards. There was no shout. Just the slap of leather going away. Len Sparks had started off in pursuit, his wonder growing at the seriousness of the effort it took to catch the other man. They had run a mile before he could reach out and get Harry Hayes by the whipping tail of his raincoat.

"What are you up to there?" the Oxford Blue had puffed, unsure of what he had in Harry.

"I just started runnin'."

"What for? Were you being chased?"

"Course I wasn't. I saw you go past and then somehow I started runnin'."

Sparks was peering to see Harry in the dark. "Are you a runner, then?"

"No. I'm a printer."

"Then what in the blazes were you running about? You were going as though the devil was after you."

Harry looked about. "I dunno. You went past and I just started up."

"Just like that?"

"Yeah," Harry said, beginning to grin.

"Look, if you want to run you should join a club. Where do you live?"

"Down the hill."

"Then you could join my club, Royal Park, if you live in the district."

"I don't know that I've heard of it."

"Do you know Abbot's Terrace?"

"Yeah. I think so."

"Look for the big green gates, halfway down on the right. I'm Len Sparks, the Marathon captain. You can ask for me if you like. I'll be in the clubhouse on Sunday afternoon."

"Thanks," Harry had said, "maybe I will."

"Good night, then. I'm off."

Harry had watched the white shirt go out of sight and was then struck by the loss of his suitcase. He must have dropped it. Worried, he hurried back, searching the footpath and gutter.

10

BILL PERSONS usually came up to London on the last day of each month. Lately, his visits had been more frequent. When he visited on a Friday, Harry would travel back to the farm with him in the car.

As Hayes ran his last mile, Bill Persons moved across the grass inside the track, careless of the field men training. As Harry lapped he could hear his shouts: "Pull your chin down. Arms! Drive with those arms."

Cooling off, Harry said, "I don't seem to be properly relaxed."

Contemptuously Persons said, "Relaxed. Do you think a tiger's relaxed when it strikes down its prey? When your mind is right and your posture is right you don't need to think about relaxing. Look at that slack-jawed idiot jumping over there. He's so bloody relaxed he can' hardly get off the ground. Come on, into the shower with you. I want to get this ant heap behind me. I've had enough of diesel stink and clockwork men for one day."

The old Vauxhall was almost vintage. Harry had never seen it washed or polished but the engine was carefully maintained. It was a tourer and the top was always down except in the worst of weather. Persons drove hard and fast, in silence. He was still riding his anger. As they bypassed Windsor, the old crenellated castle hung for a minute on the sky. Pushing like this, Persons could do the trip in under two hours. Outside Newbury a hush of leafy lanes passed an isolated pub used by the field laborers. Past The Three Swans the lane dipped toward a picture-card village which had once starred in a film. At the bottom of the dip, a rusted iron-pipe gate opened on a rutted track twisting through stands of corn. Ten minutes in first gear led to the sixteenth-century farmhouse which Bill Persons had restored.

Three years ago, on a walking trip, he had crossed the stubbled fields. A hare had started from a hiding place at his feet and gone bounding and crouching in the stubble, uncertain about the need or direction of its flight. There was nothing and nobody else in the wide harvested fields resting in the sunshine. Bill Persons had chased the hare, imitating its jumps, through the stubble into a windbreak of trees and the abandoned cottage. He had walked on crumbling floorboards under black beams, prying and poking at the walls, scratching with a nail at the woodwork. He followed a track outside the house boundary to the village and inquired about the old place. Before nightfall he had met the owner of the grainfield and the ruin was his for a peppercorn rent on the condition he did not keep a dog which might disturb the pheasants in the farmer's breeding paddock.

Persons had worked for six months tearing out the rotted woodwork, sometimes with the village carpenter to help him. He had slept on a bedroll to begin and later on a canvas cot in the big room first made livable. He set tiles on the ground floors and patched the plaster. When Harry Hayes came to visit, invited after the evening in the restaurant at Royal Park, the aged cottage had been restored, sparkling with whitewash in the moonlight. There were four bedrooms and a new bathroom upstairs; two living rooms, a study and a kitchen on the ground.

That first night Persons said little. He had gone to bed early with a book. Breakfast had been prepared when Harry got down next morning. Rolled oats dry in a bowl with sliced fruit and yoghurt. When he had eaten, Persons had pulled on a track suit that hung on a nail near the entrance. Harry had only the clothes he had arrived in. Persons made no comment. He laced on a pair of gym boots and said, "It's a nice day. Let's run." Miserably uncomfortable in slipping shoes, Harry had followed him. Persons had not turned or waited. He had stepped out the door and started running.

There was a track, the barest path in the grass. It went up the hill to a storage barn, followed a tractor path and ran across the fields to the farm's north boundary. There it followed an old cart path sunk between banks and sharp with flints. Near the village the track circled in the lane back to the iron-pipe gate and the rutted road to the cottage. It was a five-mile circuit. Persons had marked it out when he first began to live there. Harry Hayes dropped behind to unknot his tie. As his feet moistened the woolen socks, the slipping shoes took up purchase on his heels. Wild berries grew in places and brier hedges were in bloom. In a creek bed Persons pointed out a badger set. Pheasants took occasional flight. Harry Hayes forgot the discomfort of his clothing. He was once again the boy who had stolen away from the Quakers, through the fence and down the bank of the river.

That day, that night, Bill Persons talked. They ran the circuit again and walked for hours in the lanes. It seemed to Harry Hayes that Persons talked about everything in the world. There was not much he could understand, but it sounded like something he might once have known and forgotten.

Over the fire at night Persons asked Harry about his training schedule. He did not want to explain that he had no schedule, that he was so new in the club that nobody had been interested enough to give him one. He repeated one from memory which he had seen pinned up on the notice board by the track coach.

Persons reacted angrily. "Coaches like that should be shot," he said. "A man isn't a bloody machine to be wound up until his spring breaks. These schedule addicts with their treadmills are only fit to train apes. We're not apes, boy, we are men. We can be supermen. A great athlete is like a great artist: his motive is self-expression. When he is perfect, and he can be, the great athlete functions at levels the nothingmen never know. Effort, even agonizing effort, comes out of him like birdsong. These bloody cinders and concrete they pelt over kill a man in the end. They are too artificial. There's nothing natural there. The spiked shoe isn't natural either. Two much of either will ruin a man. You have to run in nature and with nature, get the skin of your feet on the soil. You can't run without love, pushing yourself over an environment as synthetic as plastic. You have to feel the joy to balance the pain and you only get the joy in nature. I'm fifty-eight do you hear me? Now, tonight, at my age, I could run your clockwork men into the ground."

He had glared his pale eyes at Harry, paced about in front of the fire.

"Zatopek did it and everyone copied him. Zatopek was mad. A freak who crucified himself. You run for speed, Zatopek said, and then you repeat it for endurance. He'd run five times two hundred meters, twenty times four hundred meters, five times two hundred meters and then he would step it up to forty times two hundred meters. He was a freak, a god. But he crucified himself. He could have set physical and mental boundaries that would have freed men to take a new look at themselves. But he broke himself with work. He never realized the divine power within him. No, boy, it won't be done that way. Nature is too cunning. You've got to join forces with nature, push her back bit by bit. You can't do it by working until every cell in your body explodes."

Persons quietened and sat moodily chipping at the crusted red embers on the fire logs.

"You see," he said softly, "it's the fear that a man has to beat. That kind of crucifixion is no good in the end against fear. In the beginning it helps push the fear away but then the effort becomes fearful itself."

He had put his eyes on Harry, the rare, gentle smile on his face. "Do you know about fear, Harry?"

"I dunno, really." Harry remembered the pain as he lay on the cinders. "I got the wind up like, the other day. You know, when I fell down on the track."

"That is part of it. What were you afraid of?"

"You know, I felt bad. I'd never felt like that before."

"Did you think you were going to die?"

"I s'pose I did in a way."

Persons poked at the log again. The harsh, thinning hair brushed stiffly back and the clipped mustache and wide, blunt features gave him a military look.

"That is one of the fears, but it is still the first and the worst of them. Sometimes, though, a man can fear not dying. I sometimes did, in prison camp."

The war was a romance to Harry. "Yeah? Were you in prison camp?"

"I was taken at Singapore. There can be worst things than dying."

Harry had watched him, waiting for more.

"Most of us live in one fear or another all our lives. Fear of a heart attack or cancer, fear of the sack, or of being passed over. Fear of the Church, fear of authority, fear of loneliness and old age. The world is rotted with fear. All of us, everywhere, are being pushed back into our fear. The machines we build to free us only make us more captive. Our bodies are rotting around us. An unfit man can't fight fear. The track man has one of the last freedoms to fashion his own destiny to his physical and mental limits. He's the last of the frontiersmen, Harry."

When Harry went to bed, the lamp he carried lit a plaque nailed over the stairs:

WHEN HEALTH IS ABSENT
WISDOM CANNOT REVEAL ITSELF,
ART CANNOT BECOME MANIFEST,
STRENGTH CANNOT FIGHT,
WEALTH BECOMES USELESS,
AND INTELLIGENCE CANNOT BE APPLIED.

—HEROPHILUS, *physician*
to Alexander the Great

In the next two months, Harry Hayes returned twice to Bill Person's cottage. They spent one weekend improving the garden, working almost in silence.

Toward the end of the second visit, after a run, sitting before the fire. Harry Hayes got up his courage: "Mr. Persons, would you teach me? I mean take on my trainin'? I've got this feelin' I could do somethin' but I don't know how to go about it."

Bill Persons showed no surprise. He had been writing on his knee and simply closed the pad. "If you go with me you go all the way."

"That's what I'm after. I want to go all the way." Harry felt himself tremble.

"It won't be easy. Nothing worthwhile is."

"It's what I want. It's, well—I've *got* to have it."

"Then you will withhold nothing. I will be your father, mother, wife, lover, priest. You'll go to the last drop of your blood and energy and then get up and go again."

"It's what I want."

"Give me your hand, then." Persons' eyes shone like glass. "We will start tomorrow. Not get yourself up to bed."

11

THE CLUB blazer had cost eight pounds. Harry had checked the price before he bought it. He had that much and a little more saved for his holidays. He wore the blazer at home, trying it out in the mirror, before he wore it in the street. The Club badge on the pocket was embroidered in red, white and blue with RPAC in a shield.

Old Mrs. Hayes had been pleased with the blazer. "You look real nice, Harry. That shade of blue, it brings out the color in your eyes."

A clear night had followed a clear day. Harry climbed the long hill out of the Saturday night bustle of the London road into the quiet of Royal Park's wide streets and old houses. His shoes shone and his heavy dark hair was slick with water and grease. Passing the green gates of the club, he rattled a proprietorial knock with his knuckles.

Young men he did not know laughed and smoked cigarettes in groups around the hall's entrance. Inside, young couples leaned elbows on the steel tables with straws in fizzing drinks or queued at the counter. The cheaply lined roof of the hall made flat echoes of the loud rock music. Most of the young men wore Club blazers. It comforted Harry until he noticed how stiff and new his looked in comparison. He became uncomfortably aware of the shop creases in the sleeves and wished that he had thought to iron them out.

On the platform at the end of the hall four young men in Beatle haircuts, white turtleneck sweaters and jeans were playing the new sound on electric guitars. Girls in long hair and twirling skirts stamped and twisted near the musical group. He recognized nobody Len Sparks had introduced him to. In that crush it would have been hard to find a face had he known one. The guitars loudened their volume, the dancers gyrated more fiercely than ever.

It seemed to go on like that forever. Harry sat down near the door where the chairs were empty. Once when the musicians took a break to refresh themselves at the panel van with THE WILD ONES lettered on the sides, Harry had queued with the other blazers for a soft drink.

He took his drink outside in the yellow shaft of light from the door where other Club blazers chatted confidentially. Nobody spoke to him. He felt more solitary than ever. He went to the lavatory for something to do, waiting his turn in the odd comradeship of men queuing to empty their bladders. When "The Wild Ones" returned, he followed them inside and took his seat near the door. The girls' twirling skirts, baring the pink flesh above their stocking tops in teasing glimpses, thickened his chest and left him somehow sad.

When Len Sparks came in late he saw Harry as soon as he crossed through the partition. "Well, you did come along?"

Harry stood up.

"Let me introduce my wife. Liz, this is Harry Hayes, the young chap I told you about."

Mrs. Sparks smiled. "Oh. The instant runner?"

"Pleased to meet you."

"He's got a fair turn of speed in an overcoat. We're going

63

to see how he shapes up on the track." To Harry he said, "Are you getting acquainted, Hayes? Meeting your club-mates?"

Harry did not like to admit he had spoken to nobody. "Haven't looked about much. I've been watchin' the dancers."

Sparks looked at him closely. "Let me buy you a drink. I can't take much more of this noise. . . . Whisky, vodka or gin?"

Hayes was confused. "Ah, I dunno . . ."

"I'm pulling your leg. You can have a frightful red squash or a frightful pink squash or a frightful cola."

"A cola, then. Thanks."

They leaned on the counter.

"What's it going to be, Hayes? Are you going to try out for the Marathon?"

"I dunno, really. Haven't thought about it much. Maybe the mile. You know, you read about it in the papers. I dunno really if I'd be much use at anything."

"The mile, eh? Like to be another Roger Bannister, would you?"

"Nothing like that," Harry said, embarrassed. "It's just that the mile's all I know about, like."

"Ah well, we will soon get you sorted out. The thing is to put yourself down for something and see how you go. You've got a miler's build, I must say. I tried out for the mile myself at Cambridge. I had no talent for it whatever. Herb Elliott was a Cambridge man, you know."

Hayes said, "He's an Aussie, isn't he?"

"Did you ever see him run?"

"No. I never."

"The Club has some slow-motion film on him. If you put yourself down for the mile you might ask to see it." He looked at his watch. "I'd better be off, Hayes. I was hoping to see George Stock. He won the Club Marathon today."

"Thanks for the drinks, anyway," Harry said. "And thanks for getting me into the club."

"My pleasure, old chap. We can't get too much young blood."

Sparks looked up then and saw the girl in the doorway.

"Len," she said, "you shouldn't be here. This is your night to swing with Liz."

She stepped inside and Sparks took her hands. "Look, sweetie, you can help here. This is Harry Hayes, a new recruit to the Club. You might introduce him about. Hayes, this is Mary Charlton."

Mary put her handbag on the counter, crossed her legs and leaned on the tips of her fingers.

"Pleased to meet you," Harry said.

Sparks pecked the girl on the forehead. "If you want to swing, Hayes, Mary is the girl to know. Good night, both."

Harry had never been studied so frankly. Glossy girls of Mary's class were strangers to him. He could think of nothing to say. The few girls he had met on excursions with his mates from the printery had been cheerfully rowdy, with accents like his own. She was fetchingly pretty, quite tall, with the long straight hair popularized by models, and extravagantly shadowed eyes. She wagged the cigarette in her fingers, waiting for Harry to light it.

"Don't you smoke?" she had to ask.

"Sorry." Harry felt more than ever clumsy taking the lighter she handed him. "I'm in trainin'. I don't smoke."

"What are you training for?"

"The mile," Harry said.

She bent to the lighter. "Oh? One of the glamour boys."

"I dunno about that," Harry said. "Would you like a drink?"

"Yes. I'd like a gin-and-tonic."

Harry remembered Len Sparks's joke. "You can have a frightful red squash or a frightful pink squash or a frightful cola." It gave him courage.

The girl said, "I'm serious. I'd like a gin-and-tonic."

"But they don't keep it."

"Of course they don't, silly. We could go to the Running Footman. I only dropped in to find an escort. Have you got a car?"

"A car?" Harry was amazed. "I've got no car. I can't even drive one." She sighed and looked bored. "Do you live hereabouts?" Harry asked, for something to say.

She told him that she lived farther down Abbot's Terrace, that her mother kept a boutique in the village. She asked Harry where he lived and he said, vaguely, down the hill. Mary Charlton was restless. Her mother was entertaining, she said, and she had come out because she couldn't bear the people anymore.

The music got louder.

"Gerry and the Pacemakers," Mary said.

"It's got The Wild Ones on the drums."

"Gerry and the Pacemakers would hardly be here in this dump, would they? It's one of their new numbers. Don't you know anything?"

Harry thought miserably that he did not.

"Let's go in and dance," she said.

"I've been in," Harry said helplessly.

Her bold look was on him again. "Don't tell me you don't dance, in addition to everything else."

"I'm sorry. I don't."

"You *are* new," Mary said. "I've not met a boy like you before. What in the world do you do with yourself?"

"I'm studyin' mostly. I'm workin' to be a master printer."

"Sounds ghastly," Mary said and got up holding her hand out.

"Anybody can twist. Come on, I'll teach you."

He felt panic-stricken. "No, really. I wouldn't know how to go about it."

"You can do this, can't you?" She wagged her long hips, her elbows up, the handbag swinging on her arm. "That's all there is to it. It's easy. Come on, now."

She pulled him up. His face felt shapeless to him as he walked down the hall. In the uncaring crush around the musical group there was no room to be conspicuous. Mary began to twist, so close that her flung hair touched his face. Harry began to follow her. She was right. It was easy.

On Abbot's Terrace when he had walked her home from the hall she looked up to the house.

"Good. They're still here. Mummy would be furious if I missed them. One must always be on hand to farewell the parting guests. God, how Victorian can you be?"

Then she had pouted the wide, thick mouth, tilted her head to Harry, bidding him. He had bent to her, his hammering breath a confusion and obstacle.

"My," she had said, "you *are* new."

Then she waved her handbag and went up the path, her skirt swinging.

12

EXCEPT FOR the years in a boarding school at Brighton, Mary Charlton had lived all her life in Royal Park. Her father had been night news editor on a national newspaper and had taught Mary squash on his afternoons off, largely to get out of the house. Mark Charlton had been a philanderer, cited in two divorces. After the second shock he and Gabby Charlton agreed to stay together for Mary's sake but the remainder of his life had been a martyrdom. He took the night editorship to be spared the cold comfort of domestic evenings and although Gabby made him account for his time, Mark Charlton had had a new mistress beside him when he crashed his car in a fog and died.

Mary still played squash at the Club; her mother said it was good for her figure. She was fast and skilled and had no trouble finding partners among the men. The squash players had made a pet of Mary. In her short skirt and lace panties she made a disturbing figure. Mary flirted with the men she partnered. She gave the impression of being available. There had been visits to obscure pubs and restaurants which left the older men bad-tempered. They would get so far with Mary and that would be the end of it.

On her visits to the squash courts Mary met Harry Hayes again. He was coming off the track in running shorts.

"The new boy," Mary said, giving him her bold look. "You could do with some fattening. Don't they feed you at home?"

Harry had flushed, pushed back the damp hair on his forehead. "I didn't know you came here," he said.

"I've been coming here since I was twelve."

"Play squash, do you?" Harry indicated the racquet.

"Yes. Do you?"

"Never tried it."

"You should. I'll teach you if you like."

"Not me."

Mary made a pass with her racquet. "It's good for you. Are you going to have a drink when you've changed?"

Harry was about to tell her again that he didn't drink in training.

Mary showed impatience. "A coffee won't hurt you, will it, Mr. Purity?"

"I s'pose not." Harry smiled.

"That's better," Mary told him. "You should smile more often. I will wait for you at the hall. Hurry up, now."

It had been easier for Harry this time; he listened while Mary talked. Afterwards they walked down Abbot's Terrace to her gate.

"You can come in if you like. I've got some new records."

Harry had looked uneasily up to the house.

"There's nothing to be frightened of. Mother is at the shop, if that bothers you."

"I'm not bothered. It's just I've got a few things to do. Thanks all the same."

Mary shrugged. "Suit yourself. I'll see you."

She did, a week later at the Club, coming from the squash courts again. Harry had his pay in his pocket.

"Are you going for a drink?" Mary asked.

Harry was ready. "I'll take you for a proper drink if you like."

"The boy's gone mad," she said.

At the Running Footman Harry led Mary to the saloon.

She pulled at his blazer. "Not in there, silly. They have a lounge for ladies."

Mary had expertly drunk three gin-and-tonics. Harry had been clumsy with three beers. The prices appalled him.

Mary asked, "Why do you do your hair like that?"

"How d'you mean?" Harry tried to see himself in a mirror across the room. He wondered what was wrong.

"It's pretty hair and you spoil it. Look."

She reached up and showed him her fingers.

He was glad of the clean handkerchief in the breast pocket of his blazer. Her hand came quickly into his. She smiled at him, without mockery.

Harry never greased his hair like that again. It was the first of many lessons Mary Charlton was to give him, the beginning of his awareness of the subtle imprints of class.

At the gate she turned her wide mouth to him again, businesslike about it. She had come up on her toes, pushed herself strongly against him. His whole body trembled.

Leaving, she touched his cheek. "So new," she said. "So new and sweet."

It was almost two months before Harry Hayes and Mary Charlton met again, for a coffee at the hall on their way home from the Club. He used to watch for her at the squash courts. Then six months had passed without a sight of her, until his heart bumped seeing her long, bare legs in the lace pants and short skirt walking down the path between the plane trees.

"My, look at you," Mary said. "You've got a suntan."

"The coach has had us under the lamp. He reckons it tones up the system."

"It has certainly toned you up. You look marvelous."

He found it hard to be casual. "Haven't seen you round much."

"I haven't been round much. Look."

"What is it?"

"It's a ring, silly. An engagement ring."

Harry stood forever, trying words which broke up before he could speak them. His throat was too dry to work properly. "That's great," he said at last. "Congratulations."

"I suppose so. It's an old family friend. We've known each other for ages."

"Best of luck, anyway," Harry said.

"Would you like a coffee?"

"No, thanks. I'm just goin' in. Best of luck. I'll be seein' you."

"Harry?"

He pushed past her, swallowing on the obstruction in his throat. He had met Bill Persons then, and the upset that Mary Charlton had caused in him was washed away. Shortly before the White City championships Harry went on a Saturday morning to the village bookstore. Mary was buying a fashion magazine.

"How different you look," Mary told him, her long, uninhibited inspection missing nothing.

"I've put on a bit. Bill has had me working with the weights."

"Yes, it suits you. But it's not that. You just look different."

Harry asked for the book he had ordered.

"Good heavens. Don't tell me you read poetry?"

"I like it. Bill started me off on it."

"Who is this Bill?"

"Bill Persons. He's my trainer."

"Are you in a hurry?"

"No. I'm in no hurry. It's nice to see you."

"Let's have a coffee, then. I've been hearing things about you. You're becoming quite a celebrity."

"Nothing like that," Harry said.

"Oh yes you are. The papers have been writing about you."

"That's only Club stuff. How do you know about it?"

"Len Sparks keeps me in touch."

He realized that Mary must have asked about him, and was flooded with pleasure.

Mary said, in the coffee shop, "You talk differently, don't you? And do you realize it's been nothing but Bill, Bill, Bill for the past half hour? Is that where you get all these odd ideas?"

Harry said, a little surprised, "I'm sorry. I hadn't noticed. I do get a bit carried away these days. How about you, then? Are you married yet?"

"Soon. In the spring."

She looked at her watch. "I'll have to go, Harry. I've got a lunch date with a girl friend."

When they separated outside the shop, Harry said, "It's been great seeing you. Best of luck in the spring."

When he saw the stocky figure striding out of the clubhouse, Harry had only time to scan him quickly before Persons was surrounded. He seemed fit and well, even exuberant, giving Harry a wink as the track men pressed him with questions about his methods of training.

"Get back to nature," he told them. "How can you expect to run? Most of you don't know how to walk. Look at you." He poked one of them in the chest. "You're all bloody leg, son. Get some pectorals on your chest."

As more athletes came up from the track and field, Persons got more excited. Harry Hayes had never seen him like this. He was going off like fireworks. Persons flung off his tweed hat and went down on invisible blocks, showing them how to balance for the start. He talked theory and names and performances too fast for most of his audience to follow. He withered accepted training techniques.

"What do you say to that, Mr. Hagerty?" a runner asked the track coach who had come up quietly.

"Hagerty?" Persons said. "Are you the Hagerty who trained that three-thousand-meter runner about ten years back? What was his name? Bertie Chivvers?"

"That's right," the coach said. "I saw you run in those days."

"You bloody well butchered him. You had him running on concrete. That's why his knee blew up."

The coach said in a strained voice, "He'd had a bad cartilage from his school days."

"He didn't have a bad cartilage when he came second to Kutz. You butchered that boy on the roads."

They fell quiet and still, looking from Persons to Hagerty in embarrassment.

Hagerty said, making an effort, "If that's what you believe, I'm sorry," and turned to walk away.

Persons' pale eyes were widened on his back. "Sorry?" he shouted after him. "It's too bloody late to be sorry. You, all of you, you shouldn't be allowed to train seals."

70

They broke up, trying to be casual.

"See you, Harry. See you, Mr. Persons."

Persons picked up his tweed hat and banged it against his knee. "Bloody idiot," he said, staring up at the clubhouse. Then he gave his changing smile, put his hand on Harry's shoulder. "How are you coping, now that you're famous?"

"I'm all right. But I was worried about you. Why didn't I hear from you? You look as fit as a fiddle."

"Why wouldn't I be?"

"You said you'd been falling off, in your telegram."

"Oh, that's an old thing. It doesn't signify. A bit of the past coming back. A young man like you with the future at his feet shouldn't trouble about other men's pasts."

"I don't know, Bill. You get me worried at times."

"All you've got to worry about is running over the top of the world. Come on, I'll take you to dinner. That bloody idiot," he said.

Two months after his White City win, Harry Hayes ran again at an open meeting at Cardiff. Invitations from as far as Sweden had come to him addressed care of the Club. It was a bewilderment to him when it began and he took the letters to Bill Persons. Some of it was fan mail, requests for diet and training schedules.

"Sticky-nosed bastards," Persons said. "They're all looking for a miracle. Some little trick they don't know about, something to make it all easy."

The Cardiff invitation interested him and he answered it, asking for details.

"I will handle this stuff in future. Just let me have the mail at the end of the week."

When he told Harry that they would run at Cardiff, Harry worried about his job and the cost of the trip.

"To hell with the job," Persons said. "Why do you think the manager wants to take you to the pub? Every time he looks down at his fat gut it makes him feel better to have you working for him. Cardiff will pay the expenses and it won't be on a shoestring either. You're a drawing card now, boy. Why do you think they want you? The bloody parasites with their sanctimonious amateur oaths. What they want is that clicking at the turnstiles. You mean money in the bank to them."

At Cardiff, in the great arena which had staged the Empire Games, Harry Hayes was favored by fortune to draw the inside lane a second time. In front of a near-record crowd he led from the start and stayed there. His time was 3 minutes 58 seconds. Out of nowhere, in his second big public appearance, Harry Hayes had run through the four-minute barrier.

SUNNY

13

THEY HAD BEEN mates in the army. They had fought inside and outside the wire at Tobruk, spat sand in dugouts rocked by dive bombers, helped chase the Eyetie into Libya. They had fought the English M.P.'s in Alex and Cairo and had not paid in brothels and bars.

When the Australians were pulled out of the desert to help stop the Jap in New Guinea, the mates fought with the Yanks in Brisbane while they waited on the troopships. When Harcourt got a waitress knocked up, Gilmour loaned him the money to quieten her. When Drew went five days AWOL, Harcourt and Gilmour covered for him. They enlisted when the first recruiting office opened and were discharged five years afterwards as privates. Harcourt was briefly a sergeant because he was given no option; most of the platoon had been killed. Drew was machine-gunned in Tobruk, hit in the thigh at Kokoda, took a bayonet thrust through his shirt in the Lae attack and was presented while on leave with gonorrhea by a girl two houses down from his parents, whom he had known as long as he remembered.

Harcourt and Gilmour got malaria in New Guinea and Drewie got it worse.

They had been coming up, when they could, for years. Drew managed a cattle station outside Alice Springs, in the great red heart of Australia.

Two whitewashed posts, swinging a board with AFGHAN WATERS burned into it, marked the entrance to Drew's property. Seven miles up the red, rutted track the buildings lay under pepper trees. A windmill turned above an artesian bore. The overseer's house and the manager's house faced each other across harness sheds, a small forge, a butcher's shop, the grain-and-feed store. An open-fronted garage sheltered trucks, a utility, the overseer's Volkswagen, workbenches and petrol and oil drums. The stockmen's hut opened its rooms on a long, crooked veranda.

They were in from a lily-padded lake a long drive out near a mustering camp. There had been good rains. In a month the lake would be a parched depression. The men sat on the homestead veranda over pannikins of rum, their feet up, and wondered at the stunning, star-crowded sky as covered as a great field of wildflowers. Harcourt sucked his teeth. They had brought back wild duck for dinner.

Mick Drew asked, "You still running that two-up school?"

"She's a beauty," Harcourt said with satisfaction. "I've moved her out to French's Forest. The vice squad knocked me off at the other place. I'd squared the wrong copper. The old lady went up like Vesuvius."

"You must be making a few quid," Drew observed.

Harcourt looked pleased. "I'm not complaining, Drewie. It's up and down. I took a hammering on the Melbourne Cup."

"I told you to lay off your bets," Gilmour said. "That bangtail was home and hosed before he went to the barrier. He wouldn't listen," he told Drew. "You remember the book he made on the donkey derby when we went back from Tobruk?"

"Get stuffed," Harcourt said.

The night was deep and velvet now, the heaped stars brighter than ever. The settlement noises had quietened. They were thinking about bed when the yellow bulb dimmed, flickered, dimmed and went out.

Mick Drew banged his feet off the rail. "That bloody generator."

The buildings reshaped themselves in the darkness.

"Been giving trouble?" Gilmour felt carefully for his pannikin.

"It's clapped out. I've got a new one on order."

They heard a call from the overseer's wife: "Sun-ny!"

Drew listened and then stepped off the veranda. "Sunny," he shouted. "Hul-lo, Sunny."

"How long is it likely to be out?" asked Harcourt.

"Depends on Sunny. I don't know how he has kept the thing going this long."

They filled the pannikins and waited. When the light snapped on, there was a derisory cheer from the stockmen.

Drew stretched an arm. He said, "I tell you. That Sunny's a bloody wizard."

An aboriginal boy, finer-featured than the Arunta, his hair

glossy and waving, tapped bare feet up the stone steps and stood wiping his hands on dirty cotton waste.

He smiled and nodded to Harcourt and Gilmour. "She's just about done in, boss. I can't patch that old fella wirin' much more."

Drew said, "They told me at the Alice that the new plant should be up in a week. Reckon you can keep her going?"

"You talk-talk the stockmen use lamps, boss. That old one loaded too much."

"I'll do that. Thanks, Sunny."

Drew watched the boy go. "He's right, you know. That generator was only meant for the homestead and the meat house."

Harcourt said, "He's a smart little fella. Where did you get him? He doesn't look like the Arunta."

"He's a Pintubi. Did you notice his eyes?"

"Can't say I did. Why?"

"Yeah," Gilmour said. "I thought I noticed something."

"They're blue. He's got white blood."

Harcourt said, "That wouldn't be new. There was plenty of gin jockeys in the old days."

"Not in Pintubi country," Mick Drew said. "They didn't know there were blacks in that desert up until a few years ago."

Gilmour said, "I saw something about that on the box."

"You could have done. It made a bit of a stir. Chips Vogel, the patrol officer out at Papunya, got a tame Pintubi to guide him. Chips found people in the Gibson Desert who had never seen a white man. About the only other living things in the Gibson are lizards and a few rodents. Tucker's so scarce the families have to break up to keep going. Chips came across a toddler hunting on his own. The kid had a fit when he saw the jeeps. Chips put up a smoke to bring his father in and he reckons he must have been hunting five miles from where he found the kid. Sunny was brought in by an old man, back in '54. He was a bit of a curiosity, on account of his blue eyes. They bunged him up to the mission. I've got him on loan. He's a bloody wizard with machinery. They're trying to get him to school in Adelaide. The Fathers can't teach him any more."

Harcourt yawned. "The Pintubi would have to be ratbags to live in that bloody desert."

They were sleepy with rum now.

Drew got up and corked the rum bottle, stretched himself and grunted. "I don't know about you, but I'm turning in."

"And you reckon there are big mobs of roos at No. 3 bore, do you, Drewie?" Gilmour got up and tossed the dregs from his pannikin.

"They were there a week ago. There's been no stock around that bore lately. The roos have come in for the green feed."

"They'll get green feed," Harcourt said. "Right up the Khyber Pass."

"You'd better take Sunny with you," Drew advised. "That old shooting truck's in worse shape than the generator."

Billy Two-Toes had once been stamped by a horse and now helped raise vegetables in the station garden. Mischief was a roustabout and impartially useless. They set out with Sunny Pintubi in the back of the bouncing truck. Drew had sent them along as skinners. There was a track to follow. When it became doubtful, Gilmour leaned from the cabin and took instructions from Billy Two-Toes. Mischief had given advice. He had shot out his arm to point the way with a butcher's knife and had frightened the life out of Gilmour.

"If I was as lucky as old Drewie, that black bastard would have taken my skull off."

They had driven for an hour when Mischief hammered on the roof of the cabin. Gilmour leaned out cautiously. Mischief waved the knife and pointed.

"Big fella mob. Plenty too much." It was still early. There was no heat haze. Away to the left where the red earth was smudged green, they saw movement.

"There must be a couple of hundred," Harcourt said, squinting. "Toss you for first shot."

Harcourt lost. They pulled the rifles from under the seat and shucked the canvas covers. The rifles were old army models with grafted barrels. The heavy .303 cartridge cases were crimped on a .22 lead. The velocity produced by this hybrid could stop a six-foot kangaroo in as long as he took to hit the earth.

Gilmour climbed to the tray. Harcourt handed up a wide webbing harness. There were anchor points bolted to the sides of the truck and to the cab, behind the driver. Gilmour strapped himself into the harness while Sunny Pintubi snapped on the traces.

"How does it feel?" Harcourt asked.

Gilmour was braced, leaning slightly back, looking out over the cab top. "Hand up the rifles, will you?" He swept the barrel in an arc, letting himself hang in the harness. "She's right. Who's got the shells?"

Gilmour loaded both rifles. "Here, Sunny. Hand me this one when I call for it." He considered Mischief and Billy Two-Toes. "Mischief had better ride in the cab, Jim. I don't want him banging about behind a man's kidneys with that bloody great knife he's got."

Mischief grinned and wagged the butcher's knife.

Harcourt said, "No? Well, I don't want him banging about with that bloody great knife in the cab."

"Put Billy Two-Toes in between you."

"Up Billy Two-Toes," Harcourt said. "He's got a bloody great knife of his own."

The old bucks of the browsing mob came up hard on the props of their buttressed tails. The truck was still distant, fuming dust. The does took notice, cropped nervously. A few joeys played. Others peeked from their mothers' bulging pouches. The bucks laid their ears forward and watched. Some hopped a few yards uncertainly, spreading alarm through the mob.

Harcourt's big bare arms were laid over the jumping wheel, accelerator pedal hard down. He saw the mob mill and swore at Gilmour. The first shot crashed loudly in the cabin. The mob began to move. The cabin crashed twice. On the edge of the mob a big buck took a few wheeling jumps, went down in a spurt of dust. The kangaroos were off now, bent forward in huge flying leaps, their heavy tails cocked, black-palmed hands curled on their chests. Above the racket in the truck and the crash of Gilmour's rifle, the ground boomed under the mob. A doe went over, turning like a wheel in hoops of red dirt. Harcourt jinked hard to miss her, aimed the car's hood at a group shepherded by an old buck. Gilmour's shot exploded in his spine. The big wheels of his hams thumped into his rib cage, splitting the belly and spilling the entrails in a flailing mess about him.

Harcourt wrinkled his nose, pulled the truck into a slide, picked out another big buck. That skin would be a write-off. As the truck jinked, Billy Two-Toes floated over the tailgate.

Gilmour was using the second rifle, swinging in the harness, blasting off shots as fast as he could sight.

When Harcourt stopped the truck and got out, Gilmour was still firing into the distance.

Harcourt said, "Turn it up. You're not sighting that thing by radar."

For a mile behind them, still, furry bodies were heaped on the stained red earth.

The truck began to give trouble in the early afternoon. Mischief had not replaced the petrol cap when the tank was filled that morning. Now the truck coughed on the powdered dust which had mixed into the petrol. Sunny Pintubi cleaned the carburetor, blew out the fuel lines, but the truck was unreliable. There were thirty hot smelling skins rolled on the tray and a heap of twitching steaks from the young kills. The truck had stalled again.

"Try her now, boss."

Gilmour was climbing into the cabin when Harcourt said, "Quick! Where's the rifle?"

A very big buck was hopping slowly across the road, targeted against thick scrub behind a dry creek bed.

"What a beauty," Gilmour whispered.

Harcourt made a quick estimate, raised the sights and went down on one knee, his elbow in the carbine sling to steady it. The rifle barrel swung. The big kangaroo slumped, picked himself up, and hopped crookedly toward the dry creek.

Harcourt fired again.

"You're over the top of him," Gilmour shouted. "Drop your sights."

Harcourt rasped the sights down, threw the rifle up and pulled on an uncocked hammer.

"You great ape. You didn't eject. If he gets to the scrub you'll lose him."

Gilmour jumped into the truck, cursing and whirring the starter. He saw Sunny Pintubi drop his spanners and run for the disappearing kangaroo. Harcourt pulled his hat off and slammed it on the ground.

"Right across a man's line of fire. What's that black bastard think he's doing?"

The starter motor caught, cut out, caught and roared the engine. Harcourt ejected the spent shell and leaped for the cabin.

The wounded buck was getting close to the dry creek. Sunny was a distant, flying figure. The truck had begun to splutter when Harcourt's door caught up with the running boy. They stayed like that, while the scrub came up. They stayed like that until the old-man kangaroo crossed the creek and gained the shelter. Sunny was still at Harcourt's door when Gilmour had to brake and pull the wheel hard over in a fury of spraying dust. Sunny raced over the creek bed and was closed out by the scrub.

"Bugger it," Gilmour said. "What a beauty. That's the biggest roo I ever saw. What's wrong with you?"

Big Jim Harcourt rubbed his face. He knocked a knuckle on the cracked glass of the speedometer. "You reckon that thing's working?"

Gilmour said, "Who gives a stuff?"

"That thing was hitting thirty back there."

"So was that old-man roo."

"Yeah," Harcourt said, looking hard at his mate. "So was that Pintubi kid."

Gilmour asked, "How do you mean?"

"What do you mean, how do I mean?" Harcourt asked impatiently. "I mean that Pintubi kid was running a photo finish with the truck for a bloody half mile or more."

They talked about it on the homestead veranda that night, rum and ice in their pannikins. Drew said, "They reckon those Gibson Desert Pintubi do thirty miles between water holes. If they come to a dry one, they do another thirty miles to the next. You take a myall, one of the wild fellas. They'll run as far as a white man can ride. When they pull up they wouldn't blow out a candle."

Harcourt persuaded Sunny Pintubi to run for him next day. Drew had to help. The boy was embarrassed, could not understand their reason. He insisted on leaving the station, where he could not be seen by others.

"Go on," Harcourt said. "Show us what you can do. There's a quid in it for you."

They followed Sunny in the Land Rover. He moved off, looking over his shoulder.

"Get right up on him, Drewie." Harcourt leaned across, holding the horn down. Sunny sprinted for a quarter mile and stopped. He hung his head, scuffed his bare feet.

"It's silly fella," he said shyly.

That night they talked about it again.

"He wasn't trying," Harcourt said. "But for a bit there, he fairly flew."

The next evening, Harcourt brought it up again.

In the room they shared, Charlie Gilmour pulled off his boots and sat on the army cot, smoking. "Come on. What's on your mind?"

Harcourt looked at him innocently. "How do you mean?"

"You know bloody well what I mean. You've been on about this Pintubi kid for days."

Harcourt pulled off his trousers and dropped them on the floor. "He's got me interested."

"He's got you interested, right enough. When you're interested there's a quid in it somewhere."

Harcourt lay back in singlet and underpants, scratching the hair on his belly. He put an arm behind his head and stared at the sagging ceiling.

"Remember Gus Drake? You've met him at the two-up game. He runs a book in Parramatta."

"I know Gus."

"Well, he's been cleaning up, laying the odds on athletics. He won the bundle on Delanoy at the Melbourne Olympics. Sent the Pommy visitors home broke."

"Go on," Gilmour said.

"Suppose I got this kid down south. Run him in private matches. You know, have a come-on for the two-up. A man might do all right, Charlie."

Gilmour did not know whether to be amazed or amused. "How would you run him at the game? You're so far into the bush the coppers can't find you."

Harcourt said, "Along with firebreak. I've been thinking about it. That firebreak would be ready-made."

Gilmour thought about the firebreak, the clearing wider than a road, running miles through the gums and ti trees, behind the stamped hide where Harcourt ran his illegal two-up game. Some of the gamblers walked to the game along the firebreak, their cars parked inconspicuously on a lake racketing with motorboats and water-skiers.

"It's as rough as guts on that firebreak," Gilmour said.

"It's a bit stony, that's all. A man would only need to fix a half mile. That would be enough to run laps."

They lay looking at the ceiling. White moonlight slanted through the open window, across the parched, bare floorboards. The night was loud with small noises.

Gilmour had many reasons to respect Harcourt's instinct for an advantage. After a long time, he said, "You awake, Jim?"

"Yeah."

"You seem pretty sure of this kid."

"I've worked it out off the speedometer. That kid can fly half a mile."

After another silence, Gilmore creaked restlessly on his cot. "Anyway, you'd never get him south. These blacks are all wards of the Government."

"We'd have to go through the Aborigines' Protection Board. You heard what Drewie said. The Fathers at the mission want to get the kid south, to learn a trade. If we had a proposition, an apprenticeship, they'd fall over their rosary beads to help."

Gilmour got up on an elbow. "An apprenticeship? Who's going to give him an apprenticeship?"

Harcourt concentrated on the ceiling. He said, vaguely, "Shouldn't be too much trouble. You could, for instance."

"What's that?" Gilmour asked incredulously.

Harcourt said, vaguely again, "You're registered as a factory. You could apprentice him as an oxywelder, on those lawn-mower petrol tanks of yours."

Gilmour was sitting up now. "Me apprentice him? You're stark-staring mad."

Harcourt swung his feet off the bed. "Listen, Charlie—"

"I'll be buggered if I'll listen."

"This could be a good thing. Now take it easy, listen—"

They were both sitting up, bare feet on the floor.

"I knew you were brooding on something," Gilmour said wildly, "but this beats the lot."

Big Jim Harcourt bent and fumbled in his trousers for cigarettes.

14

IT TOOK nine months to arrange for the custody of Sunny Pintubi. Gilmour made the application. The factory had prospered, Gilmour's background was respectable. Mick Drew was persuaded to help.

"Drewie knows the Fathers. He's a tyke himself and that gives him the run on the rails."

Mick Drew said, "It can't do any harm, I suppose. Father O'Malley wanted him to go to Adelaide, anyway. He's a bright kid. There's nothing up here for him. But I don't want him mucked about."

When Big Jim Harcourt flew into Alice Springs to get his "dark horse," as he called Sunny, to Gilmour, he saw on Mick Drew's face that something had happened.

They made the customary fast ride into town, Drew remote and frowning. In a bar they drank the first cold beer, waited for the second.

Harcourt rolled his glass. "How's Sunny?" he asked, expecting something.

Drew stared at the bar and propped his stiff leg on the footrail. He looked worn, his temples hollowed under the short mousy hair.

He said, careful not to be overheard, "The bloody Arunta got him."

Harcourt's fleshy features were blank. "I don't get you."

"The Arunta. The wild fellas. There's been a bunch of them on walkabout. They caught Sunny out at the Twenty-mile Camp. I don't know what to do about it. If Father O'Malley gets to know, a man's life won't be worth living."

The Arunta were 150 miles off their own country, a big group, mostly old men. They had been three months on the walkabout. A patrol had gone out, found the Arunta camped, urged them back to the reservation. Walkabouts were common; the Arunta had done no harm. There had been no reports of theft or cattle speared.

Sunny had twice been to Twenty-mile Camp with loads of cattle cake and salt lick. There were stockyards there, a store shed and a shelter. The camp was being prepared for branding. Drew had sent Sunny because the boy loved to drive the truck and could coax it along in trouble. The old men of the Arunta had watched him from the shelter of red gums along a watercourse. They had pointed with their lips, murmured in their deep, crooning voices, clacked their spears as they talked. When he left, the Arunta came out of the red gums, stalked the huts and rattled the doors. They bent over Sunny's bared footprints. Tracks of a boy ready for manhood, tracks of a white man's boy. The old ones sat hunkered, talked in soft calls, their scrawny dogs tonguing beside them. Chips of salt lick had broken at a hut. The Arunta bit on chips from a salt lick and spat into their beards, wiped their hands on hair rancid with kangaroo grease. At the camp in the red gums the running meat of the kill charred on the cooking fires. The old men sat on one leg. They were the keepers of the law.

Sunny Pintubi did not know that the Arunta were there until he backed out of the hut to shut the door. They had watched him for an hour, reswinging a gate on the stockyards; had come out of the gums like shadows when he went to work in the hut. He was startled and frightened by the naked men; wild fellas were strangers to him. They spoke in Arunta, touched his blue eyes as he stood in the sunlight and shivered. They put their hands on him when he pushed toward the truck, bumped their spears on the ground in warning. One of the old Arunta spoke and a man gently took

Sunny by each arm. He was sweating with fear now, did not know what they wanted from him.

The old man stood on one leg, the sole of a foot against his thigh, leaning on his handful of spears. Behind them the women came out to peep. The old man put his wisping beard in his mouth and chewed on it. He made finger talk. Sunny shook his head. The old man walked forward and pulled at the belt Billy Two-Toes had plaited. In alarm now, Sunny struggled and kicked. The old Arunta undid the belt, dragged down the boy's khaki shorts. When they fell the men looked and grunted. The old one spoke gravely, turned and walked toward the trees, clattering his spears at the women. The others followed, pulling Sunny with them. When he shouted, braking his heels in the dirt, a young hunter struck him with a spear.

There would be no help. He had little will to resist. He sat against a tree where they had put him, a hair belt lashed on his ankles, a hunter there to guard him. He knew dimly what was to be done. His eyes were closed on fear and revulsion. They had taken his shirt; he was naked, blazing with shame at the giggles of the women, the excitement with which they peeped at him. He called Father O'Malley's name and called on Boss Drew. The hunter answered, began to whisper a chant, nodding his head, the petals of his soft, wide nostrils flaring. Shadows began dropping like rain among the red gums. A screech of cockatoos flew overhead. The women went at a command from his guard. The boy leaned quivering against the wide-butted tree, almost in a drug of waiting, his memory flickering pictures on his lids: the old man with lizards in his hair, the sweet flowers they had sucked in the good place. As darkness came, from the distance the others had gone to, sticks began to beat on the ground.

A space had been cleared and bedded with a layer of leaves off the red gums. A big fire blazed on the clearing, cracking with flames and tossing sparks. Some of the old ones had stuck duck down on their faces and bodies. They stamped as they ran, put their beards in their mouths, a mesmerizing monotony of sound. At the tree another man unlashed Sunny's ankles, drew him up on his feet. He carried a paste of red ocher on a bark, began to daub the boy's body. The sticks beat louder on the ground. The smell of the man was strong. He was chanting something that sounded like words.

Sunny heard the low voices of women, their feet scraping dry leaves beside him, and tightened his closed eyes. The guard grunted over their whispers and giggles. When the hand touched his belly, the fingers long, thin and cold, his body winced with shame. The fingers fluttered across his skin and lightly, delicately, lifted the sacrificial penis. Sunny rose on his elbows, eyes wide with outrage. The gin smiled broken teeth at him, her oily old eyes glinting. He struck at her, felt the rasp on his forearm of her scaled breasts, as thin and leathery as empty purses. The blow from the guard's spear took him heavily on the temple, searing his vision. The haft in his throat pushed him back. The guard shook his head.

"Better," he said. "Him better fella bimeby."

There was no anger in the Arunta, only the waiting for understanding while he watched Sunny gravely, the haft of the spear held tight against his throat. The Arunta turned his head to speak. The old gin began to work with both hands. The spear's pressure relaxed, permitting Sunny to lift his blazing face. He saw the other gin now, for the first time, crouched near his feet, a plump young shape in the shadows. The hag smiled and nodded, rolling her eyes, whispering, indicating the girl. From a bark beside her she scraped a lump of kangaroo fat and rubbed it on Sunny's genitals. Then shyly, giggling, her head averted, the young gin took him in her hands. The guard watched, frowning, then turned and walked off. It was the custom of the old gin's people, meant to delay a possible tumescence after the operation. The young gin's fingers were urgent and decisive on him now. Helplessly, fearfully, incredulously, Sunny felt his own dark stirring and rise. The old gin cackled, whispered to the girl, and scrabbled away to sit and watch.

The deft fingers commanded him now, beyond the reach of denial. He lifted his head once again and stared directly into the girl's eyes. Her face was quite changed, softened and slackened, all shyness departed. Her eyes were hot with arrogance and power. As he hardened in her fingers her breath blew on her thick, parted lips. She crouched lower over Sunny's bound feet, intent on the betrayal worked by her hands. She was grunting, circling her squatted hips, when Sunny fell back, his tears streaming.

They tied back his hair, gagged his mouth with a ball of hair string. Sunny Pintubi was lost now, gone back on a tide of blood beyond thinking. Back past the old man of the lizards to the ghosts of other places, other fires, in a pink-and-red desert that filled the world. The pounding sticks, the stamping feet, the miasma of flame and shadow, the "Arr, Arr, Arr" of voices thumping like wind in a pipe, congested in his brain, swelled in his heart to bursting. Their hands were laid on him everywhere, touching and plucking with excitement. Three men stooped to take his body on their backs; other hands lifted him across. Crowded about, they followed the stooped men to the fire. New bodies spread-eagled on the red gum carpet, their hands and arms clutching upward. The stooped men went down over them. On this operating table of heaped humanity, fierce arms pinned the boy's body. Now another sound went up from the singers, a booming, humming, shrieking note in imitation of the presiding spirit. The women heard, trembled and fell still. The men holding Sunny's feet forced his legs wide apart. One of the old men with duck down on his body, his beard between his teeth, eyes rolling, stepped into the space between the thighs. He held up a knife of chipped quartz on a handpiece of resin. His other hand felt for the penis, grasped the prepuce and pulled it forward. The singing stopped. The quartz knife swung, hacking. The boy's body convulsed. His teeth tore into the ball of human hair. The operator held up the bloodied skin, passed it behind him on an outburst of appreciation. Then he bent again and deftly cut a slit in the urethra. Sunny's body had slumped, no longer needed restraining. The blood gushing from him was collected on a bark and carried away with the skin for burial. Quietly, the wound was dressed with paper bark, clay and fat. The old man who had operated touched the boy's body tenderly and proudly.

The sticks beat softly on the ground, the chant became a whisper. They untangled themselves and laid the shocked body gently on the leaves of red gum. They removed the bitten gag. Blood ran in Sunny's mouth, choked his whimpers. He turned his head to retch.

They heard the Land Rover while it was still distant. The gins heard it and began to clamor. A man rose and scattered the fire with his spear. A dog barked in the women's camp. Before Mick Drew reached the outpost, the Arunta had gone through the gums, black ghosts moving fast in the moonlight, back toward their own country, the old men grave with having kept the law.

"There's the truck, anyhow," Mick Drew said with relief, seeing its shape ahead. "Sunny must have bedded down for the night." He blew the horn. That should wake him. But no figure came from the hut. As he switched off, Drew saw that the truck was still unloaded. Apprehension chilled him. He blew the horn again. Billy Two-Toes limped toward the huts and stopped, went down on his haunches in the dust.

There was no sound or movement in the moon's white light.

Drew felt the need to clear his throat. "What is it, Billy?"

Billy Two-Toes put up a warning finger. He cocked his head, listening. "Wild fella bin here, boss. Plenty wild fella."

"What wild fella?" Drew said, getting out of the Land Rover. "What would wild fellas be doing out here?"

"Sunny with wild fellas," Billy Two-Toes said. "Wild fella make talk-talk. Tracks say wild fella bin take-um Sunny."

"Which way, Billy?"

"Longa scrub boss."

"For Christ's sake," Mick Drew said.

"For Christ's sake," he said again, kneeling by the hardly recognizable boy, daubed with blood and red ocher, grinding his teeth on the leaves of red gum in the scattered burnings of the fire. He lifted Sunny's head, stared unbelievingly at the wadded mess between his thighs.

"Oh, for Christ's sake. What did they do to him?"

Billy Two-Toes said cheerfully, "Ha-i, Ha-i, them wild fellas bin make-um Sunny man."

15

THE COAST there folds beach after beach between headlands that crouch over fallen rock like humped and furry animals asleep. In the winter, fishermen sit on stools, their great rods tethered on heavy sinkers beyond the surge. In summer the sands are covered by bodies fashionably naked. In the curl of green rollers the young speed on surfboards down the rushing slopes, their walnut bodies balanced like sculptures. In the hills that back the beaches, bright new houses see over bright new gardens to bright new clubs, hotels and supermarkets. The traffic of bright new cars keeps the motorcycle policemen busy. It suited Big Jim Harcourt. He could run his two-up game in peace on the coast. In the rush through French's Forest to the beaches, his customers drew no attention.

Harcourt's game was run a half mile from the road that roared through the forest reserve. Logs edged the hard-stamped clearing and made a seat for the players. They walked in along a grass-flattened track or down the firebreak from an approach farther out. They were native born and English, Scotch, Irish, Italian, Greek, German, Lebanese,

Dutch, Maltese and Spanish. They were hard men, some of them, known at every game around Sydney, and they used the broad Australian idiom in the accent of their mother tongues.

Harcourt presided impartially over this immigrant melting. Betting arguments were settled briefly and without benefit of too much discussion. Harcourt had the weight, height and experience and his fattening belly only slowed him a bit. The real gamblers liked it that way; there was always plenty of money at Harcourt's game. A big winner got an escort to his transport and a half hour's start, to be on the safe side. A big loser got a handout from Harcourt to drink himself out of depression. Thousands of pounds changed hands on a good Sunday. Harcourt took ten percent out of the "center," the stake of the spinner who headed or tailed the tossed pennies, and expected a "chuck-in" from big winners betting against the fall of the coins on the side.

Out of Harcourt's take he paid the ring keepers and the lookouts stationed up the firebreak and near the road to watch for police.

"Ten pounds he heads them."

"I want a hundred in the center to see him go. Any part of a hundred in the guts."

"I'll back the tail. I'll take any money he tails them."

The formal cries of the game and the flash of the polished pennies spinning against the blue sky continued until the darkening of shadows. Magpies and kurrawongs watched from old trees. The summer cicadas drummed louder than the men's voices. In the center of the ring Big Jim Harcourt called the tune, keeping his eye on everyone and everything.

A year had greatly changed Sunny. It had not been as hard for him as Gilmour had feared. His skin had lightened startlingly, out of the burning sun of the center. The mystery of his inheritance had only been signaled before in the curiosity of his eyes and vaguely in the definition of his features. Duriny that first southern winter the white ancestor lost in the Pintubi's dreaming surfaced in the boy and began to look out like a genie uncorked from its bottle. It was something Harcourt and Gilmour were unprepared for. They were puzzled by the difference in the boy before it dawned on them what it was.

"I tell you," Harcourt said, "it's bloody well spooky. The way he's going, he could pass for a wog."

The men in Gilmour's small factory got over their surprise.

Sunny's painful shyness and confusion bothered them to begin with. But he only needed to be told once how to do a job. He could use his hands even if they couldn't get more than a nod from him.

"It was a mad idea from the start," Gilmour said gloomily. "I want my brains crushed for getting talked into it."

"Give him a go," Harcourt said, but he was troubled too.

Within a month the men at the factory had adopted Sunny as a wonder. He wasn't just an abo in an affluent new suburb. He was a Pintubi, one of the lost people. They mentioned him importantly over their beers, invoking the boy like a curious possession.

"You heard about those Pintubi they came across up in the center? There's one working out at Gilmour's. They reckon he's got more brains than any of these wog new Australians. Tell them about Sunny Pintubi, Alf."

The men would give Sunny a pound and send him out for cigarettes or something else they did not need. He had a lot to get used to; it was good training for him, they said. A kid like that, down from a mission, he'd never even seen the ocean. They would send him farther afield, for something else they did not want, giving him careful instructions about bus routes, streets, and the proper cost of the fares.

"The change is right," they would observe, nodding at each other. "He went clear to Balgowlah for that screwdriver."

And to Sunny, "All right, was it? No trouble? Nobody chipped you, did they?"

If Sunny did not understand, they would repeat it.

"I mean chipped you. Say anything funny. No? Well, if anyone chips you, Sunny, just come back and blow down my ear."

Sunny never used the factory urinal. He would go into the closet and shut the door.

"What do you do in there, Sunny?" one of the men joked. "I reckon you must sit down to pee."

Gilmour was in the factory. He swung on the man, all stringy eleven stone of him, fierce beyond any need. "You shut your trap. You hear me? Shut your trap or you'll be out on your arse."

"What did I say? All I said—"

"I know what you said." Gilmour was shaking. "Leave the kid alone. Just keep your big trap shut."

Mae Harcourt was childless. She had married against her parents' better judgment and often remarked on their insight to her husband. She had ceased, after ten years of eruptions,

88

to hope any longer for the miracle of Harcourt's reformation. As the price of peace, Harcourt was liberal with Mae. Money became her comfort. She had her own car, the most conspicuous house in the street, and would say, when other women inquired about her husband's business, "Jim? Oh, Jim's in everything. He deals in things, you know."

It was a surprise to Big Jim Harcourt when his wife became interested in Sunny. She had told the neighbors how her husband had brought back an aboriginal boy from the center, had got him a job with a friend. The neighbor's thought it quaint, but charitable. All were curious and impressed. It made Mae feel important. She wanted to see for herself and worried Harcourt about it.

"All right. Get off my back. I'll bring him in on the way to the game."

While Harcourt opened a bottle of beer in the kitchen, Mae offered Sunny lemonade. He wore tan cotton slacks and an open-necked shirt, the summer uniform of boys his age. Mae Harcourt came into the kitchen, quite fluttery.

She said, "He doesn't look like a black at all. I mean not like that one on the stamps. And his manners, he's so respectful. I don't know, but I just expected something different."

Harcourt said, "He wouldn't come in riding a bloody boomerang, would he? Don't be all day; you've got the kid confused enough as it is."

After she had met Sunny again, Mae Harcourt said, "It's cruel to have that boy living in a room at the factory. What does he do about his food?"

Harcourt said, "The cleaning woman gets him a meal. It wouldn't be any worse than some of the meals I get."

"Yes." Mae Harcourt tightened her mouth. "You can see by that gut of yours you don't get enough on your plate."

Sunny moved in with the Harcourts a month after he turned eighteen. Father O'Malley had written to Gilmour suggesting that they might give Sunny a party. He said Sunny had always had a little something at the mission. Father O'Malley had given Sunny his birthday. It was the day the old man with the lizards in his hair had stumbled into the settlement at Papunya. The flying doctor had estimated the boy's age. It was as near as anyone would ever get.

They did give him a party, at the factory. Gilmour turned on a nine-gallon keg. Some of the men with teen-age boys of their own were invited to bring them along.

"This little bastard's taking over," Harcourt said moodily.

"Look at him. He's as much at home as a ponce in a brothel. I'd have laid a hundred to one against this six months ago."

Gilmour said, "It's a turn-up, right enough. You know you can't top him in the shop. He's one of the best hands I've got."

"Yeah?" Harcourt said. "Well, I wasn't flying up and down to the Alice as a gift to the lawn-mower business. I've got an investment in him and it's just about time it came good."

Gilmour had almost forgotten the reason for Sunny. "Go on," he said. "You're not still on about that, are you?"

"You're right I am. He can fly a half mile. I'm not having him over to my place just so Mae can swank. I'm going to start him training. That's the only reason I'm having him. I want to watch his diet."

Gilmour snorted. "His diet? What do you know about diet?"

Harcourt got angry. "I know what we fed to that grey-hound of mine and he won eight in a row."

"And dropped down dead."

"Get stuffed," Harcourt said. "That was the overdose."

"How about if you're wrong? How about if he can't run?"

"I'll kick his arse all the way back to Drewie's."

After Sunny Pintubi moved from his room at the factory into the shelter of the Harcourt basement, Big Jim bought a stopwatch and proceeded to reconnoiter athletic events.

In the early mornings Harcourt drove Sunny to empty dirt roads in the forest reserve, marking out distances by the car's trip meter. He and Gilmour were doing a lot for Sunny, he told him; this was a way he could pay them back. Harcourt also told Sunny that if he did not run, he would kick his backside up around his neck where he could wear it for a collar.

Sunny went gratefully to the factory each day. He was at peace with the machines that answered his dark hands as readily as they did a white man's. The clatter of the work-shop was as much a release to him as its silence was to the others. The painful thoughts that struggled for a tongue in him were stilled in the work and noise.

Often, at night, when the houses in the streets were still, the roads emptied and silent, the sea heard mouthing at the cliffs, he would walk in heartbreak for the wide, red country, the pale river gums and the infinite, star-crowded skies.

This was his wide, red country. A dark road aching away

between houses with dead, glinting eyes of glass. He would think of Father O'Malley for comfort and because he was alone among the hard, white men's faces, thin-nosed, thin-lipped, their cheeks as narrow as whips, he would invent black faces as he walked, use blackfellows' talk to himself. The faces he made were of nobody he knew. He made them out of the shapes of the hills or the rearing of a far headland. Their nostrils were as wide and soft as flowers, the lips curved and thick and wide, the eyes dark and secret, like pools held in rocked water holes.

There was a hollow on a headland, sheltered from the wind. It became Sunny's place. The crash and suck of the waves below him was a comfort, like the noise of the factory. The bent thoughts that he labored to straighten were less disturbing there. His eye could reach as far as it could see. On the great plain of the sea he was rested. It spread toward forever in the moonbeams, like the wide, red country that was his own. He would sit there, the strange one among strangers torn even from the acceptance of himself.

Sunny ran because it was natural to him, because he wanted to please Harcourt and because he was frightened of the big man. Harcourt checked his times against the record he had made at the amateur meetings. Inside a month he knew beyond doubt that Sunny was something unusual. He would lope a mile—Harcourt on his heels in the car, blowing the horn at him, one eye on his stopwatch—and pull up at the tree Harcourt had marked as casually as though he had walked.

BOMBAY

16

ON THE afternoon that Harvey Tonkin took leave of his friends and family to fly to his Bombay posting, he had done so in a misery separate from the massive hangover that troubled him. Harvey was built for the pace and comforts of a sophisticated manufacturing society. A young man from the Consulate met him at the airport with a chauffeur bearing a king-sized umbrella. As far as Harvey could see through the downpour, he had arrived to find India in the grip of floods.

"Good lord," the young man observed, "this is nothing. The last flutter of the monsoon. You should have been here last month."

On the hideous drive from the airport, between miserable hutments, the coolie crowding of the narrow, broken roads the dirt and scramble of petty industry, the continuous note of the horn, the sheeting rain and spraying brown puddles, Harvey determined that at the first opportunity the State Department would have his resignation.

"We've booked you into the Taj Mahal. You will be comfortable there until you find digs to suit you."

Harvey knew about the Taj Mahal. He had seen it on postcards. He had never thought of it as a place to book into.

"Don't they have regular hotels?" Harvey asked gloomily, bracing himself against the headache which had not left him.

"How do you mean?"

"Regular hotels. Hotel hotels. That place is built around a tomb or something."

"A tomb? In the Taj?" The young man puzzled about it. "Good lord, you don't mean *the* Taj Mahal."

Harvey was rubbing at the window, trying to see through the downpour. He turned and inspected his companion. "Look," he said, "it's been a long flight. I'm tired and I've got a headache. What in hell are you talking about?"

"The Taj. There's no tomb in the Taj. The only Taj with a

tomb in it is the Taj Mahal at Agra. Up north. Near Delhi. The famous temple."

Harvey felt silly. "All right," he said. "To hell with it anyhow."

By the time Harvey had been in Bombay a month his nostalgia for home needed resuscitating when he wrote to his family. In the second month he moved into his own flat in Pallonji Mansions on Cuffe Parade. By the time he wired Scott Reynolds, he was a figure in Bombay society.

The prohibition of alcohol, which is written into the Indian Constitution, has many effects on the society it is designed to benefit. The coolie castes, for whom alcohol is often the solitary comfort of their abiding misery, drink—when they do —the bathtub country liquor which reliably hastens blindness, paralysis and an earlier death than they might expect in the nature of things. The Treasury comforts itself about the millions lost to it in alcohol taxes because of the moral advantages the population enjoys by not being able to buy legitimate distillations. But for the privileged, prohibition keens the edge of interracial socializing. There is a readiness to start a party at the drop of a cork, a gay and rare frivolity, a vague erotic excitement found in other cities only during wars.

This was the Bombay Harvey Tonkin inherited, an environment so matched to his tastes and talents that he was inclined to share orthodox Hindu belief in the forces of predestination.

Harvey was well settled at Pallonji Mansions when he learned that the State Department planned to send a team of American athletes on an Indian tour. Jesse Owens, the great Negro Olympic Gold Medalist, had made a celebrated visit in the fifties, lecturing at schools and colleges. An official in the Delhi Embassy had remembered it, striving over details of the Cultural Aid program. Harvey had made an immediate telephone call to the Embassy, another to Washington, and had written a number of letters.

After weeks of unremitting string pulling he cabled Scott Reynolds at Yale: WHAT SAY LECTURE TOUR INDIA? CAN FIX. NO PROHIBITION MY PLACE! HARVEY.

By return he got the reply: LECTURE WHAT? SCOTT.

LECTURE SCHOOLS. HARVEY, he answered.

LECTURE SCHOOLS WHAT? SCOTT.

LECTURE SCHOOLS ATHLETICS! WHAT YOU THINK? LETTER FOLLOWS. HARVEY.

Harvey had just mailed the letter, detailing the delights waiting for Scott Reynolds in Bombay, when he got his cable: ORDER TURBAN. RUSH DETAILS. WARN HAREM. CITING YOU MEDAL OF HONOR. REYNOLDS SAHIB.

Harvey left the Consulate and drove directly home. His flat was on the fifth floor of an old apartment house. The rooms were big, with tiled floors and ceiling fans and a frontage view of the sea. Dhobie men spread Bombay's washing to dry on the rocks there. Arab dhows with scimitar sails beat across the Gulf.

When Harvey had showered and changed, he called his bearer and instructed him to serve champagne with two glasses.

Manuel filled the two glasses and waited.

"Go ahead. Drink up."

It was hard for Manuel to get used to.

"All this caste crap has got to go," Harvey had told him when they moved to the flat. "The first drink I ever had was from my old man's gardener."

Now he lifted his glass. "Manuel, a great thing is going to happen."

"Yes, Sahib," Manuel said, wrinkling his nose against the champagne bubbles.

"An old buddy of mine, a great buddy, is coming to stay awhile."

"A memsahib," Manuel said.

"Hell, no. A sahib. An American sahib. When he gets here we're going to have the biggest party Pallonji Mansions ever saw."

In the Santa Anna Bureau Bob Schultz was beginning to feel the strain. He was waking in the mornings hot behind the eyes, weary and unrested. The responsibility for Operation Gold Medal, which was the code name heading the growing stacks of paper, was his now, by declaration. George Cole had said, after a review, "This looks very encouraging. From here on I want you to make your own decisions. You will, of course, keep me informed. But from here on regard this as your operation."

In this way, Cole made it clear to the others. There had been difficulty and coldness but Bob Schultz had found an authority in the simple pressures of the job. His overwrought concentration made it difficult to sleep. With reluctance he had taken to resting himself with sleeping pills.

The net which would be drawn in Bombay had already

spread wide. CIA was at work. In the classified files there were names of IOC members who would be tractable. Whether these men had been coerced, bought or persuaded was not observed on the reports that concerned them. They had merely been marked "Reliable."

The names of the applicant cities for the 1968 Games had been announced. No press comment had appeared about Santa Anna although there was conjecture about Prague.

It was otherwise among the delegates who would vote in Bombay and otherwise in the national Olympic committees. Partisan lines were forming. The Soviet lobby was hard at work, and in the intelligence that crossed his table there was much for Schultz to worry about.

On a Sunday afternoon in their Madison Avenue office, Sam Clark and Rex Prentice had been introduced by the Public Relations Director of Inter-Americas to Robert E. Schultz. For five hours the partners presented the progress they had made on the Santa Anna assignment. At the end of that time the visitors thanked them and left.

George Cole asked Bob, "How long will you need to establish yourself?"

"A week. Just long enough to get the feel of the place."

"Is there anybody there who might be able to identify you?"

"The Vice-Consul is an old friend."

"That could be useful," Cole said. "Would he be in a position to house you?"

"I've been depending on it. He has a bachelor flat."

"Better and better," Cole said.

"I think he might be a help. Would it be possible to make some kind of arrangement with the Consul?"

Cole opened his gold-initialed diary. "What is his name?"

That afternoon Bob Schultz gave himself the pleasure of writing to Harvey Tonkin. The little man was going to be surprised. Schultz said he would explain when he got there.

Two weeks before Scott Reynolds was due to report for briefing with the other American athletes at the Embassy in Delhi, he arrived at Bombay Airport according to the arrangement made by Harvey. The official who had written the tour into Cultural Aid was being much congratulated on his foresight due to the publicity being given the coming IOC meeting in Bombay, which he had had no idea about when he framed the proposal. The *Times* of India had front-paged the event: ROME, BERNE, PARIS, HAMBURG, NOW IT'S BOMBAY'S TURN!

Scott landed to find himself a social celebrity by the accident of being an athlete.

The party that night rocked Pallonji Mansions. Harvey had been saving up his diplomatic liquor ration. By calculated exchanges within the corps he had mounted a variety of drinks which popped the eyes of the short-supplied guests who came parched to the flat.

The beauty of growth and the freshened air that follows the monsoon rains speeded the morning recoveries which Scott and Harvey took at the Services Club sea pool. Now Scott Reynolds sat in the sun with his eyes closed. Short blond hair sparkled on his legs. The wide chest was smooth and hairless.

"What are these Consulate parties like, Harvey?"

"A big pain in the ass."

"But we have to go?"

"I have to go."

"I'm with you, buddy."

Harvey got up and laid back his deck chair. He rolled his towel for a pillow. "Think I'll take a nap," he said. "T'hell with it."

Sam Clark, Pip Harris and Luba Ivanova flew in a week before the opening of the IOC conference.

Sam Clark took a pill and slept eighteen straight hours after arrival. That afternoon, he paid his call on the American Consul. The Consul had received advice about Clark, and could be depended on to offer him every aid and facility during his visit. He invited Clark and his party to attend a cocktail party that evening.

Scott Reynolds had got his looks from his mother. At fifty-five Marjorie Reynolds could still draw whistles in a hotel lobby. Scott's father had a talent for unlucky investments, and the offer of an athletic scholarship had come when the family fortunes were suffering from one of the market fluctuations which Reynolds, Senior, found incomprehensible.

As an only child, Scott had been indulged inside and outside the home. Beauty has the equal advantage of brains as a social asset.

At school Scott had not troubled himself much about grades. He had been a football star on the junior team. The privileges of a golden boy had come to him early. In his first

96

year at Yale a romantic notion that he would study law had sagged on the difficulties of the course. He had switched his efforts to business administration and the prospects of a career in professional football. Scott had a lively distaste for routine, and when he imagined a future of desk work or selling farm machinery with his father it drove him into his training with an enthusiasm his coaches found puzzling. His hope of an Olympic distinction was more important to him than he let show. Scott had realized early that the world prefers a man to be careless of his gifts.

In the afternoon a Sepoy from the Consulate delivered the guest list for that night's party.

"I'm supposed to know who to give the big hello to," Harvey explained, studying the names.

"The Maharaja of Sardar," he read, "President All-India Hockey Federation and member International Olympic Committee."

"What are they like, these maharajas?"

"Never met one."

"Who else have we got?"

"Coupla industrialists. These fruit-juice politicians. Coupla film stars. Coupla newspaper editors. The diplomatic mob. Luba Ivanova, American. Philip Harris, British, Samuel Clark, American."

"Who gets the big hello?"

"These fruit-juice politicians. This maharaja. These coupla newspaper editors."

"How about the industrialists?"

"They give us the big hello."

"Luba Ivanova, American?"

"Depends how many big hellos I got. It's been one helluva week."

The glory of the climate that follows the monsoon giddies the foreign population like spring. Excursions are made to the western ghats, into the sparkling air of the mountains, where every outcrop and rock face tumbles a fall of water. Gray monkeys watch the climbing trains and feed off the new growth in the jungle.

In Bombay the parties move outside, air conditioning no longer needed.

On the enclosed lawn of the Consulate, bearers in cockaded turbans and crimson sashes had set up tables. Glasses and bottles sparkled under the colored lights. Indian and Western appetizers were laid out among bowls of blossoms.

The guard marines were pressed and polished in the dress uniforms of their corps. In his office the Consul gave himself his third and stiffest whisky. He had made it a rule to drink only fruit juice when he entertained Indian politicians.

In the piled granite of the Taj Mahal Hotel, which the architect was said to have built back to front, Luba Ivanova hummed happily. She had soaked for an hour in a perfumed tub and afterwards sat in the window looking down on the Gateway to India, built before the First World War for a visit by the Prince of Wales.

Luba had bought a bottle of crème de menthe on her permit and carried a small glass of it now, sucking the drink over blocks of ice as noisily as a child. She had bobbed her dense black hair before leaving New York. It was combed back over her small, flat ears and fringed on her forehead like a helmet. Naked, she was bigger-breasted than she appeared in clothing. The breasts were long, rather than full, and rounded and cupped at the base. The nipples started from the hot soaking. Luba had made up her face for the party with darkly shadowed eyes and a pale lipstick that focused the small mouth and babyish underlip. Talcum powder nested in the pubic hair she kept cropped.

Working the peppermint of the iced liqueur on her tongue, she sat absorbed, a hand on her flat belly or absently feathering the nipple of a breast with her fingers for the tingle of pleasure it gave her. She was bigger-hipped too, out of clothing, a softness that flared and spread when she crossed her legs on the stool in front of the mirror. Her used clothing littered the floor with a child's carelessness. When Clark telephoned from the permit room to say it was late, Luba was still sucking crème de menthe, dreaming and feathering her nipples.

The white-uniformed bearers waiting on the balcony for any summons from the rooms straightened up when Luba came out and descended the staircase. She wore gold lamé trousers as tight as a skin, drawn between her legs like a wet bathing suit. A short, sleeveless lamé jacket glittered with jet bead piping. She carried a tiny gold lamé bag swinging on a long golden chain.

In the permit room the entrance of Luba, swinging the bag, cut off all conversation. Clark turned his head, prodded by Pip Harris, and got no farther for a fixed minute than the gold lamé mount of Venus presented at his shoulder.

"Nice like this, no?" Luba asked and pirouetted for them.

"Crissake, Luba," Clark said, "get your crotch out of my face."

It was probably the first time a trouser suit had been seen in Bombay. They were still new in New York.

From the Consulate's green lawn, which ran at this hour into the darker green of the Arabian Sea, the last hot colors of sunset edged wisps of cloud on the horizon's rim. It drew attention, this end of the day, like a last speech that has to be listened through before the pleasures of the table may be enjoyed. European women in cocktail dresses cut low to exhibit their suntans competed for color with the Indian women's saris. The men wore tropical suits and the universal white, soft-collared shirts.

Scott Reynolds was not finding the party the bore that Harvey had promised. When he could Scott said. "There's some talent here you've been keeping quiet about."

"The tropics gets them," Harvey said. "Tonkin's law is never crap on your own doorstep. I need a fast belt."

He was swallowing his drink when Scott touched him on the arm with his glass. "How's the big hello supply?"

"I'm fresh out," Harvey said.

"You'd better dig one up. Look over there, buddy."

Luba Ivanova had arrived.

The sea was a dark shadow now. The bearers had put out the metal torches mounted on sharp poles with wicks in a mixture of fuel and citronella as a provision against the stirring mosquitoes. Most of the guests and the Consul had gone on to dinner appointments, leaving Harvey in charge of the serious drinkers.

Harvey had given Luba Ivanova a big hello. She introduced Sam Clark and Pip Harris. Harvey decided the evening had improved and hooked his jacket over a chair. Elegance was not required for the stayers-on: the camels, as the Consul called them.

Earlier in the evening the Consul had told Harvey that they were to look after Sam Clark, who was in Bombay to make a presentation to the International Olympic Committee. Harvey collected Scott to introduce him to Clark with the warning to talk about athletics. Scott dutifully tried but Clark appeared unable to follow him. In a painful silence Pip Harris wondered if Scott had ever played cricket. They were stuck like that, each puzzled by the other, when a marine came to look for Harvey. The Maharaja of Sardar, who had no longer been expected when the Consul left, had been announced by his aide-de-camp.

"Not as late as this," Harvey said. "What you've got is a messenger. A messenger to apologize for the Maharaja."

"What I got's the Maharaja," the marine said. "He's sitting out there in a car as big as a battlewagon."

Harvey looked about at the camels settled down at the water hole. There was no help for it.

"Get back there. I'm coming. T'hell with it," he said, and searched about for his jacket.

A very big man, well over six feet, stood quietly behind his aide. The marine was at attention. The aide was an elderly Rajput in cotton jodhpurs and a high-necked jacket. His gray beard was enormous, parted in the middle and brushed stiffly to either side. He bowed and said, "His Highness the Maharaja of Sardar."

Harvey was not sure whether to offer his hand or bow. He did both. "Good evening, Your Highness," he began.

The big man came forward and took his hand. Harvey had to crane his neck to welcome him.

"Sorry to be late, old boy," the Maharaja said. "I've been looking at a polo pony and Jaiwant Singh here insisted on putting him through his paces."

He beamed at Harvey and looked up the long corridor to the distant flicker of the torches.

"I'm Harvey Tonkin, the Vice-Consul. I'm afraid the Consul had to go on to a dinner engagement."

"Oh, bad luck. He and I have met before, you know. Still, better late than never."

The Maharaja clearly expected to come in.

"There are a few of us here if you'd care to join us, Your Highness."

"Call me Sardar," the Maharaja said. "Jaiwant Singh, you take the car back. I'll telephone when I'm ready."

The old Rajput bowed and wished Harvey good evening.

Harvey wondered about protocol, leading the Maharaja up the corridor. On the lawn he waited a minute to be noticed and then, feeling foolish, raised his voice and announced, "His Highness the Maharaja of Sardar."

"Call me Sardar," the Maharaja added.

Half the guests had not heard. The others gave no signal of understanding.

Harvey said, "Let me present Scott Reynolds. Scott, this is the Maharaja of Sardar."

"Sardar will do. Glad to know you, old boy."

"Scott is one of our American athletes. He's doing a lecture tour of India."

Sardar was interested. "Heard about you chaps. What's your game, old boy?"

"Scott's a track man. We expect him to be on our Olympic team."

"Really. Tell me, is it true that you Americans are as badly off for runners as they say? From what I hear, old chap, you haven't got a four-minute man in the country."

Harvey left to find others to entertain the Maharaja. From what he had heard these Indian princes were ladies' men. When he came back with Luba Ivanova and a young Swiss girl whose husband had left in a temper after an argument about her drinking, one of the few Indians left at the party was listening to Scott and Sardar. The Indian edited a left-wing paper and was cordially anti-American. He wore the dhoti and Congress cap of the Hindu nationalist and was drunk in defiance of the Constitution. Harvey introduced the girls to "His Highness" and the Maharaja said, "Call me Sardar."

Luba said, "You don't look like a maharaja."

"How should a maharaja look, Miss Luba?"

"In the books they have turbans, no? And elephants and big diamond rings. It's nice like that."

Sardar said, "I do have a turban, Miss Luba, and at home in Udapair I wear it. But I have no elephants. Cawnpore now, he's the one with elephants."

"Cawnpore is a fat pig, isn't it?" the Indian editor said.

Sardar looked down on his countryman, his dark, almost black eyes drawn for a moment.

Luba said, critically, "I think you would look nice in a turban. A turban with some big jewel in it, no?"

Sardar said, "I think you would look nice in a sari, Miss Luba."

"God, who is this creature?" the Swiss girl asked Harvey.

Luba heard her. "I am Luba Ivanova. Who are you?"

She poised her hips and half turned, blocking out any answer the Swiss girl might have made.

Clark and Harris had joined the group around the Maharaja. They wanted to leave and had come for Luba. Harvey got back too late to get rid of the Indian editor, who had established that Scott Reynolds was one of the touring American athletes.

"How many rupees, you tell me, we are paying to bring you here?"

Scott Reynolds took a hint from the others and paid the editor no attention.

The Indian pulled at Scott's sleeve angrily. "We don't need you here. I am making that clear, isn't it? We don't have rupees for you to be eating."

Scott Reynolds lost his temper. "I'm not eating your goddamned rupees. I'm paid for by the American Government. Get your hand off my sleeve."

The editor had not been to a Consulate party before. He was drunk and had been politely overlooked all evening. His anti-Americanism was both his livelihood and his principle.

"Meat eaters," he shouted. "Whisky soaks. Our Indian runners will win you all."

It was quite ridiculous. The glass he waved and splashed over the Swiss girl was half full of bourbon.

"Oh, oh, look what you've done. Look at my frock."

"Steady, buddy," Harvey said. "Let's settle down here."

It was too late for that. Scott Reynolds was no longer sober. It had been a long evening.

"I'll run against anybody you put up," he said. "I'll run against anybody in this country."

"Crissake," Clark said. "Settle down."

It was no good.

"Settle down?" the editor shouted. "I am making it clear. We don't want any of you to settle down, isn't it?"

Sardar reached down and caught the editor under the armpit, holding him up on the tips of his toes.

"Sorry, old boy," he said to Harvey. "Our friend and I will have a talk."

Teetering, spilling his drink on himself, the editor was pushed across the lawn out of the torchlight into shadows.

The Swiss girl scrubbed her frock.

Luba said, "Better like this, no? You watch."

She poured gin and tonic on her lamé jacket. It ran off as though from metal.

"If I dressed like that," the Swiss girl said, "I'd be expecting to go to a brothel."

Luba sucked in her breath, pivoted and swiped the Swiss girl behind the ear with her evening bag. They were hitting at each other before the men came out of shock.

"You bitch. You savage little bitch." The Swiss girl struggled in tears. Scott Reynolds had her arms pinned. Luba was quite calm.

Harvey took the Swiss girl from Scott and walked her over

the lawn, comforting her, and up the long corridor out to a Consulate car.

"Sorry about this," he said to the Maharaja when he got back. "Some party."

"Worse things happen at sea," Sardar said. "Now, why don't all of you join me in a nightcap at my hotel?"

Harvey wanted to get home and relax. "Look," he said. "We've got iced champagne waiting at the flat. The way I feel, I need it."

"That," Sardar said, "is different." He put a hand on Harvey's shoulder. "Lead on, Tonkin. Miss Luba?"

Luba clapped her hands. "Nice," she said.

Clark had hired a car for his stay in Bombay. It wasn't worth calling Sardar's car. They agreed he should travel with Clark. Harvey gave the driver instructions and he and Scott shot off in the MG.

"We'll probably be seeing a lot of you, Highness," Clark said.

"Oh?" Sardar asked politely over the head of Luba, who was wagging herself into comfort beside him.

"You're on the International Olympic Committee, aren't you?"

"I am."

"Well, Harris here and Luba and I, we're making the pitch for Santa Anna."

"Are you, indeed? What do you do, Miss Luba?"

"Luba's the all-round help. She's going to interpret for the Santa Anna delegation."

"Clever as well as pretty." Sardar smiled. "Luba is not a Spanish name, is it?"

"No. It is Russian. You see I had this Russian father and this Spanish mother in Saigon . . ."

"Shut up, Luba," Clark said. "How do these meetings go, Highness?"

"What do you want to know, old boy?"

"What kinda chance would you give Santa Anna?"

"I wouldn't think you have a hope, old boy."

"You wouldn't think—we had—a hope?"

"Not a hope."

They were under the lights of Marine Drive now, on the dual highway. A long-term one-shot, he had been told. Here was an IOC member and a maharaja on the side and he didn't think Santa Anna had a hope. Clark felt gloomily for his cigarettes.

In Harvey's flat, Clark was introspective. He refused champagne and gave himself large whiskies. Now that he was home, Harvey relaxed. The stiffness of duty troubled him at Consulate parties. The phonograph played. Everybody danced except Clark and Harvey.

When Sardar came to sit next to Scott Reynolds, with Luba Ivanova on his knee, he said, "At the Consulate, old boy, you told our angry little friend that you'd run against anyone in India."

"Oh, that," Scott said, dismissing it.

"I'd like to take you up on it."

"You?"

Scott was holding his shirt open under the ceiling fan. He had danced himself into a sweat.

"Good lord, no. Not me. A competitor I will nominate."

"Trot 'em out," Harvey said. "You put 'em up, old Scotty'll knock 'em over."

"I was thinking of a horse."

Reynolds sat up. Sardar's dark eyes were barely smiling.

"You must be joking."

"On the contrary."

"Trot 'em out," Harvey said. He was weaving. "You trot 'em out, old Scott will race 'em."

Reynolds said, "Just a minute, Harvey."

"Well?" Sardar asked.

"A man doesn't run against a horse."

"Jesse Owens did."

Sardar's big hands held Luba lightly by the shoulders. He was intent on Scott Reynolds. Neither man made any pretense of smiling.

"Over what distance?"

"A hundred yards? Jesse Owens' distance?"

"You realize I'm not a sprinter?"

"Yes."

"Okay. When and where?"

"At my palace in Udapair. I have to return briefly tomorrow. Would you like to see my palace, Miss Luba?"

"Please, please," Luba said bouncing. "But Clark. You fix Clark, no?"

"I fix Clark, yes."

Scott stood up. "You're serious about this?"

"Very."

"Where is Udapair?"

"A few hundred miles north. I have a carriage on tomorrow's train."

Scott said, "Harvey? Can we go to Udapair?"

"What the hell you want to go to Udapair?" Harvey said to Sardar. "Trot your horse out here."

Sardar smiled. "That's where the horse is, old thing. Besides, I think you will enjoy it. You can fly back next day. As my guests, of course."

"Oh, please," Luba said. "Please, Harvey."

"I dunno."

Sardar stretched and looked at the time. "Well, Reynolds?"

"Harvey?"

"OK," Harvey said. "T'hell with it."

Sardar stood and clapped each of them on the shoulder. "Tomorrow at noon, then. Jaiwant Singh will collect you, say about eleven thirty. Where are you staying, Miss Luba?"

"At the Taj Mahal, with Clark and Harris."

"That's no trouble, then. So am I."

Harvey closed down the party after Sardar called his car. Clark went with him. If Luba was to go to Udapair he could see ways that she might make Sardar useful. When the flat had emptied and Manuel had come in to clear up, Harvey and Scott sat wondering what they had let themselves in for. Schultz was expected in three days. Scott was due in Delhi that same day. The social calendar was getting crowded.

17

SARDAR HAD inherited his title ten years ago at the age of thirty-three. Until then most of his life had been lived in Europe. He had been educated at Eton and at Caius College, Cambridge.

His family was an old one in northern India, distantly related to the great Shah Jehan who had built the Taj Mahal at Agra as a monument to his love for the young wife whom he entombed there, but he was English in everything but ancestry. He had forgotten most of his father's tongue long before he succeeded to the title. The mixed arrogance and puritanism of most Hindu politicians was neither understood nor appreciated by him. The orthodoxies of his given religion shamed him.

After a few months in India he was generally glad to get back to the farm in Sussex which he managed with enterprise and energy, to the small stable of polo ponies and the hunters he bred and dealt in. His challenge to Scott Reynolds had been laid down in the sporting tradition of the English counties, but it had a subjective side too. Both the Indian and the

Englishman in him could take an American down a peg. Besides, he was interested in Luba Ivanova.

The Delhi express leaves Bombay Central at midday. Harvey Tonkin and Scott had risen late, missing their dip in the sea pool and feeling the worse for it. Jaiwant Singh dismissed the car at the station—apparently it was kept in Bombay—and led the Americans through the beggars who made a vantage point of the station, to the air-conditioned coach reserved by Sardar. Luba and Sardar were already on board and waved from the window. A whistle blew and the carriage jarred and slowly began rolling. The hawkers, whose fingers had tapped the window, holding up trays of drinks, sweets and newspapers, now mouthing silently at the thick glass, slid away. Then they were out of cover, picking up speed for the long run up the subcontinent to Delhi.

In the coach there were four lounges that converted to beds, each sleeping two passengers. The big coach was further provided with a kitchen, a refrigerator, crockery, cutlery, chairs, tables and servants' quarters. There was a lot of luggage. Sardar had not been home for nine months. Jaiwant Singh and the servants had traveled to Bombay to meet him. He was making this visit for the IOC conference.

Scott excused himself immediately after dinner. The habits of training were giving him worry. When Harvey went to bed an hour later Scott was in undershorts, wet with perspiration, doing press-ups and sit-ups on the floor between the bunks.

Sardar's returns to Udapair were treated as occasions. The next morning the palace staff, local officials and the stationmaster in his good uniform waited on the platform with greetings. The stationmaster said a few words of welcome and decorated the party with garlands handed him from a trolley by a porter. An old Lanchester with a special body, like an outsize station wagon, was at the station gates. Following Sardar's lead, Harvey and Scott took off their garlands and handed them to the children crowding and shouting at their legs. Luba buried her nose in the drifting jasmine petals and refused to be parted from them. The air was thinner and cooler here, with a touch of desert dryness, the sunlight hard on the eyes, a brilliance like shards of glass.

With an Indian's instinct for drama, Sardar had turned aside all their questions about his palace. He was familiar with the impression a first visit made on his guests. Against tree-covered banks, with a bald mountain outcrop behind it, the cream-colored confection of marble and granite was set in the middle of a lake, on a small rocky island.

A motorboat and a collapsible raft for the Lanchester were tethered at the landing. The palace looked like a complicated cake, the porticoed walls set with tiny towers in the shape of flat-bottomed bells. The rosy domes and pillars repeated themselves by reflections in the water. Bushy trees branched out of the courtyard and overhung the walls.

Her voice small, Luba said, "Oh, Sardar, it's like a fairy castle in a book."

"It is rather, is it not?"

They all stood fixed on the unbridled theatricality of the old structure across the bright water.

The palace was many times bigger than it appeared. Beyond the intimate courtyard with fountains over lily and lotus pools, there were stables through gates, a polo field and a garage of old cars and carriages.

In the evening, bathed and changed, Scott and Harvey sat in the courtyard, watching the peacocks parading on the garden walls.

Sardar's height and breadth, his dark-eyed, olive-skinned looks, had made him a presence in Western clothing. They found him a bit breathtaking now. He had changed out of their world into his father's. He wore a turban, as he had told Luba he would, fastened with a stage-maharaja's ruby, a Muslim kurta, a fine embroidered shirt, over churida pajamas. Big stones were set in rings on each hand.

"My national dress." He smiled rather wistfully. Scott got out of his chair. "Sardar. You look magnificent."

"Thanks, old boy. Now I have a little surprise. I would like to introduce you to an Indian princess."

He clapped his hands. Behind them, in Sardar's private apartments, double doors opened. Two young girls stood there giggling, presenting another, her hair wound with silver jewelry, a diadem on her forehead, earrings hanging to her shoulders, bracelets gleaming on her arms, gold embroidery gleaming on a purple sari. She pointed a silver slipper.

"Gentlemen," announced Sardar, "I give you the Princess Luba."

After dinner a liqueur was served in cups as small as thimbles.

"In a few years, when this supply is gone, there won't be any more."

"What you call it again?" asked Harvey.

"Pronounce each syllable, old boy. Ah-ha-sa."

They were drinking the princely liqueur of India, distilled from the crushed flesh of birds, fermented with cardamom seeds, rose petals, orange skins and gold leaf.

"It's supposed to be an aphrodisiac. This was put down by my father before I was born. It's an acquired taste, I think."

"If you can't get it on the diplomatic ration I won't acquire it," Harvey said.

Luba had lost her chatter. She was absorbed in the enjoyment of her finery as she had been in her body after the perfumed tub in the Taj.

When the men went to bed they left Luba and Sardar on the colonnaded terrace where they had walked.

"I'd like to be a fly on the wall," Scott said.

"Yeah. That Luba."

"A sari does something for a girl, that's for sure."

"That Luba," Harvey said. "She does something for a sari."

Luba touched the stone in Sardar's turban. "Is it real?"

"You won't tell?"

"Cross my heart."

"It's paste, Princess Luba. The real one was sold years ago. You see, I shouldn't have told you. You're disappointed."

Luba shook her bracelets. "More paste, no?" she asked mournfully.

"No. Those are real."

She put the flat of her hand on his chest. "Real or paste?"

"Too real. I'm getting fat."

Luba slid her hand down his belly. "A little fat here. But still strong. Why did you bring me, Sardar?"

"I thought you would like it."

"Clark told me a lot of things to ask you."

"What is it you should ask?"

"Not now. Tonight I am the princess, no?"

"A very lovely one."

"Sardar, I am a bad girl."

He laughed at her. "Little girls are made of sugar and spice and everything nice, aren't they?"

"I am bad. Don't laugh. Sometimes I am wicked. But sometimes very nice too."

"What do you do to be wicked, Princess?"

"Always the same. Always men."

Sardar tutted.

"It is true. Ever since that not nice American husband, I have been bad. You know how many men have made love to

108

me? You won't believe it. One hundred and twenty-seven men."

Sardar took off his turban. It looked like a beehive beside him on the wall they leaned against. He wondered if she were serious. She looked so demandingly grave.

"It is true. I write them all down in a book. Very bad, no?"

He loosened his hair, wondering at her. "You put them in a book? Good lord."

"Oh, yes. I keep them in a book."

"For heaven's sake, why?"

"Why?" Luba puzzled about it. "For instance, if one calls me up I look in the book and see if that one was nice or not. Then, because I am Catholic from a convent in Saigon, when I go to confession I take my book."

"Good lord! What does the priest say?"

"Oh, you know, they say many things. For a long time I had many penances. This priest I have now in New York says it must be how God made me."

Sardar said, "Well, Luba, you take my breath away."

She studied him closely. "You see. Bad, no?"

"Luba, what do you want me to say?"

"Say? What is to say? Now you know I am very bad, we can go to bed together, no?"

For a maharajah in his own palace Sardar felt sadly bemused.

In his rooms, the long, low windows open on the lake, the thin moon white on the marble balcony, Luba had undressed her hair from the loops of jewelry. She unwound the sari and folded it, unclasped the wide, studded bracelets. She stood in a dark Indian shift, drawn on her waist by a string, and stepped out naked over the dropped cotton. Her flesh shone with a dull ivory glow in the mirror. The faintest of smiles stretched the moist baby underlip. So long did she stand at the mirror that Sardar thought he might have been forgotten. Then she turned quickly. Raised on her toes, she walked to the center of the room. Deliberately she chose the shafted moonlight. And stood there, posed.

The big man came slowly to his feet.

In a rough, hoarse voice Luba whispered, "Nice like this, no?"

She continued to stand in the moonlight, up on her toes, arching the jars of her hips, almost impartial in her own appreciation of her rounded, abundant flesh. This was her gift. He had to value it. She wanted no unlit lovemaking. This man, any man, must explore her on her own terms. She was not their instrument. They were hers. She watched Sardar, calculating him, widening her knees, cupping her breasts in her hands, moving in a slow, steamy erotic display in the beamed white light. When he came to her she slipped the gown he wore off his shoulders, worked on him with her hands, her eyes scummed with introspection. He grasped at her, his face lined as though with pain, and she stopped him. "No," she said in the thick, changed voice. "Here. Like this. Where I can see you. You're big, big, big. Now, no closer. Tell me the words."

Scott Reynolds woke feeling foggy. He and Harvey were in rooms which had been furnished for the tourists in the efficient fashion of a good hotel. Scott was lost until he sat up and saw the sun-sparked lake blinking beyond the balcony. Immediately he felt the familiar clutch of pre-race nausea. Because it was a stunt, a champagne party's making, he resented this tension. He tried to lie back and forget about it but his mind kept returning to the start. It would be the start that mattered. There would be no blocks. He would have to start out of holes. Scott got up and unpacked his track gear. He lifted the spikes to his nose. They smelled of rubbing liniment. It brought him up on a lift of excitement, confirming the identity which the rushing strangeness of the past days had dislocated along with reality.

On the polo field, near the stables, Scott Reynolds put on his spikes and began to jog. An hour later he was making starts out of holes dug by the gardener. The yard servants hung around the gate to the courtyard. Harvey sat on an old shooting stick he had found at the stables and gave Scott countdowns, signaling the report of a starting pistol by banging on a petrol can with a stirrup iron. The gallery found this behavior hilarious. For their entertainment Harvey went down in the holes. Scott banged the stirrup iron on the petrol can and Harvey flung himself forward and collapsed. The delight of the spectators encouraged him to make wilder efforts.

"You can't be doing it right, old boy."

Sardar and Jaiwant Singh wished them good morning. Harvey got up feeling a little silly.

"Reynolds, old chap, I've got an idea," the Maharaja said. "Why don't I get into this act? A man, a horse and a car. I could drive my brother's Giulietta Sprint. You must admit the car has a suitable name."

Harvey said, "If you've got a cannon, Sardar, I could play. Someone could shoot me out of it."

They marked out a course at the edge of the polo field. Sardar would drive on the hard ground in front of the stables. The gardener dug holes there to Scott's instructions. He tried them until he was satisfied. It was going to be an occasion. Jaiwant Singh had gone into town yesterday afternoon to invite the local dignitaries to come and watch.

"How you feel, buddy?" Harvey asked when he and Scott had returned to their rooms to change.

"This is getting to be fun. The thing is to get the start. It takes a horse a hundred yards to get going. When Jesse Owens ran against racehorses he would be out in front before the racehorse got away. I've got to get that start. Right on the gun."

They had agreed with Sardar that he could run the engine of the Giulietta Sprint for the start but that the gears must not be engaged. It was beginning to look like a lot of fun to all of them.

Jaiwant Singh, with his huge beard stiffened by pomade and brushed fiercely from the center in the fashion of old Rajput warriors, received the guests under the arch at the landing steps. Fruit drinks and sweetmeats were laid out in the courtyard under the protection of striped umbrellas.

Luba looked very gay in a blue linen suit. The women were shyly interested in her but few of them knew English. The police chief and the retired army officers were boisterously friendly but Scott and Harvey had trouble with the accented English of the others. Their faces stiffened, strained by the smiles that so idiotically fix those who labor to understand another tongue.

The horse Scott was to run against had been introduced that morning. She was a bay mare, Star of India. Jaiwant Singh was up, exercising the horse in tightly held canters, spurring her a few yards and then holding her in, riding on a light saddle. Near the start a servant stood with a shotgun opened at the breach. The entire palace staff squatted and stood in the center of the polo field. Sardar was driving the Alfa Romeo up and down in front of the stables. He had not used it before. In fact he had never driven a sports car of any make. The police chief was full of importance. He had been given the office of starter. He instructed them about the orders he would give and took the shotgun from the servant, filling the chambers and snapping the breech shut with flourishes.

"Attaboy, Scotty," Harvey said and stood back.

"Good luck, Scott," Luba called to him.

Reynolds went down in the holes, preparing himself, straightened and went down again.

The police chief held the gun above his head for attention. When the party in the chairs quietened, he made a speech. Among other things he said that Scott Reynolds, the American, was well known as the fastest runner in the world.

At the hundred yards, two servants tightened the tape of colored cloth. Sardar climbed into the Giulietta again, gunning the motor in stirring roars. The noise bothered Star of India. She began to paw and roar. Jaiwant Singh repositioned himself, with Scott between the horse and the car.

"Let her get used to it," Sardar called and idled the engine. Jaiwant Singh walked the horse, talking to her, while Sardar ran up the engine in bursts. Star of India was trembling, a light froth on her muzzle. The old Rajput had her perfectly collected. He wore a high-necked jacket over his jodhpurs and regimental colors in his turban. The waiting was trying Scott Reynolds. His forehead was misted with sweat.

"On your marks."

As the Rajput collected the horse, getting her bunched under him, she began to back, arching her neck to chew at the bit, her hindquarters down in tiny mincing steps. Jaiwant Singh raised his hand and cantered off, making a small circle, talking into Star of India's ear, stroking the hollow of her neck. Her flanks were smoking a little.

Sardar idled the Giulietta again. "She's too fresh, Jaiwant Singh. She needs work."

The old Rajput continued to circle the mare, stroking her neck and talking to her. Scott Reynolds straightened and walked a circle, his hands on his hips. He hitched his shorts on the long-muscled thighs.

Back at the start, Jaiwant Singh slackened pressure on the bit, letting the mare put her head down. He chopped his hand at the police chief.

"On your marks . . ."

Star of India stood head down, one hoof pawing.

"Get ready to start . . ."

The Rajput hauled back, jerking the mare into the bit, bringing her down in the quarters.

Scott strained in the holes, his eyes fixed on the colored tape. The Giulietta Sprint roared, so loud that it almost drowned the blast of the shotgun. Nobody heard the old warrior's cry on which Jaiwant Singh exploded the mare with his heels and hands. Scott was gone on one breath, lungs closed for the effort. Star of India was on his eye-corner as the tape broke before him. The horse was in a tight turn at the end of the field, Jaiwant Singh sawing at the bit as Scott stiffened the run out of his legs, drew up and turned panting.

The party had left the chairs and were streaming across the grass. The Alfa Romeo had skidded, its nose pointing toward the start. Sardar was climbing ruefully out of the cockpit.

He had underestimated the power of the car. When he sprang the clutch on the roaring engine the wheels had slewed madly. One wheel had been on soft ground. The hole it cut had thrown the car out of control. The air stank of burned rubber.

Jaiwant Singh on Star of India had broken the tape an instant ahead of Scott Reynolds.

"It wasn't really fair, old boy," Sardar said, with his good arm around Scott Reynolds. "Star of India is a polo pony. They're trained to start fast, you see."

The constraint of the morning collapsed on the excitement of the match and the drama of Sardar's accident. After lunch Harvey and the army types made frequent visits to his room. It was late when the outboard motor racketed the happy guests away.

"It's back to Bombay tomorrow," Harvey said. "T'hell with it. Let's you and me hang one on, Scotty."

18

SCOTT REYNOLDS flew out to Delhi on the early morning plane and Bob Schultz arrived on that same afternoon. This coincidence had been arranged against the known itinerary of the American athletes. On the same aircraft, traveling on a journalist's passport, Lance Dobson, the CIA man, arrived to cover the International Olympic Committee's conference.

After seeing Scott off, Harvey Tonkin had lunched at the Juhu Hotel to save himself the drive into town and had afterwards slept off Scott's farewell party under an umbrella on Juhu beach. He was still in the dark about Bob's visit. Because there was no other explanation Harvey had given himself the sentimental pleasure of concluding that Schultz must value their friendships more than he had let Harvey see. After the swim and the sleep he felt better prepared to welcome Schultz with proper excitement.

But Harvey was shocked when he saw Schultz across the

barriers. He looked sick and strained, his eyes were blood-shot, his thinnish cheeks sharply drawn. The wave he gave Harvey was tense. Instead of a greeting his first words were "Has Scott gone?" He had one answer for Harvey's questions. "I'll fill you in when we get to the flat." Outside the terminal Lance Dobson passed without a glance.

Schultz showed little interest in his surroundings on the drive into town. He had no news for Harvey. He had seen nobody they knew. He kept putting his fingers to his eyes as though the sunlight troubled him. Harvey gave him his dark glasses and finished the drive squinting.

At Pallonji Mansions Schultz flopped into a chair. While the servants were paraded and introduced he drank a whisky.

"Can we be heard here?" he asked.

"Heard? What do you mean?"

"The servants."

Harvey got up worried and shut the sitting-room door. "What's bugging you, buddy? You got some kind of trouble?"

"Jesus," Schultz said, "I don't know where to begin. If this doesn't make sense, it's my fault. I couldn't sleep on the plane. I feel as though I've been worked over with a baseball bat. Anyway, here goes."

It took a long time. When Harvey had the gist of it they went over it again, filling in the holes.

"I've met Clark," Harvey said. "A girl he's got working with him was up country with Scott and me. I'll tell you about that later. This Dobson, where is he staying?"

"Green's Hotel, wherever that is."

"It's next to the Taj Mahal, where the IOC is meeting. A kind of annex. What do you know about his contacts?"

"Next to nothing. He's not very friendly. One of these hard-nosed types. He's got a pipe into the IOC, a Swiss who used to live in the States and now works for the Olympic headquarters in Lausanne."

"I just might have a pipe in there myself," Harvey said. "What do you know?"

"How's that?" Schultz asked, looking up.

"This Maharaja we been with in Udapair. He's one of the Indian members on the committee."

"That would be the Maharaja of Sardar?"

"How you know that?" Harvey said, surprised.

Schultz was weary. "Buddy, I've got them all by heart."

"Where do I come in on this? What do you want me to do?"

"Harvey, right now I couldn't tell you. I'm zapped. The

main thing is if I can hole up here. I don't want to run into Mathew C. Kaverly."

"Yeah." Harvey felt vaguely disappointed that Bob had not come to Bombay for his company. "You say that Dobson's got three or four votes he can steer?"

"That's all."

"What happens if the IOC brings in a straight result?"

"It doesn't work that way. They knock out one applicant at a time. I'm depending on the politics, on a hangup between Prague and Detroit."

Harvey leaned back, his face screwed up. "What do we do now?"

"Are you listed in the telephone book?"

"No. It's still under the old name."

"I'll phone the number to Dobson tomorrow. He said he would need a day to get checked out here. Then we go to work on what we hear from him."

"Do they start in with these presentations right away?"

"No. There's general business first. The Executive Board meets on the twenty-first. On the twenty-second they meet the national Olympic committees' delegates. On the twenty-third there's an opening ceremony. The working session meets on the twenty-fourth and on Saturday the twenty-sixth they expect to announce the next Olympic city. I tell you, Harvey, Saturday the twenty-sixth is going to take a whole lot of living through."

"Don't jump from here, buddy," Harvey said. "It isn't high enough. You'd only break a fetlock."

Schultz put his glass down. "That drink has done for me. If I don't get to bed I'll fall over."

"OK. You hit the hay, I'll wake you round about nine for dinner."

Later, Harvey did try to wake him and got a blurred response.

"Poor old buddy," Harvey said, leaving the room and closing the door. "You've ambitioned yourself right out on a limb."

The investment of Luba Ivanova's time on the visit to Udapair was accounted for by Clark under future contingencies. Sardar might be useful. In her paradoxically practical way Luba had learned something. Sardar had told her that the delegates were so wined and dined during these conferences that many of them had difficulty remaining awake in the afternoon sessions.

"We can't depend on a morning session," Clark said. "This agenda is all over the place. What we got to be sure of is that these guys don't go to sleep on us."

After discussion he and Pip Harris decided to make Santa Anna's presentation in the dark.

"We hit 'em with the black," Clark said, marching round the room. "We sit 'em down in the dark, usherettes with flashlights. They fall over each other all the better. Then we fade in light on the working models. Pip's voice over. You know, the BBC bit. We got the Mayor on his rostrum, blacked out. We cut to the Mayor with a spotlight. He's got ten minutes. Bang! We cut the spot. Up and under with all these bongo drums. Fade in the color film. End of film. Music track comes on strong. Bang! We spotlight the second rostrum, ten minutes. Cut! Luba's got the girls in through the side door. There they are in their national costumes, these big tits hanging out. We hit them with a pencil spot and widen. In comes the track for the Santa Anna song. The girls belt it out with actions. On the line 'Santa Anna takes it away'— bang! First color slide on the screen. Spotlight first rostrum. Cut and spotlight second rostrum. Click! A color slide. Click! Another color slide. Recorded voice over. We're in the old city, the night-life bit. Up loud with the sound track. Anyone's asleep, we blast him out of his chair. End of color slides. Blackout the screen. A full thirty seconds' silence here. These guys think we've finished. They sit back scratching their crotches, Bang! Up and out with the bongos. Now, very faintly, fade in the national anthem. On the screen the five Olympic circles dissolve into one. President's head fills circle. He's got three minutes. As the camera pulls back for the long shot of the Presidential guard, in comes the national anthem again. Close-up of the President taking salute. Freeze the frame and hold. Now the spot is on the girls, these big tits hanging out. They go into 'Santa Anna Takes It Away' and goose-step down center screen, the President in freeze frame behind them. Fade in house lights. The girls go right out among the members, handing out the color books and souvenirs. We start the turntable on the model displays and hold the Santa Anna song until the room empties. If these guys sleep through that," Clark advised Harris, "they've all been bitten by the tsetse fly."

Pip Harris said, "We're going to need a lot of rehearsal time, Sam."

"What we're going to need, Crissake, is split-second timing scripts on sound and lighting. One thing we've got going for us is this alphabetical order of presentation. We've got time to shake down. Now this party. That's another place we got to hit 'em. All these other delegations—they're throwing their parties here in the Taj."

Luba said, "So are we, no? You asked me to make the booking."

Clark scrubbed his crew cut. "Yeah, well, I've been thinking about that. If you take a look in the register you'll see a lot of these committee members have their wives with them. These gals will be looking for a good time. They're going to be fed up with parties in the Taj. Come over here. Take a look." He went to the window. "What do you see?"

"The Gateway to India," the Englishman said.

"Luba?"

"The Gateway, no?"

"Raise your sights, Crissake. What do you see over there?"

"A fishing boat, no? An island."

"Yeah, an island. You know what they got on that island?" Harris said, "Yes. The Elephanta caves."

"You're damn right. You seen those caves? They got sculptures in those caves thirty feet high. Gods and goddesses. Now a party in those caves, torchlight, carpets, you'd have these old ladies wetting their britches."

Harris said, "It wouldn't work, Sam. You'd never get the permission. The party would have to be dry."

"You limeys," Clark said. "Show you a book and you go by it. I've put a feeler out. We approach this thing in the right way, we can have the Santa Anna party in those caves."

Dobson arrived at Harvey's flat soon after five. He made no concession to the difference in their surroundings. He accepted a whisky from Manuel without a glance. He remained as he had been in Washington, cool, professional and distant.

"I have an hour," he told Schultz.

"You want a table?" Harvey asked.

"I don't think so," Schultz said. "Well, Dobson, what's the picture?"

"I've talked to our man on the Executive Board. He's assistant to the Chancellor. He does the vote counting, so we can depend on knowing exactly how the votes move."

"Have you checked out the final arrivals?"

"Yes. We've lost two of our reliables. Sickness."

"That leaves us with two?"

"Yes."

Schultz worried about it. "How about their replacements?"

"Nothing doing. Our men got sick on purpose. It happens. The certain arrivals add up to five princes, four generals, two viscounts, a count, a baron, a sheik, a knight, a marquess, a maharaja and assorted millionaires. It's not an easy committee to get to."

Schultz said, "Give us a rundown on the voting blocs. I want Mr. Tonkin to hear."

"Voting will be dominated by the twenty-seven Europeans. Next biggest bloc is the eleven Arab-Asians. This isn't solid. They have their own quarrels. There are ten South Americans, two Australians, one New Zealander, one Canadian, two white Africans."

"How many black Africans?" Harvey asked.

"One."

"One?"

"One."

"We've got a tough outfit here," Harvey said.

"Well, let's have it," Schultz said. "How does this man of yours expect it to go?"

Dobson crossed his legs and leaned back. "Knockout voting is tricky. Our man expects Detroit to top the first round. He gives Detroit twenty-one votes. That would put the Americans, the Australians, the New Zealander, the Canadian, white Africa and say half the Europeans behind Detroit."

Schultz found it hard to ask the question. "And Santa Anna?"

"First round he gives Santa Anna ten. All the Latin American votes."

"Where would that put us?"

"Behind Accra. Our man expects Accra to get a certain eleven or twelve in the first round. We've got trouble with the European vote. There's a movement for them to back Lyons."

"Lyons? For Christ's sake, why?"

"Close to home. Cuts down the traveling expenses. More money, bigger teams. Bigger teams, more chances at the medals."

"How many votes could Lyons get then?"

"Maybe fifteen."

"And ten for Santa Anna?"

"That's how he sees it."

Schultz got up and began to pace. He had whitened. "I thought we were more buttoned up than this. On this forecast Prague has to go out first round to leave Santa Anna in the running. That's not going to happen. The Russians have been lobbying this for a year. You know that, Dobson. It's in CIA reports."

Dobson said, "This isn't my forecast. It's the forecast of a professional who has worked four of these International Committees."

Schultz could feel fright on his skin. The glossy CIA man was giving him the news with the distant satisfaction of a mechanic announcing that a cylinder block is blown.

"This makes no provision for the politics. All our information, everything we have worked on, depends on a political hangup between Prague and Detroit."

"We're only talking about the first round," Dobson said. "The first round they just flex their muscles."

"The way you tell it," Harvey said, "that first round could flex Santa Anna into the can."

Clark was working in floral bathing trunks. He was surprisingly thick in thighs and biceps, his belly ridged with muscle. The floor of the sitting room was scattered with crumpled paper. Clark was using the typewriter. He had been rehearsing the Mayor of Santa Anna.

"That fat little bastard. Any word with four syllables he falls arse over head. I'll have to rewrite all of him."

Harris was cutting up pages of script and sticking them down in a different order. "Where are you going to put the doctor?"

Clark got up. "We've got to bring the doctor forward. We could blow up on this eight-thousand-feet bit. Crissake, I got winded down there walking to the can. Putting the doctor on at the end leaves too much in their minds. I don't want those guys leaving the room thinking about any altitude problem. We want the doc on and off fast, before the big color film. All I want those guys to remember is that nobody's about to split a gut running on top of a mountain."

"How about slotting him in here?"

Clark was looking over Harris's shoulder. "Stick it down. We can try it out next rehearsal."

On Monday the twenty-first, the eight-man Executive Board met in Mathew C. Kaverly's suite in the Taj Mahal Hotel. Next day, in the ballroom, they formally received the national Olympic committees' delegates. On the twenty-third, the Governor of Maharashtra, standing in for the President of India, who was prevented by sickness from making the journey from Delhi, performed the solemn opening ceremony

119

of the sixteenth session of the International Olympic Committee. Following a roll call of members, the time of the next day's working session was announced and the meeting adjourned for a reception at Raj Bhavau, the Governor's residence. Over orange juice, mango juice and sandwiches, the extraordinary collection of counts, viscounts, princes, generals, knights, commoners and comrades of white, brown, black and yellow skins began to feel each other out according to their interests and purposes.

The business discussed at the meeting of the Executive Board on Monday the twenty-first was passed immediately to Lance Dobson by Conrad Carson, the Swiss assistant to Dr. Stein, Olympics Chancellor. The transcript of a discussion between General Maxim Versilov and Comrad Anton Jorgenyka, of the Soviet Union, with the Czech members led by Comrade Yuri Volker, held in the General's suite, was also put into Dobson's hands. This transcript was broken in sequence. The electronic recorder installed in Versilov's rooms a week earlier was not working properly, due, it was thought, to the monsoon dampness which had not been aired from the unused suite at that time.

Because the presentations of the applicant cities were to be made in alphabetical order, the Accra delegation was scheduled to open the entertainment that night with a cocktail party and a banquet in the Moghul Room of Green's Hotel. A Ghanaian national costume was to be presented to the wife of each committee member.

While the Accra delegation prepared for their cocktail party, Lance Dobson met with Schultz and Harvey Tonkin at Pallonji Mansions.

There were two alarms in the notes and transcript Dobson took to the flat. Mathew C. Kaverly, at the Executive Board meeting, had declared his support for Accra. He had said that the aspirations of Africa's emergent nations would be benefited by the Olympic ideal. In black Africa's struggle toward democracy, he had said, the internationalism of the Games could be a great and hopeful symbol, a recognition of the great and submerged talents struggling toward the light on that continent.

"Nobody talks like that," Harvey said.

"Kaverly does," Schultz said. "He believes it."

The second alarm was in the broken transcript of the discussion in General Versilov's suite. The General had argued that the Prague delegation should offer near-free accommodations to the athletes and officials to forestall the European support for Lyons. Comrade Yuri Volker had been enthusiastic. He said that he had pressed for near-free accommodations from the start. This was denied by another Czech. The last part of the broken transcript was mostly concerned with their argument.

When he had thought about it, Schultz said, "Suppose Prague does offer to subsidize accommodations. How would that affect—"

Dobson was ahead of him. "Detroit twenty-one, Lyons seven, Acccra eleven, Santa Anna ten, Prague fifteen."

Harvey looked at Schultz. "That forecast out of the same pipe as last night's?"

"It's out of several pipes," Dobson answered. "It's as reliable as we can get."

"Where would Prague pick up the extra support?" Schultz asked.

"The Norwegians, the Italians, the Greeks. Perhaps the odd British vote. In fact, anywhere from the European block not motivated by political prejudice."

"And you know which ones will act out of prejudice?" Harvey asked Dobson.

"Yes. I believe so."

"If we can upset Accra," Schultz asked, "wouldn't Santa Anna have to pick up some of their votes? On political, nationalist grounds, keeping the Games out of the West?"

"Politics is your specialty," Dobson said. "But if you're asking me, yes."

Schultz showed excitement. He said, "Accra eleven, Santa Anna ten. If we can upset Accra we'll be over the hump." He got up and began walking.

Dobson waited. When he saw that Schultz had nothing to add he said, "I have an idea about that."

Dobson took a typed paper out of an inside pocket and opened it on the table. Then he took out a spectacle case and put on glasses. The glasses seemed unnatural on him.

"This is a World Health Organization report, an extract from an official journal. I will read it."

He looked studentish in his glasses.

"Soon after the country gained independence, the Minister of Affairs for the Capital decided to eliminate the city's slums. Instead of beginning with a sewer system as recommended by the World Bank, the Minister, advised by his foreign consultants, set out to demolish an eyesore of seventy acres. By the time two-thirds of the land had been cleared and rebuilt, funds ran out and the work stopped. The city was left with dramatic skyscrapers and no sewer. The city is still drenched by sewage. Eighty-five percent of its school children have hookwork or roundworm and more than ten percent of all deaths in the city can be attributed to dysentery or diarrhea."

Dobson pocketed the paper and glasses.

Schultz was leaning across the table. "This is a current report? I can't believe it."

"It's current for Lagos, Nigeria," Dobson said.

Harvey stopped his glass on its way to his mouth. Dobson stared back unblinkingly at Schultz until Schultz leaned back, his lips pressed tight.

"You think we can make the switch," he said softly.

It wasn't a question. Dobson did not reply.

Bob Schultz got up and began to pace again, his eyes on the floor. "Accra can't handle it . . . nobody believes a black man can build a city anyhow . . . the way people are about germs these days, the reputation Africa has . . . it could work. It could work, Dobson. But it would have to be planted fast."

Dobson took the first sip of his drink. "It would have to come up in the newspapers."

Harvey looked shrewdly at Dobson. "This chief of yours? He's got that fixed?"

"We could break it tomorrow or the next day."

When Dobson had gone Schultz said, "Accra eleven, Santa Anna ten. If we can upset Accra, Harvey, if we get through the first round, we've got a chance."

"That Dobson," Harvey said. "I wondered about him. Always the facts and figures off the top of his head. You know why he memorizes like that? That hard-nosed bastard is shy about his glasses."

19

THE OLD MAN stood up, pushed back his chair, watched by the Executive Board and the members behind the flags of their countries. His face was set in the melancholy, houndlike look he had worn when Bob Schultz met him among the ticking machines in his desert command post. The thick hair had been cut since then, short on the sides. The blue tropical suit was unfashionably padded, multiplying the fattening muscle of his shoulders. In the glass-paneled box, the female translators were poised. As the old man began, their lips moved soundlessly.

122

"Gentlemen, the following cities and candidates for the organization of the Games of the nineteenth Olympiad: Accra, Detroit, Lyons, Prague and Santa Anna. Before we hear from the representatives of these cities, I would like to make a few points for the benefit of our new members."

He shoved out his chin.

"Article Fifty-one of the Olympic Rules stipulates that the IOC and only the IOC selects the Olympic city. When applications are received from several cities belonging to the same country, it rests with the National Olympic Committee of that country to decide which city shall be put forward. This has occurred in the instance of the United States of America. Several American cities—including Los Angeles, which presented the Games in 1932—have applied for organization. After inquiry, the National Olympic Committee of the United States has selected Detroit and forwarded that city's application to this body. Lausanne and Cairo also made applications but afterwards withdrew. The city of Manila was proposed by the Philippines Athletic Federation in an application amounting to four typewritten lines."

Kaverly paused for the laughter. At the table seating the Philippines members the two became fascinated by their ashtrays.

"It is the privilege of the international sports federations to express opinion about the Games site. Since the cost of travel to our host city, Bombay, has been high, your Executive Board discussed the choice of venue with the various federations at a joint meeting at Lausanne headquarters two months before this congress. The Executive Board is familiar with the views of the federations and these views will be considered in advising you, when the time comes to vote. Gentlemen, the business of deciding the site for the next Olympiad will now begin. I remind you to deliberate carefully. Once a decision is made there can be no reversal of that decision."

The old man turned to Conrad Carson. "Please ask the delegation from Accra to present their application to the members."

Carson left the executive table and crossed the ballroom. He was a small, fiftyish man in a dismal black suit, almost totally bald.

At the national tables the distinguished members coughed and arranged their papers, sitting up straight in their chairs. The game inside the Games was beginning. Across the big room, the Accra delegation in their colored robes filed in.

Daniel Obalisi, the delegation's leader, introduced himself

and his colleagues. He spoke in fruity English, a tremendously commanding figure as black as paint, with a huge chest and biceps. He was an Oxford graduate in economics.

"It is an honor to lead this delegation, gentlemen. As you know, the Olympic Games have never been to Africa. This is an error we propose to remedy by convincing you that Ghana's capital, Accra, one of the most exciting cities in the world today, is the most suitable, the most dramatic choice this congress could make."

Sam Clark's hotel suite was crowded. Clark had been giving himself drinks and was muzzy with excitement, tiredness and gin. Like a general who has led an attack from behind, he waited for intelligence to calculate the fortunes of the day.

The Santa Anna presentation had followed on Prague's, that afternoon. The slide sequence had got momentarily out of synchronization with the sound track, but otherwise the complicated staging had worked according to script. The fat Mayor had experienced trouble with his nerves and his English, as Clark had feared he would. When the spot had lit him on the blacked-out rostrum, the Mayor had been riveted. He had stared into it, hypnotized, his dry tongue working uselessly. It was more noticeable to the agonized Clark, standing in the dark at the end of the ballroom, than it was to the committee members. They too had needed time to adjust to the dramatics of Santa Anna's presentation.

As the delegates and Clark's team hurried in and out of the suite with eavesdropped information from the lounges and permit bar, Clark had good reason for a celebrating drink. In show-business terms, the Prentice and Clark presentation had been a sockeroo. When the house lights had come up on the girls singing "Santa Anna Takes It Away," a number of members at the national tables had got to their feet and applauded. The big Detroit presentation, much remarked until then, was on its way to being forgotten.

In Daniel Obalisi's suite, while Clark heard the reports in his, the distressed and confused Accra delegation read a prepared statement to a conference of the world press. Obalisi, holding a clipping from the *Express and Mail,* issued his indignant denial.

Lagos, Nigeria, he said, could in no way be compared to Accra under Nkrumah. Accra was one of the great cities of Africa, a modern metropolis. He could absolutely refute that there would be a health risk to athletes or visitors in Accra. To prove this, he had got from Ghana's Embassy in Delhi the most up-to-date figures available on hookworm, round-worm, dysentery and diarrhea in Accra.

"You got any of those go-go pills left?" Clark asked Pip Harris.

Harris handed him a small bottle.

"What's the dose?"

"One will do."

Clark swallowed the pill and looked at his watch. "Cris-sake, we've only got an hour. Luba's on Elephanta, is she? You heard from her?"

"Everything is OK."

Clark's proposal for the party on Elephanta had been made in ignorance of all of the difficulties. From blank re-fusal the chief customs officer had been moved into accep-tance, by slow and painful degrees. Clark had arranged coverage with the stringer for *Time* magazine and the rep-resentative for *Paris Match* as the most unusual party of the year. This had been underlined when the Director of Tourism was approached for permission to use Elephanta. Everything had been arranged, down to the boats that would transport the guests to Elephanta from the Gateway's sea steps.

The alphabetical order in which the presentations had been made was a bonus from fortune which Clark valued highly in the science of image making. It was his belief and conviction that few people can hold more than one idea in their heads about anything at one time. For that reason he had scheduled the Santa Anna party as close to the voting as possible. It had been a calculated risk. Had the congress got through its busi-ness a half day earlier and voted that afternoon, the Ele-phanta party might have proved to be a wake.

Tomorrow's voting was a concern Sam Clark did not allow himself. His rule in life and business was to concentrate on one worry at a time. The presentation had been worry num-ber one. The Elephanta party was worry number two. Worry number three, the big one, was something he would sweat about tomorrow.

While Clark lay in a hot tub, making himself relax, the Accra delegation was in the suite of General Versilov, plead-ing through an interpreter for the General to make a state-ment immediately the congress opened the next day, refuting the dangerous publicity that could ruin Accra's chances in the voting. Black Africa had no member to speak for it in the secret session. Ghana's friend, Russia, must take a stand for them, Obalisi said. When the Accra delegation left the suite feeling encouraged, the General smiled and toasted his comrades. Any upset in Accra's following could only mean more votes for Prague.

Harvey Tonkin had been conducting his own research in the permit bars of two hotels on the reception given the Santa Anna presentation. It seemed to have been a big success.

He needed the information to take back to the flat. Schultz would still not go near the Taj Mahal for fear of meeting Kaverly. There would have been little chance of their meeting. The old man was as aloof as a monarch at these congresses. He attended no receptions, entertainments, lunches or dinners. Outside working sessions he remained in his suite, taking his meals there, only approachable through Dr. Hans Stein, the Chancellor. If he required a committee member he summoned him. In the old man's mind the ideals of the Games were invested in his person, sanctifying him like a pope. The jutted eyebrows and falling jowls, the heavy shoulders and the menace of his mood changes dominated the multiracial assembly as it did the house and estate on the wastes below Mount San Jacinto.

In the past there had been conspiracies to unseat him, but the old man's intelligence service left him at no plotter's mercy. For the majority of the IOC members Mathew Kaverly was as invulnerable as General de Gaulle.

The left-wing newspaper, *Kreig,* was published in Bombay on each Wednesday. It was Kaverly's rule that the IOC office should provide him with clippings of mentions of the IOC made by the press of the country in which they were guests. A tear sheet from *Kreig* was on his table. The old man was flushed, his neck swollen. He pounded again on the telephone and then called the IOC office in the hotel's arcade, demanding that Hans Stein and Conrad Carson should be found and brought to him immediately.

The *Kreig* report was headed: DO NOT SQUANDER THE FLOWERS OF THE GODS ON THE UNDESERVING—Rabindranath Tagore. The report read:

> While two out of three of our people go to bed hungry every night, and the Banias tighten their grip on Mother India, the stately princes of the country, the puppets of the former British raj, continue to grow fat.

> With government pensions of up to twenty lakhs per annum and no apparent shortage of foreign exchange, these "men bedecked like women," as Ghandiji called them, spend

their time traveling between the fleshpots of Europe and their palaces here.

While genuine men of industry have to battle for foreign exchange to buy from abroad parts essential to their machinery, these princes spend valuable pounds and dollars on vulgar foreign cars. Many of them are sufficiently well educated to be of some use to their country. Some with consciences have gone into government and are rendering services, however slight. But the vast majority are useless wastrels, squandering their time on childish pursuits.

It has come to our notice, for instance, that a certain maharaja recently entertained his guests one morning to a race between a man, a horse and a car. We are happy to notice that it was not a son of India who took part in this demanding display. The runner, as you might have guessed, being a visiting American, Scott Reynolds by name.

We urge the Government of India to cut the props from under these prancing princes and abolish their pensions which would feed tens of thousands of hungry families. We also urge that the International Olympic Committee, now meeting in Bombay, take steps to prevent its charges from aiding and abetting the infantile pranks of our alleged aristocracy.

The old man got up, went to the table and read the report again. The thick, wide hands trembled on the paper. Uselessly, frighteningly in the empty room he shouted, "Stein, Carson . . . get up here!"

That last night before the voting, the air sparkling, perfumed by the green growth and blossoms soon to be hammered to death by the sun and the long wait between rains, was sleepless for the lobbyists, the vote peddlers and the anxious leaders of delegations who dealt and conspired through the still, pale night.

The transcripts from the bug in General Versilov's suite remained broken. Dobson had been unable to get the device replaced. The General's aide left the suite only to go to his own bed at night. With the maddening recalcitrance of machinery, like a television set which blows a tube in the middle of a world title fight, the bug saved its failures for the words in which Bob Schultz was most interested. It was clear enough that every influence was being used to get the Games for Prague. The General remarked to the Russian members that he did not give a damn about Prague personally but that a win for Prague was a necessary staging camp to get the Games to Moscow.

Conrad Carson had told Schultz he had no doubt that Accra had been eliminated as a serious competitor. Now it was time to eliminate Lyons.

Schultz was prepared for that. He had kept his own counsel about it before, but now was the time for a discussion with Harvey Tonkin and Lance Dobson.

"Harvey tells me it went over big," Schultz said.

"The English didn't like it," Dobson told him. "Too professional. Not in the true amateur spirit."

"What's your overall impression?"

"Overall? Very good."

"Worth votes?"

"Conrad Carson thinks so."

"That's good enough," Schultz said. "After that press conference of Obalisi's we can take it that Accra is out?"

"He buried himself. The Iron Curtain boys have already cut up the Accra vote."

"That leaves us with Lyons to worry about?"

"Yes. If you're right about the political hangup you've been working on. The Prague offer of subsidized accommodations isn't official, by the way. They're handling it carefully, by direct lobbying. Kaverly takes the view that free accommodations are contrary to the Olympic idea, that it would be a bid to buy the Games. The Commies don't want any trouble with Kaverly. They're treading very softly on this."

"What help can you give us on Lyons?"

"We've got a very strong lobby going; it's beginning to catch fire now. There's a lot of support to get the Games out of the West."

"That's a lobby for Santa Anna. It's not an anti-Lyons lobby."

"It is by implication. Lyons is in the West."

"Check," Harvey said. "I've seen a map."

Dobson began to be wary. Because he did not like Schultz he sensed something about him now. "You got any ideas?" he asked.

"Yes. Something I need action on."

"You're the boss," Dobson said, as though he did not mean it.

Schultz let it pass. He got up to pace. "Here's the picture. In 1962 the world ski championship was held at Chamonix, France. The East Germans had trained hard for it. At the last minute the East German team had their visas refused. NATO countries don't recognize East German passports."

Harvey said, "Just a minute, buddy. East Germans travel in Europe."

"They do and they don't. If an East German citizen wants to visit a NATO country, he has to apply for a travel pass or a safe-conduct from the Allied Travel Office in West Berlin."

"I know about that," Dobson said.

"No government body has any control over the Allied Travel Office. There are three representatives, one French, one English and one American. You know, the old postwar Allied control. Here's the clincher. Any one of those representatives can veto the decision of the other two. He need give no reason. Theoretically, he's answerable to nobody. Like the IOC, Allied Travel is a closed shop. Nobody knows today which of the three decided to keep the East Germans out of Chamonix."

Dobson was alerted. "Lyons must know about this," he said, his attention clamped on Bob Schultz. "They must have got an assurance that the East Germans can travel."

"I can tell you what they've got." Schultz opened the file beside him and read. "Provided that the present conditions remain unchanged, when the time comes, the three Western Powers will not raise any objection to issuing the necessary documents to the athletes of East Germany who are to participate in the Games."

"Goddammit," Harvey said. "That's woolly enough to wear."

Dobson was taut, leaned forward. "And one of the representatives on Allied travel will veto the East German visas?"

"I didn't say that."

"And you didn't say that they won't?"

"That's about it."

"Why didn't you break this earlier?"

"Accra was our first problem. The time for this is tomorrow morning, on the IOC floor, before the voting begins."

"So that it's too late for Lyons to get a harder assurance?"

"That's one point. In any case, the way things are between East and West Germany, there are no hard assurances that could be given four years ahead."

If Schultz had wanted Dobson's respect he had it.

"What do you want me to do?"

"I want you to get the issue raised on the congress floor."

Dobson worried about it. "That won't be easy. The European members we could get to would balk at that. To get emotional force behind it the question should come from one of the neutral members."

"Just a minute here," Harvey said. "Just a minute. I haven't been much help to you guys, but how about this Maharaja Scott and I were with?"

"The Maharaja of Sardar," Schultz told Dobson.

"Why would he want to do it?" asked Dobson.

"Why not? It's a fair question. I know a girl who could put it to him. You can't get much more neutral than an Indian."

Schultz said, "We would have to be absolutely sure of him, Harvey. There won't be any second prizes tomorrow morning."

"We could know about it tonight. I could set it up through Clark."

"All right, Dobson?"

"All right. If you can get the question asked I can organize a lot of hell to support it. But like you said, there won't be any second prizes."

When they were alone, Harvey asked admiringly, "How long you been sitting on this?"

"It came up months ago. We had most things covered. The mistake I made was about Accra. I didn't provide for Kaverly being behind Accra. Who is the girl who knows Sardar?"

"This big doll of Clark's, the one up at Udapair with Scott and me."

"You think she can swing him?"

"Over her shoulder is my guess," Harvey said.

At the big parties given by the applicant cities, anxiety ran unbridled. These provided the only opportunity the delegations had to lobby the members in mass. The success of a party was counted by the rate of acceptances. Absences of members from an important voting bloc quickly caused nerves and depression. The success of the Santa Anna presentation had benefited the Santa Anna party. Clark had reckoned on a seventy-five percent acceptance of invitations. It was more like ninety. The English members and their wives appeared in force, curious for something further to gloom over.

In the last colors of sunset the little open ferries shuttled from the Gateway to the island, their broken seats and parched timbers decorated with paper ribbons. The guests were garlanded on embarking. A transistor radio on each boat played music from Air-India. The long pier on the humped island had been swept of litter. Coolies with old sedan chairs carried the fluttering memsahibs and the elderly up the long, steep climb to the caves. Across the water the atomic research station at Trombay reared a monolith of silvered steel like the phallus in a Hindu temple. A striped marquee, the sides rolled, was set at the entrance to the caves. Behind the tables of food and drink the caves were lit with pale pink lamps, flickering shapes on the massive inertia of the sculptured limbs of gods and goddesses carved out of the granite more than a thousand years before. In the immemorial dream of the Hindu pantheon the voices of the guests flattened on the walls and the lofty dark of the rock ceilings.

Dazzled by the setting, the impassive haunt of the old carvings, the beauty of the evening and the eerie acoustical effect of the classical Indian orchestra set on a bamboo platform in the cave's echoing mouth, the guests expanded and fraternized. The Elephanta villagers, men, and women and children, peeked in dumb awe through the bushes.

The leader of the Prague delegation, an elegantly polished and handsome man, busied himself among the ladies. In romantically accented English he compared the beauties of Bombay to those of Prague. He spoke about Prague's historically famous crystal and mentioned that it would be the city's pleasure, should Prague get the Games, to present the lady wives of ICO members with crystal services.

Clark got hold of Pip Harris. "Get that fat Mayor or somebody. Get in there and break it up. That guy's using our party to sell his own soap powder."

The fat Mayor had troubles of his own. He had just been told that the committee member for the Argentine had been lobbying the South American bloc not to vote for Santa Anna. The Argentine planned to apply for the next Games. If Santa Anna were to win by some accident tomorrow, it might be twenty years before the Games went to Latin America again. The Argentine member said that Santa Anna was hopelessly unstable politically, that it did not have the money to stage the Olympics, that it did not have the brains to stage the Olympics, and that the Argentine would make South Americans proud. The fat Mayor had to be quietened by Luba Ivanova. He had challenged the Argentine member to a duel.

In his suite Kaverly waited while Conrad Carson read the *Kreig* article. Dr. Stein had not been found. Carson was pale. The congestion in the old man's neck and jowls was a signal he feared.

"Nobody else seems to have read this, sir. I've not heard it mentioned. I don't think it's anything to worry about."

"The IOC dirtied while a congress is in session? You don't think that's anything to worry about?"

"Sir, the article only mentions the IOC by drawing attention to the—"

"Damn you, I know what it draws attention to. Who is this man Reynolds? What is he doing in India? I won't have the IOC referred to in this way. You get this man, Carson. You get him here."

"But, Mr. Kaverly, the voting starts tomorrow."

"To hell with voting," the old man shouted. "I want to know what this man is doing here! Who is paying him?"

"He could be a tourist."

"Amateurs can't afford to be tourists. If this man is taking money in a foreign country, being paid for, I'll see to it that he never competes again. Do you hear me?"

Carson's head was bent hopelessly over the tear sheet. "Very well, Mr. Kaverly, I will see what I can do."

"Get on to the Consul," Kaverly shouted. "Check on this man's passport. If you see Stein, tell him to come here."

Outside the door Conrad Carson looked down the great staircase to the shortened figures crowding in the lobby. His dark suit and tie, as sober as an undertaker's, marked the cold pallor that topped the polished head. The years of abuse he had borne from Kaverly had been inside him as a cold and useless malice. Now, in ways he neither knew nor cared about, he was paying him back. He went to his room to telephone. A building constructor in the Lyons delegation had offered the Chancellor a bribe. Dobson might want to know about it.

Shortly after ten, Harvey Tonkin parked his sports car outside the Taj and asked at the desk for Clark. The receptionist thought that Clark was in his suite; his key had gone. Harvey walked up the staircase. He met Clark on the balcony, looking for a bearer.

"How did the party go?"

"Big deal," Clark said. "I'm pooped. Join me in a drink, Tonkin?"

"I'll take a raincheck on it," Harvey said. "I've got a letter for you." He handed Clark the envelope.

"Yeah? What's this, fan mail?"

"It's from Schultz."

"Yeah?" Clark said. "Who's Schultz?"

"Robert E. Schultz."

"Yeah? Who's Robert E.—" Clark stopped, his lips pointed

with surprise. "Chrissake. That Schultz. I didn't know he was here." He tore the envelope open and read the letter quickly. "Where you come in on this?"

"Just a friend of the family."

"Yeah?"

"It's clear, then, is it?"

"I got it," Clark said. He crumpled the paper and put it in his pocket, holding his hand there.

"There's a telephone number on that," Harvey reminded him.

"Yeah," Clark said. "OK. I got it."

"We will hear from you, then?"

"Sure, sure," Clark said.

Harvey waved, going down the staircase. Clark was still standing there with his hand in his pocket. He looked rattled.

At midnight Clark called Pallonji Mansions. He was drunk. Harvey answered the telephone.

"It's OK," Clark said.

"You're absolutely sure of that?"

"Sure I'm sure. It's in the bag."

20

BOB SCHULTZ sat on Harvey Tonkin's balcony, the hard shine of the sun-struck sea dazzling his eyes, heating his skin through the cotton pajamas. He watched idly as the dhobis spread their washing to bleach and harden on the hot rocks beyond the seawall; he could see them as he had not until that morning. Because it was beyond him he was relaxed and free. He sat there almost mindless, so slack that reaching to pour the coffee his arm was clumsy. The sun whirled patterns on the closed skin of his eyes.

Harvey came to the balcony doors, stuffing tobacco in his pipe. Schultz was leaning back in the safari chair, his eyes closed. Harvey put a finger on his lips to Manuel and sat down, turning the pages of the morning paper with caution.

The lobbies and lounges were as thronged as they had been all week, but the raised voices, the called names and the women's laughter had changed into charged quietness. The shut doors on the first-floor ballroom magnetized attention like a totem or an effigy, demanding respect and notice, the gossip, rumors and speculation had shrunk into tentative remarks.

At ten thirty, the press and delegates waiting in the permit bar rushed to the first-floor landing. Conrad Carson, assistant to the Chancellor, had called for the leader of the Lyons delegation. In the minutes before he was found, the first rumor had exploded and left the hotel for the city: "Lyons has the Games." The leader of the delegation was brought from his suite and joined the pushing journalists around Conrad Carson, who quickly dashed his hopes. In quick French Carson explained that the Committee wished to ask him a question. The doors closed on their going. The silent waiting was over now. Everyone had some kind of conjecture.

At eleven thirty the doors opened and the Lyons leader, mottled with shock and outrage, stepped out and went from sight in the clamor around him. Had Lyons got the Games? Why had he been called? What was happening? Refusing to answer, calling on his delegation for help, his hands pushing at the weight that jostled him, the French leader forced a passage to the staircase. Journalists waited and banged on the door of the suite or made useless calls on the house telephone. It did not answer. Inside, the receiver had been taken from its hook.

At twelve thirty the doors opened again and the Committee members filed out. The congress had been adjourned for lunch. Journalists who had covered previous IOC meetings noted the peculiarity of the mood. The members were as reserved as a murder jury, the usual social exchanges between them almost absent. Each member seemed anxious to reach the privacy of his own rooms. When Mathew C. Kaverly followed with the members of the Executive Board, no comment could be had. The old man had pushed a reporter in the chest. "When this Committee reaches a decision you will be told. Not before. Now, out of the way."

Watching him go, an English journalist said, "No wonder they call him F. U. C. Kaverly."

Luba Ivanova had risen late and prepared a bath with foaming oil. By clapping her knees together she could raise big pink bubbles which she popped with concentration. She was thinking about Sardar: "That big one loves me a little." She had not asked Clark why he wanted Sardar to raise the East German question. Clark would have his reasons.

She had put the request to Sardar last night. They had dined in his rooms. Afterwards, on the balcony, Luba had been withdrawn.

"A penny for your thoughts, Princess."

134

Luba had wrinkled her forehead. "Clark wants me to get you to do something."

"Does he, now? What does he want me to do?"

"He wants you to ask a question in the session tomorrow."

"What question?"

"First you must say if you will ask the question, no?"

"Why must I do that?"

"Because if you don't want to ask it, I am to make you."

"And how will you do that, Princess?"

Luba frowned at him. "You think I couldn't? I can do some things you don't know about. Sometimes I can make men do anything."

"Why aren't you making me do it, then, instead of telling me about it?"

"I don't know. It spoils it. I don't like reasons."

"What is the question? Tell me."

Sardar thought about it after she had told him. He said, "I don't mind asking that. It's a good point. If the Games go to Lyons there *is* no guarantee that the East Germans will have access."

"Then you will do it?"

"I will do it, Princess."

Luba brightened, leaned over and kissed Sardar on the chest, nibbling at him with her teeth.

"Now there is no reason to make you, no?"

"No. No reason."

"It is nice like that. Now I will make you, anyhow. Just to show you, big one."

Luba got up and looked in her handbag for her door key.

"What are you going to do?"

"I am going to get my gold shoes with the spike heels and my black garter belt. Don't you laugh, big one. You don't know what's going to happen to you."

In Pallonji Mansions, Schultz had poured a whisky. A cable had arrived from George Cole in answer to the report he had sent back in the diplomatic pouch: EVERY CONFIDENCE. THE VERY BEST OF LUCK. COLE.

"Try him again," Schultz told Harvey. "They must have heard some news by now."

Harvey was dialing when Manuel opened the door to Dobson. Before they could ask him he said, "We're still in."

They stood stock-still. Harvey clapped Schultz on the back. In an even voice, standing as stiff as a soldier, his face emptied of the lurching relief he felt, Schultz asked flatly, "Who is out?"

"They took two votes before lunch. Accra went out on the first round. Lyons went out on the second."

Schultz made no pretense now. He folded up on the couch. "Detroit, Prague, Santa Anna. Jesus, we made it."

Dobson looked strained; he had lost his gloss. "You want to hear the voting?"

"Go ahead." Schultz waved. "Let's have it, boy."

"First vote gave Detroit twenty-two, Prague nineteen, Santa Anna ten, Lyons seven, Accra six."

"Accra goes out on its jacksie," Harvey said.

"Second vote gave Detroit twenty-four, Prague nineteen, Santa Anna fourteen and Lyons seven."

"Out on its jacksie goes Lyons," Harvey said gleefully.

Schultz asked, "Where did we pick up the votes on the second round? Let me make a guess here."

Dobson cut him off. "Two from South America. One from Eire. One from Iceland." It stopped Schultz. "Eire? Iceland? How did we pick those up?"

"According to Carson, the Iceland member's wife does his voting. Anywhere with sunshine, she votes for it. The Eire member votes for the underdog and against the British. First round he voted for Accra."

Schultz slammed the couch. "It worked. The Lyons thing worked."

"There was hell to pay," Dobson said. "Could I have a drink, Tonkin?"

Dobson drank half the whisky Harvey handed him, coughed, drank the other half and put the glass down.

"The Lyons leader must have panicked," he said. "He made out no case at all. The West German member said the East should be kept out and asked who was it built the wall. Kaverly blew his top and threatened to expel the West German member from the meeting. They had a war this morning."

"We're going to make it," Schultz said. "I can feel it. More than half the Committee has to agree on one city. They will never get more than half of Detroit or Prague. I've done hundreds of hours of this. I know what I'm talking about."

Bob Schultz could not see past his own excitement. Dobson was not giving any cheers. Watching Dobson, the way he had downed the drink he would ordinarily hardly touch, Harvey said gently, "Just a minute, buddy. I don't know what it is, but we got something sour here."

Even that was slow to bring Schultz back. Dobson waited for him.

"What do you mean?" Schultz asked.

"It's true," Dobson said. "We've got trouble."

"How can we have trouble . . . now?"

"The Russians. We got it on the bug. They're going to fix Santa Anna."

"The Russians? How? They'll be voting again in less than an hour."

"The altitude," Dobson said. "The eight thousand feet. The Russians are going to carpet Santa Anna like we did with Lyons."

Schultz was sick. "We covered the altitude in the presentation. Nobody asked questions then."

"Nobody gave Santa Anna a prayer then. It wasn't worth asking questions. The leader of the Prague delegation is a doctor. He's been with General Versilov since the adjournment, dictating questions to be asked after lunch. He's also been on to the Chancellor. Remember, Stein is a doctor. He's got him in a flap. The Russians are going to ask for Santa Anna's application to be invalidated on health grounds."

"Oh, Jesus," Harvey said. "The Accra bit again."

"Santa Anna's votes would almost surely swing the Games for Prague," Dobson said.

Schultz straightened his wide, flat shoulders. His hand went to his thinning hair, brushing it forward.

So softly that it was hard to hear him, he said, "Now, now. Not this far. We're not going to be beaten now," and then, "Dobson, the man who put the altitude case for Santa Anna is Dr. Luis Sánchez, of Santa Anna Hospital's pneumology unit. This man is an expert on his subject. That will have to be our edge. The Russians have no time to get expert advice. We've got to get hold of Sánchez, brief him and give him time to work up a water-tight case. I want him out of that hotel and holed up somewhere until he works it out. If they just hit him suddenly, we've had it."

"This Sánchez. I might not be able to move him."

"Use your journalist's cover. Tell him you have a tip for him. I don't care how you do it, but get him away from that session."

"I'll try to raise Clark," Harvey said. "He could get Sánchez to Dobson."

"Look, if I find him I'll take him to my room. I could tell him Clark is there and wants him if you can't contact Clark before I get back to town."

"Good. Get going."

On the telephone Harvey said, "You deaf, Clark? That phone's been ringing five minutes."

He held the receiver away from his ear so that Schultz could hear. The answering voice was muzzy.

"He sounds stoned," Harvey said. "Clark, are you drunk?"

The thick voice said, "Who is this?"

"Tonkin. Tonkin the Vice-Consul. Where can we find Dr. Sánchez?"

"How do I know, Chrissake?"

"Give it to me," Schultz said. "Clark, this is Schultz. Get on the ball. Try to contact Sánchez. Tonkin is on his way in. We've got an emergency."

A half hour after the sixtieth congress of the International Olympic Committee met, for the second time on that unusual day, a delegation member was summoned to answer questions on the floor. Dr. Luis Sánchez could not be found. Mathew Kaverly ordered that no Committee member was to leave the room until Sánchez's whereabouts was established. The gallery outside the green baize doors learned this from Conrad Carson. At three o'clock Carson called for the Santa Anna delegation's leader, and the fat Mayor, popeyed and gesticulating, spent twenty minutes in the secret session, having understood little and answered nothing, repeating for most of that time the name of Dr. Luis Sánchez. At three thirty Dr. Sánchez and Sam Clark were seen in the hotel lobby and the doctor was hurried to the session.

During the wait for Dr. Sánchez, the Chancellor, Dr. Hans Stein, dispatched three cables at urgent rate through the IOC office in the hotel's arcade. One was addressed to Professor Ernst Jokl at the University of Kentucky, the second to an Onnie Niskanen in Addis Ababa, Ethiopia, the third to Dr. R. N. Jefferson, Auckland, New Zealand.

During the hour Dr. Sánchez was behind the ballroom doors, Lance Dobson had been on the telephone to Bob Schultz. He told him that Sánchez had arrived in Bombay with a detailed altitude case for Santa Anna but that it had been cut by Sam Clark during rehearsals for the presentation. In Dobson's room at Green's, Sánchez had made notes from the papers brought him in his briefcase by Clark. He had been coached by Clark in deportment. "Keep your voice low and casual," Clark had said. "Smile a lot. Try to look as though you find the questions childish but tolerate them because you're such a nice guy. Where you've got a real strong

138

point, drop your voice so the bastards have to ask you to repeat it." Sánchez had results from ergometer tests on subjects under stress at eight thousand feet, quotes from world medical opinion stating that no risk of harm to athletes would occur below twelve thousand feet, and on Clark's instructions, Sánchez was to state that he had been authorized by the Santa Anna Olympics Association and the Santa Anna Organizing Committee to make an offer: if any sports federation or national Olympic committee believed its athletes would require a longer period of acclimatization than two days, the athletes would be granted a free subsidy for any period up to six weeks.

At four thirty Conrad Carson again appeared and made an announcement. The president, he told the press and delegations, had adjourned the session until the following morning to permit members time to thoroughly consider the claims of the applicant cities. No comment whatsoever would be made by any member of the IOC's Executive Board or the president. In the following hubbub the doors were pinned back and the tense, heated committee members hurried to debate and confer in their own apartments. A dinner scheduled to be given by the Executive Board that evening was canceled on the instructions of Mathew C. Kaverly. Despite the IOC's secrecy rule it soon became known that Accra and Lyons had been eliminated by the morning vote.

Conrad Carson and the thin Chancellor sat at a table opposite the old man. Neither of them had eaten. For almost five hours, member after member had been summoned to Kaverly's suite. The IOC had split down the middle in a bitter disagreement that had next to nothing to do with the Olympics. It was East against West, lobby against lobby, prejudice against prejudice, Detroit against Prague.

The old man looked sick. His migraine tormented him, weakening his limbs, pitting his stomach with nausea. There was a pillbox beside him on the table. Stein was smoking neatly, his ashtray piled. The hand that held the cigarette was kept well away from the old man, and when he expelled smoke through his nostrils, he turned his head. The old man lumbered about in the big sitting room. The pain of the migraine had blurred his vision, unbalanced his weight; he moved clumsily.

"It has to be stopped, Hans," the old man said, his back to them. "They're trying to take it away from us again. It's the last clean thing. All over the world, these young people, these strong young people . . ."

He stood weaving his head and shoulders. Then he raised one arm, the finger pointed.

"The anti-Christ is in this building."

Carson and Dr. Stein fidgeted.

"Oh, yes he is," the old man said, looking warningly at the uneasy men. "The perverts of universal death have come to assassinate hope. The gray-faced ghouls of destruction, the beauty killers, the ideal-killers, are here to contrive against us. The last nonpolitical International in the world is a suffocating stink in their nostrils. They want the young men and women for their wars, inside their filthy barricades. I won't have it, do you hear?" His voice roughened into a shout.

Stein glanced at Carson. "Come and sit down, Mathew. You should have eaten something. Let me order coffee and sandwiches."

The old man slumped down in a chair, his forearms on the table, the heavy fingers spanned. "The politicians have been trying to bring us down for years. If the press learns that the IOC has been split on a political issue . . . I wanted Accra. All those new nations in Africa—they need us."

"Here, Mathew," Stein said, "take a pill."

He hooked his head at Carson and went to the bathroom, running both taps in the bowl for cover. When Carson came in, Stein said, "It's the migraine. He will be all right shortly. Just leave him alone for a bit."

Carson made a noise of contempt.

Stein said, worrying, "He's right, you know. A conflict like this could be very damaging. The Iron Curtain countries might walk out if the Games go to America again. If Communist Europe withdrew—and they've threatened before this to start a break-away movement—others in Africa and Arab-Asia would follow. It could be the end."

Carson said in his weird Swiss-American accent, "While the Russians have a chance of getting their democratization program through, they won't withdraw. If they get that and the new contests they want, games that are hardly played in the West, it will be America who withdraws."

"They won't get that," Stein said, "not while Kaverly is president."

"Kaverly won't always be president," Carson said with satisfaction.

There was a knock outside and the rattle of wheels. Stein turned off the basin taps.

The old man sat and munched through the food, drinking the coffee thirstily. His vision was clearing, the scum lifting off his eyes. Without looking up, speaking over a packed mouth, he said, "The Games will go to Santa Anna."

"There is the altitude problem, Mathew. I'm not sure that—"

"Damn the altitude. If they can run horses there, they can run athletes. How do you think the next vote will divide?"

"I'd give it to Detroit by a small margin. The three French votes have been pledged to Detroit against a promise from the American members to support a Lyons application for the next Games."

"We beat the politicians on that one," the old man said, brightening. "There will be no Games in Europe that bar East Germans."

"One of the Lyons delegation offered me a million francs for the International Board of Olympic Aid," Stein said, smiling. "With ten percent for my favorite charity to be handed directly to me."

It was the offer Carson knew about, which he had passed on to Lance Dobson after the scene in Kaverly's room about Scott Reynolds.

"Ten percent for your favorite charity?" said the old man, his neck swelling.

"A construction man." Stein was still smiling. "It usually is."

Kaverly slammed his fist on the table, rattling the crockery. "Why didn't you tell me about this?"

"I was going to, then Lyons was voted out. It didn't seem important."

"I will have him hounded," Kaverly said. "What is his name?"

"Mathew, it has happened before. It does no good to make a rumpus. A note has been made that he will be unacceptable on any future delegation."

"They're all around us," the old man shouted. "The corrupters are everywhere."

"It has happened before, Mathew. It will happen again." Stein tried to placate him. "These building contracts can mean millions to the constructors."

The old man lumbered about again. And then he halted as though he had run into something solid. As he had turned on his houseman in the desert, he swung now, the cat-light jump on the balls of his feet.

"Who else knows about this?"

"Carson. Nobody else."

Kaverly thumped his palm. "Detroit has made a deal for the French vote, eh? Carson, get the French members up here."

"They will probably be at dinner," Carson said.

"I didn't ask you where they are," Kaverly bellowed at him. "I asked you to get them up here. Now!"

Carson looked at Stein.

"Get them," Stein advised him.

Kaverly continued to lumber about, thumping his palm. He popped his jutted eyebrows at Stein and smiled.

"Mathew, what have you got in mind?" Stein said, apprehension in his voice.

"I'm going to break this thing. I'm going to screw their damn necks, all of them."

When Carson got back with the French Committee members, Kaverly was calmly drinking from a fresh pot of coffee. He asked the visitors to seat themselves and said that the Chancellor had something to tell them.

"Gentlemen," Stein said, "I'm afraid we have a scandal on our hands."

One of the French members knew no English. A younger man translated for him. English was always spoken in Kaverly's presence.

Stein was miserable. Pinched white patches shone on either side of his nose. "An influential member of the Lyons delegation has offered the Executive Board a bribe for its influence."

He licked his thin lips and sought help from Kaverly, who was half turned away, drinking coffee.

"You are familiar with the president's views on these matters. He has decided that the matter must be publicized to discourage future repetitions."

"Chancellor, you can't do that," a French member said. "Lyons intends to apply next time around, after getting a firm commitment about East German passports. A charge like this would ruin the city's chances."

"Believe me, gentlemen, I'm very sorry," Stein said, his head down.

"Who offered the bribe?" the younger member said, waving his hand angrily. "Who offered the bribe? Let us hear his side of the story."

Kaverly said, "This is a matter for the Executive Board, not the members. The man's name is immaterial. The bribe is not."

142

The French members talked between themselves in their own language.

"What do you want us to do?" asked the elder.

Kaverly turned his head, splaying his jowls on his collar. He said nothing for a minute, running his eyes from one man to the other. "I want the French vote for Santa Anna."

It stunned them.

The older member looked amazed. "You can't suborn the vote. How dare you?"

The old man's head came up, pulling out the ligaments on the thickening neck. His voice was loaded with threat.

"You gentlemen made a deal with Detroit; now you will make a deal with me. The sixtieth IOC conference is not going to be wrecked on political interest. Before that happens I will bury Lyons and bury the whole damned Committee."

The Frenchman stood up, his voice quavering. "You go too far. France does not bend to force. Our honor will not permit it."

"This conference is concerned with only one honor," Kaverly roared at him. "The honor of the Olympic ideal. I promise you, if you make a deal with Detroit I will call a world press conference on this Lyons bribe. I'll have your French honor for garbage."

The Frenchman choked. He was beyond words. "Come," he said, and rushed from the room, not waiting for his colleague.

Stein took off his spectacles, pressing thumb and forefinger on his eyeballs. The old man sat hunched, glaring at the slammed door. Then he began to heave, whistling through his nostrils. He was laughing.

"French honor. They all think they're de Gaulle."

Stein lit a cigarette shakily, turning his head to blow away the smoke. "What will they do?"

"What can they do? Where's Carson?"

"He said he was going to the office."

"Telephone him. Ask him to get Charlie Ryder up here."

Ryder was in his sixties, the leader of the Detroit delegation, pink and smooth, almost womanish in the smallness and regularity of his features.

"Mat," he said, his hand out, "I've been wondering when you'd ask me up. Well, it looks as though we've made it this time. The city said, when they asked me to come, Detroit's applied five times for the Games and lost five times on a knockout. This time we're putting Charlie Ryder in the ring. If we can't win with Charlie we can't win with anybody."

Ryder and Kaverly had sat on the same Republican committees.

"Get Mr. Ryder a drink, would you?" Kaverly asked Carson. "He takes bourbon on the rocks. So you expect a win, do you, Charlie?"

"You're right we do. I don't have to tell you, Mat. Like they say, Mat Kaverly's got two shops. Kaverly Canneries and the International Olympic Committee."

"You can go now," Kaverly told Carson, and then turned to the other man. "You believe that, Charlie?"

"You're right I believe it."

"Then believe me now. Detroit isn't going to win."

Ryder's face fell into hard, watchful lines. "That so?" He crossed his legs slowly. "You asked me up here to tell me that?"

Kaverly poured a coffee, cold now. "That's it, Charlie."

"You're not betting on the Commies, are you, Mat?"

"It's been pitch and toss. But Prague has the French vote."

Ryder lurched, splashing his drink. He uncrossed his legs and composed himself. He said, "Do tell?"

"Charlie, I know you made a deal for the French vote," Kaverly said, looking at Ryder sadly. "You won't get it. If you and I don't get together, the next Games will go behind the Curtain."

Ryder measured him. "What are you up to here, Mat?"

"I'm trying to keep the Games in the West, Charlie."

"What makes you think Prague has the French vote?"

"Charlie, there will be just one vote on that floor tomorrow," Kaverly said, almost spilling out the words. "It will all be over in a half hour. Do you want to take the risk of seeing the Games go behind the Curtain?"

"You know the answer to that. But Detroit has been a five-time loser. We can win here tomorrow."

"You can't win, Charlie. All you can do is give it to Prague."

Now Ryder was spilling out his words. "That's if Prague *has* got the French vote."

Kaverly picked up the telephone, getting tangled in the cord, and put it on the table in front of Ryder. "Ask them, Charlie."

Carefully, Ryder put his glass down. "This thing's been close enough for us to taste, Mat. You know how I feel about Detroit. You and I been friends off and on for a long time. If you're trying to bring me down, I won't forget you for it."

The old man's face hung in clumps "Ask them, Charlie. Ask them if you can count on them."

When Ryder had replaced the telephone he almost whispered, "They say they can't promise anything."

Kaverly put a hand on his shoulder. "Charlie, we've got one chance to beat Prague on that floor tomorrow, just one. You've got to switch your lobby to Santa Anna."

"We were so close," Ryder said, who had not recovered. "So close. Suppose we took the risk?"

"There's no risk to take," Kaverly said. "One vote and the Games go to Prague."

Kaverly knew his man. At a Republican convention in 1962 Charlie Ryder had made a speech charging that John F. Kennedy was a fellow traveler.

The hotel that faced the Gateway to India was lit in almost every window. It was a rare sight, beyond most people's memory. The pavement sleepers along the seawall turned their backs against the distraction and wrapped their heads in coverings. In the lit rooms the arguments and lobbying continued. Big Daniel Obalisi, glossy black and naked, sat up in bed and wrote a report on a pad propped against his knees. He had learned that Ghana's friends the Russians had made no attempt in the congress to defend Accra on the subject of roundworm, hookworm, dysentery and diarrhea. As he wrote, Obalisi blew noisy sighs.

Mathew C. Kaverly had ordered himself tomato soup, a thick steak with salad and French-fried potatoes and a banana custard. He had telephoned the IOC office to ask for Dr. Stein. While he waited he sucked a peppermint and rocked on his heels, humming, "It Happened in Monterey." It was Kaverly's favorite composition, next to the bird music. At home he had it piped through the garden. The old man was considering how the corrupters had delivered themselves into his hands. It was a judgment. Almost a portent. He would get the result he wanted. He hadn't got Accra, but Santa Anna would be the first time the Games had been presented on the continent of South America. It was a great triumph, a great promise for the future. The old man lumbered happily about the room and shook a little on his laughter. He had beaten them all. This would be the cleanest result he could remember. A result absolutely untouched by the faintest taint of politics. It occurred to him as he rocked and looked down on the Gateway that a climate in which it rained only once a year would be deadly dull to live in. He

145

resolved that when he got home he would work out a long-range weather forecast for Santa Anna. "It broke somebody's heart," he sang, "and sad to say that it was mine."

Sardar sat on his darkened balcony. Luba Ivanova was beside him on a footstool, her arm across his legs.

"We might never meet again, Princess Luba."

"If Santa Anna wins I will see you there, no? Clark has promised I can go."

"Ifs, my pretty, do not turn the world."

Luba sat up, her nose wrinkled in thought. "I might marry you. But mixed marriage, it is not good, no?"

It hurt Sardar. "You think not?"

"No. I am this good Catholic. You are something else and won't go to heaven."

"Good lord," Sardar said.

Harvey Tonkin called Manuel to help. He and Bob Schultz had dined in a restaurant near the Towers of Silence where the Parsis laid out their dead to be picked to the bones by vultures. The Parsi religion, Harvey had remarked, must have been worked out by a very clever vulture. They had returned to the flat to have drinks with Dobson, who was calling to give Harvey a laconic goodbye. Bob Schultz had passed out, smiling idiotically. The little man struggled to support his friend's weight while Manuel took his legs. Harvey said, "This they would never believe in Washington, D. C."

Next morning, within forty minutes of convening, Mathew C. Kaverly announced to the gallery that on behalf of the sixtieth congress of the International Olympic Committee, the city of Santa Anna had been awarded the Olympic Games.

At nine that night, after returning from a closing-of-session party at the Juhu Hotel, Dr. Hans Stein was handed three cables received in answer to those he had dispatched the previous day.

They read:

REPLYING YOURS 24/10 FEAR ENDURANCE STRESS AT SANTA ANNA'S ALTITUDE COULD CAUSE CARDIAC TROUBLES. YOURS, PROFESSOR JOKL.

REFERENCE YOUR QUERY SANTA ANNA GAMES, THERE WOULD BE THOSE WHO DIE, NISKANEN.

ATHLETES DRIVE THEMSELVES LIMIT OF PHYSICAL ENDURANCE. TO DO THIS IN RAREFIED CONDITIONS COULD CAUSE DEATH OR

IRREPARABLE DAMAGE THROUGH OXYGEN LACK. YOURS, JEFFER-SON.

Stein sat at his table stricken and gray, reading and rereading the terrible verdicts.

PART TWO

HARRY

United Kingdom

21

THERE HAD always been a solitary place inside him. Persons had known it as a child. It had been ineffable then. He had felt it as a sense of displacement, an unaccountable feeling of loss for something he could not identify. His difference had not been romantic or wistful. He had played contact games at school with a disregard for hurt which frightened much bigger boys. It was more like something inside him which awaited his discovery, known about but mysterious like the far side of the moon.

Persons was twelve when his mother died. He had cried at the grave, his big brother at his side in the uniform of an Air Force cadet. But less out of love than for resentment at the cold, implacable hole, greasy with winter and puddled, crumbling its edges when his mother's coffin bumped there. His mother was doubly dead to her young son because she had never been properly alive to him. She had been the need to keep quiet, a shut-windowed room that smelled of sickness and medicine, dressing gowns, bedpans and grappling kisses from a mouth made lipless by pain. Bill Persons' revulsion for organic decay was rooted there in his childhood.

He had chosen to be a civil engineer out of contempt for people who dealt in people. To get as far from that as he could into the clean, inanimate world of structures. He had been brilliant at his work and tolerated because of it by the bosses he abused and stormed at if he thought a job mean in specifications. He felt love once, wild and desperate, and so frightened the girl that she hastened to marry another man, chiefly because he had taken a job in Canada. When the Kempei Tai took his body to savage, Persons was already a little out of reach.

When they put him in the cage, Persons had had no heroics to support him. He had taken his leave of both sides. He speculated on the bars and worked his swelling tongue to make a smile. If it became unbearable he could tear a noose from his clothing and strangle himself. They had only his life to threaten him with and Persons did not want it anymore. He considered it absurd that this should be all there is to man's tyranny of man. Obey my law, salute my flag, kneel down before my god. Or? Or I will kill you. When the prisoners in the huts looked across the compound, shattered by their impotence and pity, they could not know that the man in the cage was not helpless but terribly armed.

In the passing weeks the questions they asked him lost significance. The questions were the necessary preface to the bitter contest between them. In the will and defiance they could not crush out of him, the defeat of their kind by his kind was in him like revelation. They feared his death more than he did.

At last, on a reflex of pain, his arm had shot out, fingers clawed, toward the Kempei Tai sergeant who had interrogated him from the beginning. The man had recoiled in a start of terror from the prisoner helpless on his knees between guards. Persons had fixed him with his pale eyes, grinned over broken teeth to mock him. That had been the end of torture. The Kempei Tai never troubled him again.

After the war the doctors helped, but the repair that Persons worked on himself had little to do with medicine. His body, the muscles and organs in it, had become a projection of his will and spirit, a phenomenon he could easily produce. In the bad times he did not think "I am sick; I am hurting." He thought "It is sick; it is hurting." His love of machines and structures survived in him as a sapped passion, but he felt no requirement himself to design and build. He had discovered within himself a country without boundaries, and he built his dams and bridges there.

Before Bill Persons met young Harry Hayes his life had approached serenity. There was nothing more in the world he wanted. He had proved what he had needed to prove. He had his house, music, books, garden, a few friends, money enough. He could no more have lived under one roof with a woman that he could have with another man. In the prison camp and afterwards he had been too long solitary for that. When his sexual energy had returned with his health, it had been sublimated in training. Now, if need disturbed his peace, Persons was hardly involved. He would park the old Vauxhall off Bayswater Road and go to a house that he knew. He would take sweet sparkling wine to drink and chat with the girls over the glasses. He always arrived at midmorning, when the house was otherwise empty. When the wine had gone Persons would say "Well, Mamie?" to the eldest and least attractive. He considered that she most needed his patronage. Mamie was always uncomfortable after Persons had left. She would tell the others, "He's kind, you know what I mean? But he always leaves me feeling queer. It's like I'm not there or something."

Harry Hayes had touched Persons as Mamie never could. It was both a physical and a mental involvement. He had been attracted by the boy's good looks, his vulnerability, his "newness," as Mary Charlton had called it. He had recognized too the thing that quested in the boy, the instinct for conflict and achievement. The tenderness he felt toward Harry's long, clean body he wryly dismissed as an unexpected signal of the frustrated father in him. And then Harry had run, his face grave and still, until he had been filled by the pain. Later, in the locker room, while Harry was still shaken, that manic laughter had risen between them.

It had come to Persons then and he had resisted it. He could use that body. He had been too old himself, after the war, to show the world more than a glimpse of what he knew. He resisted it because he was truly reluctant to become netted in others. But the Kempei Tai were everywhere now, in many skins and many countries. Behind the boy's blundering words and gestures there was a flinty vessel into which Persons could pour himself and run through the rot of the world. His square hands had strangled at the wheel of the old Vauxhall. His pale eyes stretched with disgust and rage. "I'll show them," he shouted. "I'm not done yet. I'll show them."

Next day, calm, he had poked at his garden and looked over the stubbled fields. If he was right about the boy no more would be required. The boy would seek him out like a fate.

Persons was almost as famous as Harry Hayes after the sub-four-minute mile at Cardiff. The reporters went to their files and resurrected his old clippings. He had begun to behave extravagantly at meetings, attracting attention to himself. The officials resented and feared him. If his demands were not immediately satisfied he blazed at them in fury. The reporters were uneasy. They could never get Harry on his own. He would listen carefully and cautiously to their questions and then say, "You had better ask Bill." Alec McBride was the only reporter Persons would admit to any kind of intimacy.

It had happened faster and surer than Persons had reckoned. He and Harry Hayes had fused. All the potential of the boy's life was clamped and focused on doing the other man's will. He breathed the passion with which Persons filled him and kindled it with his imagination. They were one, not two, until Harry waited for the pistol, and then the gravity would overcome his face. If he looked up in the waiting there was no contact in his eyes. He had blanked them all out, including Persons. There was a testing time before him and he was pinpointed on that. He had learned to welcome the pain. It was Persons who labored to keep them fused, agonized on the field in his grotesque mime of running, with his eyes blazing, stepping the correct footfall, fingers pinched for purpose, hands pulling on invisible ropes for the balance and the drive, his head painfully arranged in spinal alignment as though by springs of will he could project these postures on Harry. When the time came for the strong to falter, Persons knew it to the instant. The screams of the body's protest were exactly the same as his tortures, the lapping panic and the mind's recoil. There was a barrier there and the human vessel could shatter on it like an aircraft thunderclapping through the wall of sound. "This is it, Harry. This is it. The difference between the men and the boys." And on the field he would drive them both through, into the peace on the other side.

He had often told Harry, "A great athlete is a distinct and different kind of man. He's the prototype of the future. Those oafs in the stand filling their bellies with buns are as far from us as the apes. They are the nothing-men, Harry. One day they will stuff them and put them behind glass so that others can wonder at what they evolved from. They need welfare states. Spineless pink crawlers like that couldn't live a day on their own. They'll never climb real mountains, Harry. They can't get higher than their wives' mounts of Venus. Those oafs in the stand don't know that if the tape was moved back another fifteen yards the great miler would die before he hit it. They make good compost. Nature needs them. Cremation should be forbidden by law."

Because it had happened faster and surer than he had reckoned, Persons had not set his targets. That came to him after Cardiff. He was having a telephone installed. In the early morning Persons had stood on his doorstep and watched the white-overalled men setting a ladder against the cottage.

"S'pose you'll be getting ready now for South America, Mr. Persons," one said smiling.

"South America? I don't follow you."

"The Olympics. Heard it on the news this morning. Next Olympics are to be in South America, place called Santa Anna. There's a bit of an argument about it. It's halfway up a bleeding great mountain."

The Olympics. An Olympic Gold Medal. Here, now, they had broken the four-minute barrier. An Olympic Gold Medal won against the supermen of the world, which he would run in Harry Hayes's body. Persons pulled at the bookcase searching for an atlas, shaking like a man in fever.

On his visits to London, Persons spent afternoons reading in the British Museum. He was disturbed by what he learned. He filled a book with notes on stress at high altitudes. The suppressed excitement Harry had noticed in him turned to bitterness and bad temper. At a weekend on the farm Harry mentioned a letter to *The Times*, which had been passed about at the club. It had been signed by a number of ex-Olympians who protested about the choice of Santa Anna. Bill Persons had blazed.

"To hell with the Olympics!" he had shouted. "Those bloody IOC lunatics. They're a pack of senile crumblers. Their average age is about seventy. A good deep breath would see half of them six feet underground."

In a book on stress in mountain climbing Persons found a reference to a Dr. Axian, described as the man who got the British climbers up K-2. Axian received him in a cupboard of an office behind an old building in Hampstead. The Medical Research Council's laboratory was set up there. The big, precise man did not agree that there would be those who'd die in Santa Anna. "Mind you," he said, "I can't prove it scientifically. Roger Bannister has warned that there will be psychological factors to consider. An Olympic contest creates a massive excitement in the athelete which is itself a form of stress. We can't synthetize that artificially."

In the laboratory, popeyed with effort, an assistant pedaled a stationary bicycle to the rhythm of a metronome and wheezed into a gas mask.

"We push his breath through a meter," Axian said, "measure it by volume. Analyze it. All part of the continuing experiment. Man under strain."

He checked the resistance of the bicycle wheel. "We can simulate all kinds of effort, but we can't satisfactorily simulate altitude. In Britain we don't have that kind of high country. It will make it hard for our athletes. The French will be all right and the Russians, of course. The Americans will probably go to the Rockies."

Persons said, "Apart from the health dangers which you don't believe in, what advantage would athletes have who already live at height? Keino in Nairobi, for instance?"

"A measurable advantage. I could calculate it for you."

"If a sea-level athlete got to Santa Anna early, how long would it take him to acclimatize?"

"Well," Axian said and rubbed his nose, "it would depend how early, wouldn't it? It can take nine months to acclimatize to height. There won't be many British athletes who can afford to get to Santa Anna for nine months." He smiled. "This could be the first Olympics at which an athlete can buy himself a medal."

Persons banged his tweed hat on his legs. "The bloody lunatics."

"Very possibly," Axian said.

On afternoons other than Fridays, when he made his collections and wrote up the cashbook, Harry was seldom more than fifteen minutes early or late for the meal Mrs. Hayes would have prepared. The kitchen table would be set, pots hot on the stove, the whistling kettle filled and ready. He would kiss his mother's cheek and hand her the afternoon paper. Mrs. Hayes would take her spectacles from her apron pocket and sit opposite her son, turning first to the sports pages for the mention of Harry's name. It was still a wonder to her. She kept his clippings pasted in the back of a half-empty photograph album.

On the day he saw the unset table and cold stove he immediately blanched with premonition. There was no sound. He called for her, unwilling to move. She was on her bed, under the chenille cover, dressed, breathing heavily in sleep.

Harry touched her. "Mum, are you all right?"

Mrs. Hayes opened her eyes and smiled. Her mouth was dragged on one side. "Harry? Are you home early?"

"No, Mum. It's three o'clock. What is it? Don't you feel well?"

She used one elbow to raise herself, looking puzzled. "I dunno, lad. I had this funny turn. I sat down to peel the potatoes and everything got dark. Me arm and me leg went like water. I had that much trouble gettin' to bed."

"Which arm is it?"

"This one. Me right."

He took her hand and lifted it. It lay flatly in his grip. There was no answering pressure of fingers.

Mrs. Hayes frowned. "That's funny. I can't feel you. I can't hardly feel my arm at all. What is it, Harry? What's happened?"

The doctor stood with his bag on the kitchen table.

"I understand that your mother is a widow?"

"That's right."

"Have the family any relatives? Somebody close by who could come in and help?"

"No. There's only the two of us."

"I see." The doctor examined the picture calendar on the wall above the stove. "She has had a stroke. Not a grave one, but I'm afraid that she won't be able to look after herself."

Harry looked about him. The cold stove was like a lump of ice in the kitchen.

"I could get a nurse," he said.

"Hm." The doctor looked at his watch. "There is that, of course, but it's rather expensive. You are out most of the day, I assume."

"I get back about three."

"Hm," said the doctor. "Even if one can afford a nurse there is always the problem of meals."

"What do you think I should do, Doctor?"

"Well, Mr. Hayes, it is not for me to say. But in cases like this it has been my experience that the most satisfactory arrangement for all parties is to let the patient go to a home. Of course," he said hurriedly, "there are some excellent homes. Excellent care and attention. Homes are not the Dickensian places they used to be, you know."

Bill Persons arrived next afternoon. Mrs. Hayes had slept untroubled and awakened to enjoy a bowl of chicken broth. Her speech had slurred a little but the doctor dismissed it.

"She has an excellent constitution," he said.

The district nurse had several times been in and out. There had been no more mention of a home.

In the tiny enclosure below the level of the street Harry was watering his mother's pot plants when he heard the old Vauxhall. He hurried up the steps. Persons' tweed hat was jammed down on his nose. He wore it that way against the wind, driving the open car.

"Well," he said, tilting his head to see under the hat brim,

157

"how is she?" He was holding the door open, his feet on the footpath.

"She's much the same. She had an easy night. The doctor gave her a sedative."

"Good," Persons said. He got out, slammed the door, pushed his hat back. "Anyone in there?"

"Not at present. The doctor was here at lunchtime. The district nurse has just left."

Persons eyed him. "You look as though you'd been dragged through a hedge backwards."

"I didn't sleep much."

"It's you the bloody doctor should have given a sedative." Persons looked with distaste up the long street. "Look at it," he said. "A mile of dirty windows and peeling brick and not a green thing in sight. No wonder people have strokes."

Mrs. Hayes was awake. Harry helped her sit up, tucked the pillows behind her. "Bill has come to see you," he said. "I'll make a cup of tea."

Persons had only been twice before to the basement. The last time had been when he came to reassure Mrs. Hayes after Harry resigned his apprenticeship and took the job with the dairy.

When the tea was ready, Harry put a cup on a tray with a sweet biscuit on the saucer.

"I'll take it to her," Persons said. "No, you stay here. I'd like to see her alone. Where's the bedroom?"

When he came back he poured a cup for himself and sweetened it with the honey he used.

"How is she? What did she say?"

Persons had continued to stir his tea. "She's finished," he said.

"Finished? How do you mean?" Harry heard his voice tremble.

"I mean finished. Done. A bundle of rags. She will never be any good."

There was nothing in Persons' voice and nothing in his face to soften the brutality of it.

Harry felt himself drift away from this man for whom he had painfully waited. A fierce instinct to protect his mother rose and focused within him. "Why do you need to say that? What do you know? You're not a doctor."

Persons had tasted his tea, quite relaxed. "I've seen more death in a day, lad, than you will see in your lifetime. I can smell it on a sick person's breath. I've smelled cancer on the
158

breath of a fit man. Your mother might live another six months. She won't live longer."

Harry breathed hard, staring at him. "You hate people, don't you?"

It surprised Persons. He looked up into the pale face that wondered at him. "Don't be silly. There will be enough ghouls about without me. Old biddies with cups of soup, congratulating themselves on their charity, using sickroom whispers and slopping their eyes at you until you'll want to blub out of self-pity. These old biddies love death. They think they've got a patent on it, like childbirth. I know how you feel, boy. I saw my own mother buried when I was half your age. But my business is with the living. So is yours. There is no substitute for what is."

Persons went to the stove, found matches and lit the gas. He stood there frowning while the water boiled. Harry said nothing, his forehead in his hand. Persons emptied the teapot, found the caddy, made fresh tea when the kettle whistled. He emptied Harry's untouched cup in the sink, preoccupied, still frowning.

"How are you going to look after her?"

"I don't know. I could get a nurse."

"For ten pounds a week. You could afford that if you cut out eating." Persons poured the tea and sat down.

"I could get a part-time nurse for the mornings."

"And look after her yourself in the afternoons, I suppose?"

"Yes. I'm home by three."

"I suppose you'd train running up and down the kitchen?"

For the first time Harry felt the burn of tears behind his eyes, a constriction in his throat. "I don't know. I just don't know. Poor Mum." He rubbed his eyes. "Poor Mum," he said again.

Persons softened his voice. "You've got to be realistic, lad. Most people find it too hard."

22

THE BUILDING was two-story, modern, aggressively bright, with lifts and ramps instead of stairs. The matron and staff were aggressively bright. Aggressively bright young doctors visited. The furniture and fittings were aggressively bright, made in materials impervious to wear. It was as though only human decay could be tolerated in that institution or that the hard, bright metal of chairs, tables and bed might lend the infirm flesh its own immortality.

Old Mrs. Hayes kept her wits. After three months she was neither better nor worse. She could walk a little now and confidently expected to be well enough soon to go home. She wasn't on charity, which mattered to her. Harry paid the home four pounds a week.

Visiting on a gray afternoon drizzled with rain, he found a car stuck with political slogans and party pennants outside the home. It was Election Day. Strangers were helping the old women to the cars, holding umbrellas over them.

"What's going on?" he asked a young man with a rosette in his buttonhole.

"We're getting out the grave vote," the party worker said cheerfully.

"The grave vote?"

"What else would you call it? There's only one way out of these places, mate. Feet first."

Harry Hayes was still loaded with violence when he latched the green gate and turned down Abbot's Terrace. Now he wanted to be free of the basement flat, to escape "that underground cave" as Bill called it. He would find a boardinghouse. A big, bright room with a high ceiling and a prospect of green in the windows. The horn that beeped insistently behind him hardly broke his thoughts. Only when the little red car slowed alongside and beeped again did Harry look.

"Who's dreaming?" Mary Charlton asked. "That's what comes, you see, of reading poetry."

They had not seen each other since the meeting in the village bookshop.

He had to bend awkwardly to the little car. "How are you?"

She looked bright and flushed. "As well as four finos can make me. I've been visiting Liz Sparks." She gave him her cool inspection. "Do you know I've never seen you out of that Club blazer? Do you wear it to bed?"

Harry said, "Only in winter."

She was still calculating him, biting a little nervously on her lip. "How about a drink? I'll show you how well I can drive. Do you like my car? I call her Mardi Gras."

Because he had accepted the black crepe but not the ordained end, Harry had the need of a relieving which had not come to him running on the track. He was suddenly sick of the discipline, had the desire to kick something over. He saw Bill Persons warning him with his pale, cold eyes and faltered for an instant. Guilt touched him and because of that he hardened.

"All bloody right," he said.

Mary Charlton changed a little, a pucker between her eyebrows. "You don't have to be so fierce about it."

Because he was stockaded, bent on himself, he did not notice Mary's nervousness. She tried to catch his attention with her hand, posing it before him on the table. The pub was almost empty, a few couples on stools at the bar. It made it harder to talk.

She had to say, "Haven't you noticed anything?" She waggled the fingers of her left hand, her voice arch and gay.

Harry was still slow about it. There was nothing to notice on her hand. And then he saw her meaning.

"Your engagement ring. There is no ring."

"Well, you're not blind after all. I must say, I was beginning to wonder."

He did notice her now, saw suddenly that she had thinned, that her eyes were changed. He was looking at her properly for the first time, coming out of himself. "What happened?"

"Didn't you know? I thought Len Sparks might have told you."

Harry shook his head, watching her nervousness.

"It's an old story. I was jilted."

Harry couldn't imagine Mary Charlton being jilted. "At the church?"

"God, no. That would have been too much. A month before the wedding. There was this Swedish girl my fiancé had met in Stockholm. She came to London to be an *au pair* and bang! That was that. Yours truly is the joke of the district. That's why Mummy bought me the Mini. It's a consolation prize."

She laughed again, her face stiff.

Harry said, "I'm sorry. I didn't know. I thought you were probably married."

"You mean you didn't think about me at all," Mary said, and wished she had not.

It was true. He had had no room or reason to think of her.

"No, it's not that. I often wondered about you. It's just that you said you were getting married in the spring."

Mary said, "Perhaps I will get married in the spring. But not this year."

"You had the wrong fiancé. You can count yourself lucky."

"It's funny. I wasn't all that keen to begin. Mummy was

mad about him. She thought he was the greatest thing ever. He's very smooth and quite well-off. But enough about my troubles. Let's talk about you."

After an hour, Harry remembered he had a train to catch. The gins they had drunk showed on Mary and were in Harry's cheeks as a heated tingle. In the car she hitched her skirt and sprawled her legs, searching in her handbag for the keys. Although she had thinned in the face, her body was heavier and fuller. Her perfume was there on the thick new-car smell of paint and rubber and leather.

She said, "You direct me. I'll drive you home."

He didn't want that. He was reluctant, as he had been at their first meeting, to have Mary know how he lived.

"No, just drop me off at your place. It's easier to walk from there."

"Why walk when I can drive you?"

"It's easier. I can do with a walk."

"I don't think you trust lady drivers," Mary said, and backed the car, swiveling in the seat to watch out the rear window, her face close to him, her breath sweet with gin.

At the house she parked with a flourish, scraping the tires on the curbing, and sat holding the wheel. "You won't let me drive you?"

"No, thanks. Really."

"Have it your own way." She turned her head and screwed her face to listen. "The telephone." She reached for the door handle. "Don't run away."

She slammed the gate open and hurried up the path. "Damn," she called from the porched entrance. "The house key. It's on the car ring, Harry."

He pulled the keys out of the ignition and walked quickly up the gravel.

"Do hurry."

Mary unlocked the door, gesturing him in. The telephone was on the hall table, a tiny black chair beside it.

Mary said, "Oh, it's you, Gabby. No, I've just come in. I heard the phone ringing from the street."

Harry waited uncomfortably, half turned to study the garden.

Mary said, "Sorry about that. It was Mother. She and a friend went up to the Chelsea Flower Show. They're going to stay in town and go on to the theater. Mother worries about me being on my own these days. She thinks I might be feeling fatal or something."

162

Her wide mouth smiled and she stood smoothing her skirt down.

Harry nodded. "Well, it was good seeing you again. I'd better get on my way."

"Must you?" Mary said. "I mean now that you're here, won't you stay for a drink or a cup of coffee?"

She was anxious about it, pressing him with her eyes. It wasn't Harry's kind of house. The rich furnishings caused him uneasiness.

"Thanks, no. It's getting late. I'd better be on my way."

But the dimmed light, the warmth and comfort, the silence that seemed to spill from the rooms, held him fixed in the doorway. There was a charge in Mary's waiting, a strain and a helplessness so different from the bantering manner she used to have.

He had to say something. "All right, then. Thanks. A cup of coffee."

Mary walked past him and shut the heavy door, making it suddenly dark in the hall, colored with the tints of the lead light paneling.

She said, "This way," and held out her hand until he took it.

In the shadowing evening the big room glowed, palely lit by halfdrawn curtains and a single lamp under a parchment shade painted with dragons. Cabinets of china, a tea cart with glasses and bottles, deep chairs and a tapestried sofa heaped with fat colored cushions were arranged on a dark carpet, deep enough to be noticed.

"No," Mary told him. "You just sit down. I'll put a record on the player. Gabby taught me to be competent in the kitchen. You've got to learn to run a house if you want to make a good marriage." She made a face. "It didn't help me much, did it?"

She was soon back with a coffee service on a silver tray. She moved a low table close to Harry.

"I've given you cream, is that all right? I can get milk if you want it."

"No, cream's fine. Thanks."

There was only one cup and saucer beside the cake tray.

"How about you? Aren't you having any?"

"I don't feel like coffee. I'll have a small gin. Here, let me pour."

He had not wanted coffee; he never drank it. But it was scalding hot and sweet as Mary had prepared it, the cream floating thick and cool, making two flavors as he sipped the coffee through it. He took a cake for good manners and because she wanted it and enjoyed that, too, although Bill had barred cake from his diet.

Mary crossed her legs beside him on the couch. "I've never known a boy to change so much in such a short time," she said, puckering her mouth at him.

"That's what you said last time I saw you."

"I know. You just go on changing."

"Bill says if you're not changing it means you're dead. He says the world is full of the walking dead. He always says that about people he doesn't like. He says 'There goes another one who won't lie down.'"

"Bill? That's the trainer you talked about last time, isn't it?"

"Yes. I probably did mention him."

"Mention him? You talked nothing else. He must mean a lot to you."

Harry laughed uncertainly. "Well, he's my trainer. He's taught me everything I know."

"And now you're the British champion."

"I was a bit lucky," Harry said.

"I don't think so. You're different. I noticed that when I first met you."

She was concentrated on him; it made Harry awkward.

"You kept saying I was new," he said, looking at his coffee.

"You remember that? I'm glad. Do you remember when I said it?"

He was faintly embarrassed now because he did remember and her insistence seemed to shrink the sofa they shared, to bring her palpably closer.

Even her voice pressed at him. "The time you kissed me good night. The first time."

He could feel the traitorous flush on his skin, wanted the conversation changed. "I'm no more changed than you are." He looked up to laugh it off.

Her wide mouth was quivering. She was quite tensed; her voice shook. "Why do you say that?"

"That you've changed?" he asked, wondering.

"You said I was more changed than you are."

"No, I didn't." He had to try to remember his words, to get it right to account for this reaction. "I said I'm no more changed than you are. That's all. Just that we have both changed."

He was talking to Mary's back. She had got up to freshen her drink.

"You don't have to pretend. I know they've been talking about me at the Club. David boasted about it. I didn't even know at the time."

"Boasted about what? Who's David? I don't know what you're on about."

"David. My ex-fiancé." She came back, pale, defying him, and tossed off half the drink. "It's quite a joke on the squash courts. Old changed me. David let them all know, damn him."

It was unfamiliar country to Harry, but he had an instinct of understanding. He stood up, looking deliberately at his watch. "You think about it too much," he said. "It's just that your pride has been hurt."

She could have left it there but did not. "You don't think it matters?"

"Of course it doesn't matter."

"Oh, I've changed right enough. I'm not a virgin anymore. I'm not a virgin by a long way."

He stood in the rich room's glow and was helpless. He had been free of it, otherwise directed, and now battened things cracked and broke in him. "No girls, Harry. We have better uses for your manhood. Time enough for that when you've got something achieved. Then you'll be able to pick and choose from the best of them." He had been free of it and it had been easy. He had not labored for purity; he had known nothing else. It was part of the power he consumed on the track.

"Did you hear me, Harry? I'm not a virgin anymore. You were right about me being changed." She was standing beside him; her voice stroked the word.

He said, "It doesn't matter. It would be better if you didn't talk about it, Mary."

"I want to talk about it."

He turned to her, and her eyes were wide and dark, her breasts lifting on her breathing. "You shouldn't have told me. It's none of my business."

"I wanted to know if you'd think any the less of me," she said, her face lifted.

He wanted to say that it did not and could not matter to him, that he wished he had never entered the house. "Of course it doesn't matter. I'll have to be going, Mary."

"Will I see you again?"

"Well, we do seem to bump into each other.'

"We do, don't we?"

He was able to smile. She had relaxed her demands. He remembered that he had left his suitcase in her car. "Thanks for the coffee."

She said, "My pleasure, sir."

Her face was tipped, the wide mouth waiting, as casual as she had been that first time, under the darkening trees at the gate. He bent to her confidently. Her mouth widened as she came up against him, her hands going to his shoulders. She fumbled away from him, breathing on shudders, the flat of her palms on his chest. He was shaken, but powerful too.

"Still new?" he asked bravely.

She only nodded. He bent ever so slightly, perhaps to brush his lips on her forehead, but her head came up, her mouth pulled almost like pain. His head came down on hers so savagely that he felt the impact of teeth. His hand was behind her head, crushing the long hair into his face. So painfully was she bent that he jarred on her struggling pelvis. A shoe slipped and scraped his ankle and still he could not let go. He was supporting her now, almost carrying her. Stumbling, pushing at him, her mouth screwed on his, she fell on the couch, got free. She thrashed her head to escape him, moaning; tears spilled on her cheeks.

"No. No. Stop it. It's just because I told you. Stop it. Leave me alone."

But Harry came down on her, his daylong anger leaping and burning. There was a part of him that knew and watched the clamoring mindlessness in his brain. He fumbled at her and she kicked at him, the long bare legs striving. And then he found her. She stiffened once and then collapsed, became billows that lapped at him.

"Oh yes. Oh, God help me. Oh, yes. I want it. So long. It's been so long." Her head was turned, pushed hard against the back of the sofa. She moaned as he fumbled at her and fear rose in him.

"Mary?" he said, choked.

She turned her head. Her eyes were lost, wide but lost, scummed like the eyes of the blind. There was smeared blood on her face.

He froze.

She cleared her eyes and reached up with a finger.

"You're bleeding. You've cut your lip. See?"

The clamor eased in his head. His hand remained under her skirt, inert where he had found her.

Mary's breath shook as she smiled at his lost, strained face.

"So new," she whispered, "so new." She put out her hand, looking for him, gripped the dark pain in his loins. "You don't know, do you, my darling? You don't know."

He felt tears and clenched his eyes against them. He had never been in such utter desolation. Very proudly and very surely, the strong fingers made him free.

"I will show you. Come to me. I will show you, my darling."

He brought his mouth down on her, gasping, his body blazing with glory.

Once they had been tools of his trade, constant in his life for years. Persons had shopped for them wryly. A drawing board with a leg that propped, like the one he had used to own. A T-square, a right-angle clamp, marking inks and pens stamped with familiar trade names.

Persons had been back several times to the Medical Research Laboratory in Hampstead, groping shrewdly for the answers he needed. On the old refectory table in the farmhouse's big room he stared through the window to the fields, making calculations. When he lifted his pencil to sketch, his face was pinched with excitement.

Later, making tea, he thought about Harry's telephone call. He had waited up late and had come down from his bedroom, roused from sleep and bad-tempered. Something had come up, Harry said. Persons had banged down the receiver. It would be his mother again. There had been enough of that. It was time he jerked the boy into the collar.

A water tank would serve for the chamber. One of those square iron ones. He estimated the volume and calculated the size of pump he would need. The door would be the difficulty. It would require a perfect seal. He was thinking about that, standing outside for the sun, watching a jet scribbling chalk marks on the sky. An escape hatch. An aircraft escape hatch. The Soho disposal store would have one. He would mount it outside, line it with a heavy rubber gasket. The vacuum inside the chamber would suck the hatch tight.

An old tin of whitewash with a paint brush fossilized in it stood against the wall. Persons skipped and booted the tin. They had almost taken it away from him with their Santa Anna Olympics. If he couldn't get Harry up a mountain to acclimatize, he would pull a mountain down to him. He would build him a mountain under his own roof. A chamber he could depressurize to any height. By the time they got to Santa Anna, Harry Hayes would be running downhill.

Bill Persons' pale eyes blazed as he paced, head bent, in the garden. The rules had been made. The rules were catch as catch can. He would tread down the world at Santa Anna.

There had been no waking, no rising to consciousness holding sleep by the hand. Harry had opened his eyes and his flesh had leaped and quivered. In the entombed silence of the basement flat his hands, mouth and nostrils were full of her. He shook with wonder and pride, his fingers screwed in the bedcovers. Fragments of recall as clear and sharp as chipped glass glinted upon his eyes. He had no management of it. The fragments spun, in and out of order, joined with each other, divided. The *tump-tump* of blood in his ears was like the moments before a race. There had been nothing to prepare him for that fury, no vestige of heard tale, dirty joke, preknowledge out of nighttime emissions. He had torn at her long past her ruin, past the revelation that had come to her, past her eventual protests, past her broken, moaning stupor, the spittle running from her mouth. Under the bedcover his skin blanched. But the strange pride in his body contested the guilt. He continued to lie there, stretched tight, instructing the images now.

She had wakened him with a warning about the time and Mother. He had not known that he had slept, had not known the room, had hardly known Mary, barefooted in a slip, lips swollen, his blood on her face. They had parted incoherently, Mary slumped against him, her lips on him hot and dry.

Harry put his legs on the floor, stood up and wondered at his weakness. Alarm touched him again. He had been like this at Cardiff, after breaking the four-minute mile. Hollow, papery, spent, his legs watery. He took the tea back to bed, was falling into sleep as he drank it. He had not once thought that he should be at the farm. Had not once thought of Bill Persons.

It was early afternoon when Harry Hayes woke again, slow this time to leave his sleep. Fright struck him. There was no pride now to combat the unfolding confusion and remorse. He had betrayed something. He wanted to isolate it but could not; the thing betrayed had too many parts. Harry got up and began mechanically to dress, as though his clothing might protect him. He would tell Bill that his mother had got bad. Bill need never know. He wouldn't see Mary Charlton again. He would order her and it out of his mind. But the guilt that

168

hung on him was not for parted innocence. It was the full-blown guilt of the adulterer.

It was three days before he heard from Persons, the usual peremptory message passed by the loading clerk at the dairy: "Club 4:30, Bill." Harry walked up the hill and cut into back streets to avoid Mary's house on Abbot's Terrace. He yarned for a while in the clubhouse, his company celebrated, the champion's privilege, keeping an eye on the clock. At 4:30 he was out on the track, jogged a few laps while he waited. He saw Persons come out, stand with his legs spread, his invariable pose as he searched over the track. Harry kept going, jogged another lap.

Persons was surprised when Harry called him. He swept off his tweed hat and banged it on his knee, the exclamatory gesture he used. "No wonder I couldn't see you. What's the fancy dress in aid of?"

Harry was wearing a new track suit. "I lost my gear," he said, and the guilt disordered his smile. The bag he had dared not go back for was locked in the trunk of Mary's car while she awaited his knock, his phone call, his tall figure walking Abbot's Terrace.

Persons grunted. "All right," he said, "let's see you run."

Harry kept his head down when he came off the track, hands on hips, chest heaving, walking the patterns of repair. Persons said nothing. When Harry had to look up, those eyes were on him.

"Is that the best you can do?"

"You didn't say to go all out."

"You were running like a bloody girl. What's wrong with you?"

"Nothing's wrong with me. I wasn't going all out, that's all."

"A man can go all out standing still," Persons said. "You were moving as though you didn't believe in it."

Harry tried to summon himself. He was hot with disappointment and anger. "If you want me to turn it on, say so."

Persons was undecided. He couldn't account for Harry's posed face, the distance he was keeping between them. "All right," he said, "put the drive in on the last lap. Watch your head carriage. You're still tensed up in the neck."

He was more at home this time. He had not run since the night with Mary, had only replaced his gear that afternoon. The unfocused resentment which had handicapped him went as he struck his rhythm. His hair flopped on his forehead.

The tension bled away. He came out of the third lap on a surge of power that blasted the obstacle inside him. The joy rose and fury slammed in his muscles. The pain came and he couldn't get enough because this was what it was about.

He came out of the last lap still running. He jogged another lap, his eyes stinging with sweat, aware of the attention he had drawn. There was no need this time to avoid the pale eyes. He could not forbid the smile stretching his face.

Bill Persons squatted on the grass, his hat tipped, lit with a smile of his own. He said, "Not good enough. Not good enough by a long way."

"I know," Harry said.

They continued to grin foolishly at each other.

Persons got up. "Come on," he said, his arm on Harry's shoulder. They walked like that, over the field to the clubhouse.

It was all right. It was more than all right. It was great.

23

MARY's broken engagement had dismayed her mother. It was unthinkable that Mary could be jilted. Her own Mary, whom everyone talked about, the belle of Royal Park since babyhood. Gabby insisted that it had been Mary, not David, who had broken the engagement. She had spent days on the telephone, fluttering her laugh.

"What do you think that daughter of mine has done?"

It had been hard for Gabby to buy Mary the car. She was terrified of accidents, had never forgotten the horror of identifying Mark Charlton's body. She was puzzled by Mary's manner. There had been no tears. Just the numbness of shock and then a hatred of David that forbade the mention of his name. Once when Gabby had made one of her telephone calls, she looked up and saw Mary in the hall.

"I've got news for you, Gabby. I was never in love with him anyhow. It was more your idea than mine."

She had been cold and hard and strange to her mother, had gone upstairs, slammed the bedroom door.

It was different now, had been different for a week. There was no more hardness, no more withdrawal. She had kept to her room that next day, drowsy with wonder and joy. She had a cold, she told her mother. She looked like it too, puffy-eyed and remote. Gabby, carrying up a late breakfast, noticed Mary's swollen mouth and worried that she might be ill with something worse than a cold.

It was another day before Mary felt the prickles of apprehension. She had not gone to the boutique as she usually did, wanting the luxury of the silent house and the telephone that seemed to fill it. Her own thoughts were companion enough, and she waited dreamily for Harry to call. By midweek she had no more waiting in her. The little red car cruised Abbot's Terrace, parked in side streets to watch the Club gates. She knew nothing about Harry. It made her cold. She did not know where he worked or lived. Because he had not come back, not even for his case, it had to be because something had happened. The thought both comforted and upset her. She asked about him at the Sparks' house, so patently nervous and casual that Liz Sparks noticed.

"Our champion?" Sparks said. "He's got a job somewhere with a dairy company. I don't see much of him. He spends most weekends training in the country. Why do you want his address, sweetie?"

"It's just that I might be throwing a party. I thought I would ask him along."

"He's not the party type," Sparks said. "That boy would have made a great Spartan. Did I tell you how I came to meet him, out training one night?"

Liz Sparks interrupted. "I'm warning you, Len. If I have to listen to you tell that story once more——"

Because her own thoughts so frightened her during the tormenting days, Mary went at last to the Club, swinging her handbag in the office doorway.

"A party?" the secretary said, when Mary made her excuse. "You can leave an invitation with me, Mary. He gets fan mail care of the Club. He usually looks in to pick it up on a Friday."

On his way to the farm that weekend, Harry collected his mail and kept off Abbot's Terrace. The secretary put the letters in one of the big, brown envelopes used for mailing the monthly bulletins.

The day had been good. Harry had run the circuit with Persons in the morning and twice alone in the afternoon. Persons had gone off after lunch in the Vauxhall. There had been a telephone call about a water tank.

In the evening, while Harry read, Bill Persons opened the brown envelope and spilled the week's mail on the table, grunting and making observations. Because the envelope was unstamped, he noticed it. He held the pink letter paper under his fingers, thoughtful.

"Dear Harry," Persons said.

Harry looked up from his book.

"Dear Harry," Persons said again.

Harry waited and smiled.

Persons looked back to the pink sheet, reading very slowly:

In case you have forgotten what happened to your suitcase, you left it in a certain red car. Don't worry. I'm keeping it safe for you.

I hope you haven't been sick. I've been worrying. I suppose you've just been busy. I don't seem to have a minute these days myself.

I'm hoping to see or hear from you very soon.

Persons raised his eyes then. Harry had frozen. Each word jarred him like a blow. He had turned away, waiting on Persons in dread.

"Love, Mary," Persons said.

The relief that that was all closed Harry's eyes. He had to say something, spoke as though he had made a grand discovery: "Well! So that's where I left it."

"Who is Mary?"

"Mary? Oh, she's just this girl at the Club. She was giving me a lift in her car." He kept away from Persons' eyes.

"How long have you known her?"

"How long? Oh, more than a year, since I first joined Royal Park."

"You've never mentioned her."

"Why should I? I only see her once in a blue moon."

"Have you been out with her?"

"Of course I haven't." Harry got hot, riffling the pages of his book. "She's just a girl I see at the Club."

" 'I'm hoping to see you or hear from you very soon,' " Persons read. "Why is she?"

"I don't know. To give me my bag back, I suppose."

"What's her other name?"

"I'm not sure," Harry said. "Charlton, I think. Yes, Charlton."

He absorbed himself in his book, waiting until he heard Persons tear another envelope.

The next day Persons drove Harry hard. He ran four laps on the five-mile farm circuit, slept, then worked with weights on the cottage lawn.

172

Afterwards, Harry lay with a blanket under him on the refectory table, his naked body sweet with the resinous odor of liniment, as Bill Persons worked on his labored muscles. They were closest at these times, joined by the laying on of hands. Harry grunted, under the probe of Persons' fingers, his eyes closed.

"Over," Persons said, spanking the flat of his hand on Harry's buttocks.

On his back, the luxury of this easement faded his thoughts.

Persons' voice was at a distance. "We've got to get you back to hard work. You've been having it too easy lately. The Athletic Association wants you for the next International."

"I thought you had ruled that out."

"I've changed my mind," Persons said.

"It's up to you, Bill. Do they know yet who will be running?"

"Otah, Vargi from Hungary. That colored boy from South Africa. Rose, from New Zealand. Leroy, the French Canadian. Brown from Ireland. Sternberg from America."

The fingers stopped kneading him. Harry's eyes opened. He did not understand. Persons watched.

"Otah? Vargi? Brown? They're not milers, Bill."

"Who said they were?"

Harry sat up. "You don't mean—"

Persons pushed him back, but Harry propped on his elbows.

"I do mean," Persons said.

"But it's not my distance. I've never raced over three miles in my life. I can't run that distance against Otah and Vargi."

Persons slammed him down hard, and began to probe again. "Can't? Who taught you that word?"

"But I'm a miler. I've got a reputation now. If I go in against men like that and do no good—"

Persons banged his fist on the table. "Can't. Can't. If I do no good. What the blazes is wrong with you? You've been mooning about ever since your old lady packed up. I've just about had enough of it. You'd better get your guts back and be quick about it."

Harry said nothing; his eyes widened at the ceiling. He could hear the other man's breathing. "My guts are all right," he said quietly.

"Glad to hear it."

Persons splashed liniment and began working again. Harry's mind was running a three-mile event.

"Do you think I could do it, Bill?"

"I'm not interested in your just doing it. If you go in, you go in to win. You go in to break thirteen minutes."

Harry came up again on his elbows. He said, "Jesus Christ."

Persons almost smiled. "You won't get any help there."

Harry lay back for a long time. "Thirteen minutes. You really think I could break it?"

Persons smiled bleakly. "I know you will. You know you will."

They began to smile for each other.

"Brown won't worry you," Persons said. "He's the glamour type. Gray track suits to match his eyes. When it starts to hurt he won't be at home. Otah's dangerous but he doesn't like soft going. If there's been a bit of rain, Otah will run barefooted. Vargi will come close to spiking him if he does, just to get him worried about his feet. Vargi's in the services like all these Communist athletes. If he can win, it will mean a promotion for him. He'll get to be a bloody colonel or something. According to the press, the American has been promised fifty thousand dollars by his old man if he beats thirteen minutes. He's a front runner. If you lead him at the right time it will break the bastard's heart."

Harry shook his head. "How long have you had this up your sleeve, Bill?"

"I just decided," Persons said.

The Internationals were to be held at White City. Harry Hayes had eight weeks to prepare. In that time he left much of the world. Day by day, he gathered up strength until it thundered in him like drums. Day by day, he grew on the spilling of it. There was no division now between job and training. One continued the other. He ran his deliveries to the milk bottles' clinking and trained to the ticking time clock in his brain. Persons' fierce eyes were always with him, Persons' voice in his ear. Nothing broke this concentration. Persons kept the dairy company's accounts, made up the cash on Friday. The world was blurred and deluding. Only their purpose was real.

He had forgotten that it had to happen, and came out on Abbot's Terrace to walk the new way home, to the big room Persons had found for him. In the little red car she had parked to watch for him, Mary Charlton trembled. Harry turned as she braked hard beside him.

He said, "Hello, Mary."

Her counterfeit gaiety could not survive the meaning of the new case in his hand.

Harry leaned down, as polite as a stranger. "How are you, then?"

Mary had beside her the old case that matched his, pushed it at him through the window, her eyes brimming, unable to speak. He had forgotten that too and, it broke him out of himself.

"Oh," he said. "My bag."

Her head was turned. She was fumbling to start the engine.

He almost let her go, but her misery stopped him. "I am sorry, Mary. I truly am."

"Why?" She was distracted. "Why wouldn't you even come back for your bag? Am I that loathsome to you?"

He looked away down the peaceful street. "You don't understand."

"Then make me understand," she said fiercely. "I don't want anything from you. You've got no right to treat me like dirt."

He said, gently and hopelessly, "You wouldn't understand. It's just that what I am trying to do, there's no room for anything else. Truly, Mary, that's the only reason."

She could see that he meant it. "What you are trying to do? How do you mean? You don't mean running?"

In their painfully awkward positions—Harry bent at the little car's window, two brown Globite cases in his hand— they wondered at each other. He was moved now, remembering the smell and touch of her.

"That is what I mean. It takes, well, it takes everything to be good at it."

She sensed that she must be careful, stilled the incredulity in her voice. "And that's the only reason you stayed away? Didn't even come back for your bag?"

She put out her hand and touched his where he held the opened window. Triumphantly, she knew that in some way everything would come right. "Can't we see each other sometimes? Like we used to do?"

"The Internationals are in a fortnight. Bill's putting me in the three-mile."

"You want to concentrate on it," Mary decided.

Harry nodded.

She was smiling, tolerating him like a mother. "Afterwards, perhaps. After you have won."

Harry puzzled at the pride in her voice. He nodded again. "All right. Afterwards."

Mary leaned and kissed his hand. "You want to leave now. I'll just sit here and watch you."

Obediently, Harry moved, looked back, and then his tall, erect figure walked away on Abbot's Terrace, two bags bunched in one hand.

In the Sunday afternoon's quiet Harry Hayes left Charing Cross Station and walked to Hyde Park through St. James's. The sun was hot. The sky clear and high. The familiar dryness was in his throat, cotton wool in his stomach, loneliness on him like a grieving.

The event was scheduled for three thirty.

"I want to see you come through those gates at three fifteen. Better late than early. Talk to nobody. Got that? Talk to nobody. Run the race in your mind. Run it every step of the way. Think of my signal. When you see it, imagine the effort."

Under the bowered trees in the painted park, drenched with the dyes of spring, Harry Hayes walked, seeing nothing.

At the round pond old people sunned themselves and commanded frisking dogs. Children ran squealing or willed their becalmed boats. With superstition Harry found the seat he had used almost a year ago. He leaned back, his bag on his knees, easing himself in the sun. Then he closed his eyes. The time clock started. The bag dimpled in his grip. For eleven minutes he sat carved. The blue towel signaled. On the bench the lean, neat-featured face went rigid.

The 18,000 spectators in the White City stands had something to remember that day. Alec McBride wrote in his column: "In the face of one man I saw the myth of the 13-minute barrier shatter. Sternberg and Vargi beat Hayes to the last turn. As he came past, my skin prickled. Had this been war instead of sport, I would have said he was going to win a Victoria Cross. In the war I saw this transformation on men about to commit a great act of bravery. It is the look of a man who is momentarily more than a man. A man whom no power can stop. Harry Hayes looked like that yesterday."

Persons had been right. Otah had tried the track and taken off his spikes before they had walked the tunnel into the carnival clamor from the stands.

"Steady," Persons said. "There's no hurry. Let the bastards bleed."

Harry head his name being chanted, the bray of the loud-speakers, the impatient calls of the officials.

Persons turned his back on them, put his hand on Harry's shoulder. "Are you ready?" His pale eyes burned.

Harry sucked in, beginning to tremble.

"There's no hurry, lad."

"I'm ready, Bill."

"Take it," Persons hissed. "It's yours."

The first mile came up in 4 minutes 15 seconds, Sternberg, the American, leading. Into the second mile Vargi cut dangerously close across Otah, got his barreling chest in front of the black man. Hayes was running wide, outside Otah's shoulders. Toward the end of the second mile, Brown was in distress. Sternberg was running wild, on his way to $50,000. Locked like that, they went into the third mile: time, 8 minutes 36 seconds.

As the meaning of the time registered, the stands hushed. Singly, in groups, they stood up as though pulled.

Sternberg was leading Vargi by five yards, Otah and Hayes by seven.

At the rails near the stands a blue towel thrashed the air. Otah labored desperately as Hayes catapulted round him. Vargi felt the blowing breath on his shoulder, twisted his head back in fear. Barely wide enough to clear him, Hayes was going past. Two laps from home Hayes and Sternberg ran almost on one stride. Sternberg dropped his chin on his agonized chest, arms and legs striving to drive. When he lifted his head, Hayes was leading, lips pulled back on a mask of trial.

In the final quarter Harry Hayes ran alone, Sternberg thrashing helplessly like a man in the backwash of a wave. The front rows of the stands were already clambering over the barriers, surging and cheering onto the track. Harry Hayes had run past pain into another country. Faster and faster he flew, down a long, bright tunnel.

He knew nothing at the tape; his pace continued unbroken until Persons dashed out and stopped him. He stood upright for an instant and then gagged and doubled under the protest of his shocked body.

Even the officials were running to reach him. A hundred yards back, Sternberg was spread-eagled at the broken tape.

The announcer's voice struggled with emotion.

"The winner of the three-mile event, Harry Hayes of Britain. Second, Sternberg of America. Third, Vargi of Hungary. The time . . . the time, 12 minutes 54 . . ."

The rest was lost.

24

WINTER FELL early and stayed late. The days telescoped into a few hours of scummy light. Grass hibernated and gardens went back to the earth. The trees stropped their naked arms. Pavements glassed with ice. The traffic mulched the sparkling snow into muddy sludge. Throughout the black, lowering months, shod for the skidding surface, Harry Hayes ran his deliveries and kept the schedule Bill Persons had laid down.

The notice he had won at Cardiff was now an unstinted celebration. His shattering three-mile run against the world's best had made him a national hero. He was "Britain's Iron Man," "Britain's next Olympic Gold Medalist."

Persons was fierce in his rejection of the job offers and social invitations that arrived in the swelling mail. He would hurl these, crumpled, into the farmhouse fire.

"Bloody parasites. You stay away from all these glad-handers. They can poison a man with their breath."

Harry would look up and go back to his book, sometimes touched by resentment. He wanted to hear from Persons what others said so freely. It wasn't Bill who crashed through the limits that tethered others to the track. In every race there was a time to be alone. He had gone out against the best and set a record to beat them. He had been alone there, in a place beyond help. He wanted that admission from Persons.

He had come back to the milk truck and recognized the sports reporter waiting with a photographer in a car.

"Sorry to badger you, Harry. But we can't get near you at the track. How about a few shots as you make your deliveries? You know, human interest. Why you are doing this job and so on."

Harry had said, "You'd better ask Bill about it."

"It's you we want a few words from, Harry. You're in the big time now."

"I'd better not. Thanks all the same. Have a word with Bill."

"Persons won't let anyone near you." The reporter stepped angrily on the butt of his cigarette. "The press has given you a good go, Harry. You're news now. You owe something to the fans."

178

"Sorry," Harry said, "I'd better be on my way. Thanks, anyhow."

He had climbed up on the truck. The reporter shouted after him. "Wake up to yourself, Hayes. It's you that goes out there and wins. Not that crazy bastard Persons. What are you, a ventriloquist's dummy?"

Through the rest of the morning he could hear the man's voice, feel the blood burn in his frozen ears.

"What are you? A ventriloquist's dummy?"

They did not understand. This was something he and Bill did together. But there was a time to be alone and it was a cold and awesome place. That was all he wanted from Bill: just the recognition that at last he had to do it alone.

And through that black, lowering winter, Mary Charlton waited for Harry Hayes as patiently as the commuters waited for their trains. Because she had thought herself in love before, had hurried into it across the frontier of her own virginity, she well knew now that it had been trite and careless. It was the dark, awkward boy whom she loved, now become a man and a mystery. The stillness of Harry's purpose was like a wooing to Mary. The importance of it became her importance. He had fallen on her like a starving god. She could wait for it again. He would need her. Meanwhile, she would be the accomplice of her own denial. Mary had no doubt, no misgivings. She had come upon maturity with the force of an accident.

Harry Hayes rarely knew peace again after his achievement in the full sun at White City. Before that it had waited to be proved, all the days of his life. With conquest done he lay in his own hands as a charge and responsibility. He was unique. Now he had to be his own keeper, the guarded and the guardian inside the one skin. He was unique and there was no escape from that. It was insisted upon by others, like a jealous right of their own. Now he would have to go out and do it again and do it again after that. Cold with sweat at night he lay on the bed, running and running through gasping pain forever toward a white light.

He only had one easement. To forget himself in training and to remember himself listening to Persons. There was never difficulty in Bill's company. Laughing and shouting and stumping the floor before the great open farmhouse fire, Persons would talk and Harry would cling to the words, his face bright with excitement. It was only alone in his room that the anxiety returned to torment him. Bill was his easement and confidence. Bill, and Mary Charlton.

He had changed once, the first time Persons had run him past exhaustion. He had changed again, after Cardiff. And he had changed forever, after the International.

Persons had told him there would be this, had promised it: "If you've got the courage for it, the manhood to drive yourself through, you'll find out something the nothing-men live and die without ever suspecting."

He had been there. It was true. And because it had happened he was no longer fearful of seeing Mary. Because he was more than ever different, he was more than ever alone. He needed her company, to be with her sometimes, connected to the careless world. He kept it from Persons. Not in guilt as he would once have done, but reserved and certain and decided.

Although Mary Charlton had his telephone number she seldom called him, and never again waited in lanes outside the Club. They met on Monday evenings, after his return from the farm, for dinner and the local cinema or sometimes a drive in the little red car. On Tuesdays, when he used the Royal Park track, Mary would wait to take them to coffee. He told her about his childhood, tried to explain why he ran and what it meant. Once Mary visited his mother at the home.

At a late winter meeting at the Royal Park Club, Harry set an unofficial 1,500-meter record. Mary Charlton was among the supporters, sitting with Liz Sparks in the members' stand. Bill Persons was there. Harry had waved to her. They did not meet. Something unsaid kept Mary away.

She asked afterwards, "Was that him? The man with you in the tweed hat?"

"That was him."

"He looks as though he's angry about something."

When Mary Charlton spoke of Bill Persons it was always as "him." He was too easily there, between them. It was better to not use his name. She was as chaste as a sister, kissing Harry good night. It was as though she wanted to assure him that he had nothing to fear, could safely await his own time. Her very carefulness not to touch him with her opulent breasts and hips when she kissed him kept their memories of what had happened more alive than any embrace or secret touch.

Toward the end of winter, in retreating cold and a stirring on the trees, Bill Persons folded the Sunday paper and handed Harry an article. It was headed HOW MANY GOLD MEDALS WILL SANTA ANNA COST BRITAIN? Harry Hayes was

180

particularized as the athlete most likely to be cheated by Britain's lack of elevation needed to acclimatize to effort at a high altitude. Despite newspaper speculation, the Olympics had not been mentioned between Harry and Persons. Harry was accustomed to Bill. Bill would take his own time.

Harry put the newspaper down. "There doesn't seem much doubt that the chaps from the high countries are going to have an advantage."

Persons was sitting at the refectory table, leaning across it on his elbows. "You know we're going to be there, don't you?"

Harry smiled. "I didn't altogether take it for granted."

"Not much," Persons said.

"It wouldn't have occurred to you before, either, would it?"

"It occurred to me the first time I saw you run."

"The first time?" Harry winkled his eyes with disbelief.

"Yes, the first time. You don't have to drink the barrel to taste the wine."

They stared at each other. Harry could hear his breath coming. It was out now, and he felt his body lighten. Now he knew again where he was going. The wheel had flattened into a pointing road.

"We're going to run over the top of them all. The world is going to know about us, lad."

"Fifteen hundred meters?"

"Fifteen hundred meters. In a time they won't be able to believe."

Harry broke away from the other man's eyes. Only now that Persons had made it real did he dare to properly conceive it. He said, wondering at it, "A gold medal."

"Not just a gold medal," Persons said. "*The* Gold Medal. The fastest mile ever run."

Harry recalled the newspaper articles, the protesting letter to *The Times* signed by Bannister, Chattaway, Brewster.

"But, Bill, how much chance will I have in Santa Anna?" He tapped the folded newspaper. "How about this? What does this height problem mean?"

"What does it mean? It means that every athlete who can find a mountain will be training on it for the next three years. It means that the bloody IOC has made a medical Olympics of Santa Anna."

There was no help in the cold, watching eyes. Fear nibbled at Harry's stomach. What was Persons asking of him? How could he cross the lonely place without an even chance?

He said decisively, "I can't will myself over this, Bill. If the newspapers are right about Santa Anna, it's too much, even for you."

Persons said, "Can't! That word again."

Because he had wanted and needed to say it for the admission Persons would never allow, Harry spoke softly and certainly.

"It's me who goes out and runs, Bill. I can't give you the world's fastest mile if my body's eight thousand feet behind me."

Briefly, Persons half shut his eyes. The boy waited, pale but resolved.

Persons stood up, half turned away. "You can't?"

"I can't."

"You'll have to have a mountain, will you?" Persons said, almost threatening.

Quietly, Harry answered, "I'll run on glass if I must. I'm only saying that if everything I've read is true, my chances are less than even."

Persons whipped about and banged the table. His eyes were wide and snapping. The rare smile was shining on him. "I've got you a mountain. What do you say to that? I've pulled a mountain down out of the sky."

Harry had flinched, prepared himself, when Persons banged the table. He came to his feet.

Persons was grinning like a boy. "You don't know what I'm talking about, do you?"

Harry shook his head.

Persons rushed out of the room and returned with the drawing board, flapping with sheets of pinned paper. "There it is. There's your mountain."

Harry puzzled at the outlined structure, looked up to wonder at Persons.

"Don't you recognize a mountain when you see one?" Persons laughed and slammed his leg, delighted by Harry's worried face.

"I don't understand, Bill. What is it?"

"He doesn't understand," Persons told the wall. "He can't see a mountain when it's under his nose. Probably because he's never heard of a bloody mountain that can huff and puff itself up and down to any height that it wants."

He stopped shouting. The smile disappeared.

"Don't stand there with your mouth open like a door. I haven't gone mad. I'm going to build you a mountain. A pressure chamber, lad. Nobody else has thought of it. I can

182

depressurize that chamber to any altitude. When the time comes, you're going to sleep in there. When the time comes, you're going to work in there. When the time comes for Santa Anna, you'll have a head start on the rest of the world."

Comprehension pieced itself together. "Good God, Bill. Will it work?"

"I was an engineer, remember? It will work. Nobody gets the best of us, lad. Did you think I was going to send you into the big one to break your heart?"

"Bill," Harry said weakly. "Bill, I'll never understand you. Really. You take my breath away."

"I'll take their bloody breath away," Persons shouted. "The Americans, the Russians, all of them. What do you think now? What do you think of old Bill?"

Harry slumped into his chair, still amazed. "Is it legal?"

"Who cares if it's legal? If it's legal for Keino to live in Nairobi or Bekula in Addis Abada, if it's legal for the Russians to take to the mountains where the rest of the world can't see them, if it's legal for Britain to go down the drain because God didn't give us any high country, then it's bloody well legal for Bill Persons to build his own bloody mountain."

"You're a wonder, Bill."

Persons said wryly, "It's you who goes out and runs, is it? Who gave you the will to run? Who reached up and pulled you down a mountain?"

Harry felt the color stain him. "I only meant—"

"I know what you meant. You've been reading too much about yourself."

But Persons saw, too, that Harry had his own pride. It was there in the level gaze that would once have dropped. It was there like the shadow of a warning. It was Persons who shifted, putting his arm about Harry's shoulders.

"How about an hour in the pub, to celebrate?"

Like that, they walked out to the old Vauxhall.

"Damn it," Persons said. "Fetch my hat, will you?"

25

IT WAS spring on the calendar but the seeds in the earth had been stunned by the long, icy winter. The days had lengthened and showed it when the gray clouds opened to grudgingly exhibit the sun. Bill Persons had accepted an invitation from the Swedish Athletic Association to lecture on the theory and practice of conditioning.

"I'm fed up with this black damp," he told Harry. "It gets into your bones like rot. It will be cold there, but at least it will be dry and bright."

He slammed his tweed hat on his leg.

"Five hundred pounds and all expenses. They wouldn't pay any other trainer in the world as much as that, lad."

Persons intended to be away five weeks, making his return through France. He was excited about it. There were two television appearances on his Swedish itinerary and another in France.

"The French couldn't train apes," Persons said. "They'll have a flea in their ear when I'm through with them."

He had been intense and absorbed for months, in an almost frivolous mood. Two studded iron tanks had been delivered to the farm. Persons had cut them himself, with oxyacetylene equipment, had himself welded the two tanks into one.

"I'm a bit rusty at this," he had said, a visor over his eyes, sparks blazing on the livid metal. "But I'm not as rusty as these tanks. They're going to take a lot of cleaning."

Harry couldn't share this craftsman's pleasure. The square, squat lines of the blackened tanks, papered with flakes of red rust, seemed to threaten. "I can't say I'm looking forward to this. It's beginning to remind me of a coffin."

"You'll get used to it," Persons said happily. "I spent over a year in a cell smaller than this. I'll hang some pictures in it for you. You can have a bedside table with a doily. It's all up here." He knocked dangerously on his head with the grip of the hissing, flaring torch. "Kant spent thirty-five years in one room and made discoveries other philosophers are still working on. Give me a bit more pressure, will you?"

Bill Persons had been away two weeks. Harry had postcards from him almost daily. Persons liked the country and some of the people. He did not like the officials who had arranged the tour and had already fallen out with them. He was cheerful enough about it. "Had a pipsqueak official on a television panel last night—blasted him!" Or: "These pipsqueak officials are the same the world over. Bugs in better men's beds." He had also accepted an invitation for Harry to appear at two Swedish meetings in late summer. "None of this amateur nonsense," he wrote. "Red carpet all the way. I squeezed these pips until they squeaked."

Old Mrs. Hayes died the day Harry received the news.

At four o'clock Mary Charlton waited outside Royal Park Club in her car. When Harry did not come out she pushed through the green gates and looked for him on the track.

"I don't know where our Iron Man is today," one of the athletes told her. "I've been here all afternoon. I haven't seen him."

Mary went to the telephone box and called Mrs. Withers, the middle-aged widow who had let Harry his room.

"Oh, Miss Charlton. I'm so glad to hear from you. Mr. Hayes's mother died. They rang from the home a few hours ago."

When she had swallowed, Mary said, "Oh, God. Where is he now, Mrs. Withers?"

"He didn't say where he was going. But he had his good blue suit on. I think he went to the home. It must have been a shock, the poor boy."

"Is anyone with him, Mrs. Withers?"

"There has been nobody here. He doesn't have friends, does he? Oh dear," Mrs. Withers said, "I mean nobody calls apart from you and Mr. Persons. I don't think he has any family."

"No. He hasn't any family."

"It was that sudden. The poor lady died in her sleep. Miss Charlton, would you like to come here and wait for him? He shouldn't be alone at a time like this. I'm afraid I'm not much use. In all the time he's been here, I've hardly got to know him."

Quickly Mary said, "Could I? That would be very kind, Mrs. Withers."

"You have the address?"

"Yes, thank you. I will come now."

Mary ran down the path to the car, her breasts swelling with pity and love. She, now, would be all he had. For once, he and she would be safely beyond that other, angry-eyed man.

"He's had nothing to eat since breakfast."

Mrs. Withers pulled on her gloves, her hat with a pin through it ready on her head.

"I've put a casserole in the oven. He always has casserole on Tuesday. Mr. Persons makes out his menus, you know, right down to the whole-meal bread I get in. Do try to make him eat, my dear. I've laid two places in the dining room. Perhaps you would care to have a meal with him? You'll find everything on the sideboard. Your mother keeps the boutique in the village, does she not?"

"Yes," Mary said, "I work with her now."

"I thought so," Mrs. Withers said. "I've known you by sight since you were little." She looked at Mary approvingly. "I won't be back until late, my dear. Use the house as your own. I'm really no good at these things. I get quite shaky."

In the strangeness of waiting, Mary Charlton looked about the room. Two ebony elephants watched a marble-faced clock on the mantel. A copper fire screen fronted with heavy glass stood with a copper shovel and tongs on the hearth. The upholstered furniture was heavy and glassy with wear. A cabinet of china oddments shone darkly in a corner. The room was different, important to her, because it was a part of Harry's life. She got nervous waiting. When a door opened and closed she brushed at her hair, made herself ready for him.

"Mary!" Harry stopped with surprise in the doorway. "What are you doing here?"

Her eyes began to sting. "Oh, Harry. Mrs. Withers told me. I telephoned."

"Where is she?"

"She went out. She invited me to come and wait. You're not angry, are you?"

"Of course not. I was going to call you. Did you go to the Club?"

Mary nodded.

When he came into the sitting room, she could see how drawn and hurt he was. She wanted to go to him but could not. He stood awkwardly, holding a large, cheap suitcase. He looked at it before he spoke.

"Mother's things. One suitcase of scraps. That's it. That's all that's left."

She did run to him then, her cheek on his chest. "Harry, Harry. My poor darling."

He put the suitcase down, his arm going absently about her. Dry and still, he looked over her head.

"She slept in a cubicle. I'd not seen it before. A cubicle with a curtain for a door. They had made up the bed and she was on it under a sheet. It's funny, but her mouth has been crooked ever since she had the stroke. It wasn't like that now. She just looked the way she used to. She never told me she slept in a cubicle."

They sat together, Mary holding his hand. Harry spoke of his mother. It seemed now that he had much to remember.

When it was later, she said, "Do you think you could eat something? Mrs. Withers left me in charge."

"I'm not hungry."

"Won't you try? I'm invited too. The table is all laid, waiting."

"I couldn't eat, Mary."

"You've had nothing since breakfast. Won't you try?"

"Very well. If it will make you happy. I think I'll take a bath. There was something there. A smell. I don't know. But it seems to be clinging to my skin."

She said, wondering, "This is your room. This is where you live. It's so bare, Harry. Haven't you any of your own things, any family photographs or anything?"

"There was a lot of junk when I came here. I had Mrs. Withers take it out."

"It's like a monk's cell, almost. Why don't you hang some pictures?"

The wide window on the garden came almost to the floor.

"That's my picture," Harry said.

He remembered the rooms in Islington, remembered the basement flat. He thought, She wouldn't understand. How could she understand what a view means?

He said, "In all her life my mother never had a picture like that. A big window into the sun, on a garden."

She looked at him, worried.

He took off his jacket and went to the warerobe, halted there for a minute while his stomach swirled again. The hatbox with its Regency beaux and hoopskirted ladies with painted parasols and painted smiles, all the colors dulling to ivory, his mother's hatbox of sad little treasures, sat on his wardrobe now as it had sat on hers from his earliest memories.

"I'll look at the casserole," she said.

There was nothing to do in the kitchen. Mary went to the sitting room and got her cigarettes, unsteadied again to be alone. Distantly, she heard water splashing. She thought, I need a drink. If Bill Persons were here, she wondered, what would he say or do? Harry had not mentioned him. But perhaps he had sent him a cable. Perhaps he was coming back to help.

Mary got up to look for an ashtray, saw the brandy flask shining down on a silver salver. She was gagging on brandy-and-water, listening for Harry, when she saw the old suitcase, in the dark by a chair where he had left it. It played on her nerves in the still room as though the absent-minded old lady, whom she had once visited, were dead inside, folded up in the felt slippers she had worn. Mary finished the drink, put out her cigarette in a saucer. She smoothed her skirt on her thighs. She wanted the suitcase put away. Out of his sight and out of hers.

Harry had turned out the light when he left the bedroom. She carried the suitcase there, holding it away from her body, and looked about for somewhere to put it. There were no hiding places in that bedroom. The case clamored more loudly in the pearling light falling through the big window. Her nerves were quite fretted. She knelt and shoved the case from her, into the dark under the bed.

"Mary? What are you doing?"

The sudden voice so frightened her that she gasped and staggered to her feet, her heart jolting. He was standing at the door, in a towel.

"You gave me such a fright."

"What were you doing?"

"Putting the suitcase away."

He came close, frowning. "You're shaking like a leaf."

"You frightened me."

"Steady down. There's nothing to be frightened about."

He held her. She began to sob, her cheek against his damp, warm chest. "I'm sorry. I'm sorry. I don't know what's wrong with me."

He said, "Steady down. There's nothing to go on about."

She was strained against him, her hands grasping at his bare back, her wet eyes and lips brushing at his chest. While she held him, she felt the dark rise of his body, the palpable surge and will of him. Her knees trembled. His arms tightened about her, crushing her breasts, his body growing into hers. She looked up, panting, trying to see into him. His dark eyes under the damp fallen hair were fixed over her head, as impersonal as stones.

"No, Harry. Please. You don't want it. You don't want it, Harry. Leave me."

He gave no answer. There was no recognition in the dark, fixed eyes that looked over her into nothingness. He continued to crush her, grow into her.

All her breath seemed to leave her body on one shuddering gasp. She slumped helplessly against him.

"No . . . please . . . no."

But he did not hear. His hand went between them. She was still slumped, but a heat and a strength and a triumph stretched and lifted inside her. He was looking at her now

188

with a dark, fixed gaze that seemed to see nothing, or beyond.

She asked, steadily, "Are you sure?"

"I'm sure."

She faltered away from him. His face was as hard as a carving. For a long time she looked at him. She stood for a minute with her eyes closed. And then, slowly, deliberately, she crossed her arms and pulled the jumper top over her head. She held it for an instant in her fingertips, let it fall. He stood like a carving in the shadows that darkened the tints of his bare chest and arms.

She reached behind her then, unclipping the frothy brassiere, pulled it over her arms, dropped it. She stood with her eyes closed again, as though afraid to see her own familiar body, the dark nipples starting on the heaving pointed breasts. He said nothing, made no movement.

She stepped out of the pleated skirt, her eyes on him like a pleading, then dropped the slip. He moved toward her and stopped.

She whispered "Harry," not knowing what she asked for, her body shaking. She took a few steps toward him.

"No," he said.

She looked down at herself, filled with pride. Her eyes were as clear as his were clouded. Without shyness, almost in defiance, she turned her back, bent, freed herself of the filmy briefs and faced him.

At last he said, "I didn't know." And then again, "I didn't know."

She was the carved one now. All the fruit of her body filled with singing, perfect and victorious and frank and free as perhaps she could never be again.

"What didn't you know?" she whispered.

"I didn't know anything could be so beautiful. I didn't know."

Mary said, "I love you, Harry. I've loved you since before I was born."

26

BILL PERSONS had stayed an extra week in Paris, to make an appearance at an athletic meeting sponsored by a French magazine. He returned suddenly and telephoned Harry, who was leaving the dairy for the day. He told Harry he was still at the airport. There was a disposal store in Soho he wanted to call on; it was getting him the aircraft escape hatch he needed for the mountain. It was always the mountain now, never the pressure chamber. He arranged to meet Harry at the Red Lion for a beer. They could have an early dinner before he drove on to the farm. He had a lot to tell Harry, he said.

In three years, Harry Hayes and Bill Persons had not been apart for longer than a week. Watching over his shandy in the saloon bar, it seemed to Harry that life had waited for Persons' absence to reach out and shake him. His heart beat a little harder at the prospect of reunion, but the hole Persons had left by his going had closed on his mother's death, had darkened on the deepened meaning of his connection with Mary Charlton. He felt the worrying guilt about it as he had from the instant of the other man's telephone call. It troubled him like an unresolved priority that niggled to be ordered, a demand that specified no reason. When he thought of Persons he thought of Mary. When Mary came to his mind, Persons shadowed her.

Persons came in with a great grin, his pale eyes searching Harry's face, an arm out in a hug. He slammed his tweed hat on the bar.

"Well, how do I look? The coat, lad. I bought it for television. The Swedes called me a genius so I thought I should dress like one."

He was wearing a wine-colored corduroy jacket with a flapped-top pocket, as pleased as a boy about it. Harry felt the familiar peace as though it had never been absent. All else washed away on Bill's excitement, Bill's warmth, the privacy of their understanding. Over dinner Persons was still talking about what he had said and done. It wasn't until he had worn himself out that he asked, "How's the old lady keeping?"

It had not been forgotten in him, but it had been distanced, now that he was with Persons again. It was such an intrusion that he wished not to answer, found it hard to get the voice or the words.

Harry said, "My mother's dead."

Persons had his chair tipped. He was looking about the pleasant restaurant with a hand on his wineglass. All the smiling left his face. The chair legs knocked, coming down.

"What?"

"Two weeks ago. She died in her sleep, one afternoon."

"But you didn't let me know?"

"It wouldn't have helped," Harry said, looking at the table. With no attempt at concealment, as jealous as a woman, his eyes snapping, Persons said, "Then who did help you? Who did you get to help?"

Harry looked up and shook his head. "Nobody. The home seemed to know an undertaker. It's over now."

"Who was there? Who went to the funeral?"

"Nobody. Oh, I suppose I could have told the people who lived above us; they were always kind to Mum. There didn't seem any point. It didn't matter, really, to anybody except me."

Persons said, "You should have told me, lad. You didn't have to do it on your own."

Harry smiled a little. "Your business is with the living, remember?"

They held each other across the starched tablecloth and the tall bottle and wineglasses, in the polite chatter of gossip and laughter. There was an instant before Persons eased. He reached out and put his hand over Harry's.

"You are right. My business is with the living."

Harry smiled again, into the eyes which had once so frightened him.

"I know, Bill. It's over. I'm all right. What I need now is a record to break."

On the following weekend, at the farm, Bill Persons announced that he had entered Harry in the Internationals at London's Crystal Palace. He had decided on the mile and wanted a crushing run.

"That gives you just on two months to get ready. We're going in there to run it in three minutes and fifty-five seconds. You said you wanted a record to break. Can you do it?"

"I think so. If the weather is reasonable, Bill."

"Good," Persons said. "With a run like that to back us it will be roses all the way when we go to Sweden. Come on. You can give me a hand to cut a door in the mountain."

On the day Harry's mother died, Mary Charlton came home at two in the morning. Gabby had been frantic with worry. Mary had left the boutique in the afternoon for coffee. Gabby had telephoned everybody. She was still terrified of the little red car. When she heard the door open and shut, Gabby was in the kitchen making tea. She dropped the pot and rushed to the hall. Mary stood, handbag dangling, swollen-looking, dazed.

"My God. Where have you been? What has happened?"

191

Mary's eyes were heavy with sleep, her body slow and full. She said, "Did you wait up?"

"Of course I waited up. I've been frantic. Where have you been?"

"With Harry," Mary said.

"Harry Hayes?"

Mary nodded.

"Where have you been with him? What have you been doing?"

"His mother died this afternoon."

"Oh." Gabby's anxiety had been so painful that she was exasperated in spite of her relief. "Oh, dear, the poor boy. But really, Mary, it's two o'clock. You could have telephoned. It's not good manners to intrude on a family at such a time."

Mary shook her head. "He has no family."

"No family? No family at all?"

"No."

"Where does he live, then?"

"With Mrs. Withers in Elm Street. She says she knows you."

Gabby puzzled for a minute. "With Mrs. Withers? Is that where his mother died?"

"No. His mother was in the Old People's Home."

"Would you like tea?" Gabby asked bravely.

"Too tired," Mary said.

Gabby watched Mary climb the stairs and then went to the kitchen to think. This had gone far enough. She would insist on meeting Harry Hayes. She wondered, with a clutch of fear, what she had allowed Mary to get into.

Harry Hayes met Mary's mother the day before Persons got back from Paris. Gabby Charlton had worried Mary about him every day.

Mary said, "Harry, will you do something for me?"

"What is it?"

"Gabby wants to meet you."

It had surprised him. "I don't know, Mary. I'm not much good at meeting people."

"I met your mother," Mary said.

Harry frowned. "Why does she want to meet me?"

"She knows I have been going out with you. She just wants to meet you. It's natural enough. You will like Gabby. Everybody does."

Harry knew Mary's mother by sight. He had seen her

through the window at the boutique, smart, young-looking, chatting and laughing with the customers. To be taken home and introduced would be an involvement he could not afford.

He had drifted into the relationship with Mary and he needed her now. He accepted that and could manage it because they were as alone together as two people on an island. It was real and unreal; he could lay it aside when he had to. Step back from the soft, sweet touch and smell of her into the hard, clean, free world he shared with Bill Persons.

"I'd rather not, Mary."

"Oh, please, Harry. Just meet her. It will make things so much easier for me. I'm proud of you. We never see anybody together. Can't I at least show you off to my own mother? It needn't be formal. Just come in for afternoon tea."

Harry said, "I don't know, Mary."

Gabby Charlton had her hair done for Harry's visit. Because so much of her life was lived through Mary she prepared for Harry as she might have done for a flirtation of her own. If Mary liked the boy he must be acceptable. Mary could have anyone she wanted. Gabby quite forgot the outrage of Mary's jilting. She was determined to be winning and gay, although the memory that the boy's mother had died in a home upset her like something disagreeable she had eaten.

"You must call me Gabby," she told Harry when they met. "Everybody does. Including this naughty daughter of mine."

She expressed sympathy about the death of his mother and, rid of that, fluttered nervously over the cups and cakes, smoothing the skirt on her long hips in the exact habit Mary had.

Harry's gravity and careful manners did not ease her. The trace of Islington in his accent was a shock to her. But he was undeniably attractive. She held back the personal questions she needed to ask. It was too soon after his mother's death. The frustration of that drove her further into frivolity, worrying Mary who was so anxious that each should make a good impression on the other.

"I believe you are an athlete, Harry?"

Mary said quickly, "Harry is preparing for the next Olympics."

Gabby was impressed. "Goodness me. Olympics. How exciting for you. Do you know Len Sparks? He was a Cambridge Blue."

"Yes. Sparks introduced me to the Royal Park Club."

"Really?" Gabby said. "Len is such a dear. The family

have been friends for years. And what do you do, Harry, when you are not being an athlete?"

"I work for a diary company."

Gabby wondered what one did in a dairy company. "Oh, in London?"

"No, in Gillsham."

"Our Gillsham? Over the hill?" Gabby frowned.

The tall boy, watching her, said softly, "Yes, Mrs. Charlton. I'm a milkman."

When they had gone Gabby shut the door and leaned on it. She could hardly believe it. A milkman—it was unbelievable. Thank goodness she knew nobody in Gillsham. The thought that he might be delivering milk to one of her friends made her feel quite ill.

In the car Mary said anxiously, "Harry, you must forgive Gabby. She doesn't understand. She doesn't know what it is you are doing."

Harry nodded. He said tiredly, "Don't worry about it. I know what I'm doing. That's all that matters."

Still anxious, Mary asked, "Did you like her just a little bit?"

"She's attractive. But I don't live in her world, Mary. I wouldn't want to."

They drove to the country, with little to say. For the first time in months Harry wanted to get away from Mary Charlton, back to the track, back to the farm, back to Persons.

He was back and at peace in his clean, hard, free world, bent on the preparation. There was little room or need for Mary in the fierce satisfactions of the training schedule he kept. Persons had him running 80 and 100 miles a week.

"You will have to reach inside farther than you have ever done. You are going to feel that your pulse is bursting. Every rational impulse will cry out in protest. Your kidneys will fill with poison. Your muscles and brain will scream for oxygen. Three minutes fifty-five won't come easy, lad. It will be you and your manhood against the agony." Persons had watched him closely. "Can you handle it?"

Harry had needed a breath. "Yes," he said, "I can handle it."

Persons clapped Harry on the shoulder, his face close, inquiring into his eyes. He smiled a little. "You're getting used to the pain, lad, aren't you?"

There would be no tactics run at the Crystal Palace. Persons had refused to tell Harry which athletes would be in the race. He had forbidden him to read any comment on the coming meeting.

"There will be nobody in the stands except me. There will be nobody on the green except me. There will be nobody on the track except you and me."

The meeting was to be an International between Oxford and Cambridge and Cornell and Pennsylvania universities. Persons had only told Harry that much as a warning.

"If you hear it talked about at the Club, walk away. If anybody tries to talk about it to you, walk away. If you hear it talked about on the radio, switch it off. You got that?"

Harry nodded. "Yes, Bill. I've got it."

Harry Hayes was to appear in the Invitation Mile.

Because there had never been more than spats between Mary Charlton and her mother, neither of them knew how to manage conflict. Gabby's headlong indulgence of her daughter had been proof against Mary's errors. Len Sparks called Mary "Princess." Gabby thought of her in that way. She was a princess by right of being quick, clever and beautiful. Because she attracted attention, because strangers had stopped in the street to admire her ever since she was tiny. Although Gabby had contrived Mary's engagement, she never doubted that her daughter would make a brilliant marriage. It would be as ordained as the sunrise. The jilting had shaken Gabby more than she let herself know. She was already convinced about the truth of her story that her naughty daughter had broken it off. But a milkman. A milkman whose accent made it clear that his background was unfortunate. A milkman whose mother had died in a Council home for the aged. It was too much for Gabby.

Because that was hard enough to believe, it was harder to believe Mary's attitude: she was unmoved by her mother's upset and had tried to explain something she did not properly understand herself.

Gabby said furiously, "What nonsense. I've never heard such rubbish. You're saying that because the wretched fellow has a sport, he has to be a milkman. A milkman, good heavens! Len Sparks has a sport and he's in the Foreign Office. I won't have it. You're not meeting people who could be an advantage to you. You don't go out and have fun. You haven't accepted a party invitation in ages." Gabby threw her hands up. "I just can't understand what's come over you. I'll just have to put my foot down."

They were both tired. The argument had continued for hours. Because of what Gabby did not know and Mary could not tell her, the tears rose in Mary's eyes. Instantly, Gabby was contrite, more upset than ever, patting Mary and blaming herself.

"Let's just forget it for the time being, shall we? You know how fussed I get. We will just forget about your friend. I am sure he is a nice enough boy, really. It's not that I've got anything personal against him, dear. It's just that he's an unsuitable companion for you, you must see that. Look, why don't we have a big party and ask all your old friends?"

Mary sobbed. "You don't understand, Gabby. You've got no idea. You don't understand."

"No. Well, I suppose I don't. If he must be a milkman, he must. There, now."

Mary looked across at her mother, tears splashing wildly. "But Gabby, I love him. Can't you understand? I'm in love with him."

Gabby sat down as though her legs had folded. She was beyond speech.

Mary said, wiping at her eyes, "He's the only thing in the world I want and I don't even know if he loves me."

"Good grief," Gabby whispered.

Mary buried her head in the chair, sobbing.

In the next few months the thoughtful silences in the house on Abbot's Terrace were many. Mary had been so secretive, so impossibly up and down, that Gabby had to take care. She knew that Mary was seldom seeing the boy, because she was either at the boutique or at home. She had diagnosed Mary's declaration of love as the rebound from the broken engagement. This explanation comforted her. Mary would come to her senses. Meanwhile, Gabby had her thoughtful silences.

Mary's thoughtful silences were otherwise. She had missed one period and had waited for the next; it would be all right, she had missed before. But she was overdue now again. Mary waited through the slow passing days, trying to keep the implications out of her mind. She had heard about hot baths and gin and had made herself quite sick by overdoing it. But the days passed. Her breasts began to tingle and harden. Blue veins ran a tracery on the tender milky skin. She could no longer bear the suspense. In mixed calm and hysteria she telephoned the doctor who had always looked after the family.

27

"WELL, young lady, you're pregnant." Old Dr. Pitt was rough and direct. "Does your mother know?"

Mary shook her head, clasping and unclasping her handbag.

"Hmmm. Will I tell her or will you?"

"I will, Dr. Pitt."

"Yes. Far the best way. Now, you must not worry, young lady. Mustn't upset the little chap."

It came to Mary then. She suddenly felt faint.

"I'll want to see you again in a month. Remember, you've got a job to do now. For the present just carry on. You've been feeling well enough, haven't you?"

"Yes," Mary said weakly.

"So you should. A fine, healthy girl like you. I've never seen you looking rosier."

When Mary had gone the old doctor thoughtfully washed his hands. Gabby Charlton's Mary. There would be a stir about this. He sighed. The nurse let in the next patient.

Gabby told Liz Sparks that she was ready to give up. Mary had become impossible to live with. Her moods were unmanageable, Gabby said. She was either up in the attic or down in the cellar. Gabby was afraid to say two words. At the least thing, Mary would storm into tears or anger.

"The child's not well, I'm positive. I'm going to talk to Dr. Pitt about it."

Mary's skirts had begun to pinch. Her breasts swelled and hardened. She was exhausted by the moods that shook her, could not bring herself to tell Harry or her mother. When she thought she was carrying a part of Harry inside her, the pride and wonder of it left her weak.

As the seed grew, Mary's calm grew with it. The quickness to tears, the panic, ebbed and departed. She kept more often to the house now, waiting greedily for Gabby to leave in the mornings so that she could wander and dream unchecked. On the few occasions she saw Harry her love affected her like pain. It stabbed in her, squeezed her breath, like a pain which had no hurting. She hardly heard his words, while her eyes made new discoveries: the fine bones in his wrists and fingers, how small and even were his teeth, the flatness and the strength of his shoulders. The shadow of Persons, of "him," did not exist anymore. She was beyond Persons now, with the part of Harry she carried inside her. While Harry talked, Mary told him, whispering it on her lips so that he would stop and ask "Did you say something?" She would shake her head and in a minute say it to herself again: "I'm going to have your baby."

Gabby Charlton went to see Dr. Pitt.

"Well, Gabby, still getting younger every day, I see."

Gabby fluttered a laugh. "That bedside manner of yours will get you into trouble one day, George."

"A bit past it now," the doctor said. "Well, Gabby, what is ailing you? That sinus again?"

"It's not me, George. It's Mary."

Gabby had taken it well, the doctor thought. He wouldn't have expected less of her. "Yes. Well, there's nothing to worry about there. Mary's in fine shape. You're going to make a very attractive grandmother, Gabby."

Gabby's eyes flickered. Her hand went out to the desk. She said, "What? What did you say?" staring at him, her lips trembling.

Dr. Pitt took off his glasses and rubbed both hands in his eyes.

He said, "Oh, Lord."

The week before the Crystal Palace International, Bill Persons drove up from the farm on a Friday to take Harry Hayes back. That evening, late, when the track was empty, Harry was to attempt the three-minute fifty-five mark. It was almost dark when they walked out of the clubhouse. Persons carried a starting pistol.

He said, "Look about you, who do you see?"

Harry looked. "Nobody."

"You see me?"

"If you're the funny-looking chap in the tweed hat, then yes, I see you."

"That's all you will see at the Crystal Palace. Now, reach for the mark as close as you can, but don't overdo it. If it hits you too hard, back off. When you are ready, I'll give you a count."

Harry breathed deep, turned and walked away, summoning up the charge of power as Persons had taught him. He began to run in his mind, began to tremble. As the big spring in his chest wound tight, he grimaced. The pistol exploded. He was gone, his time clock ticking, the cinders squeaking to the long, light footfall on the darkened track.

When he had recovered, was walking weakly in circles, Persons showed him the stop watch.

"Look, lad. Three minutes, fifty-six. It's there. You can do it."

Harry nodded, bent over.

"I know. I went up to it and stopped. I could have gone through."

Dr. Pitt had given Gabby a sedative. Her shock, her unbelief, still denied acceptance as she walked on the thronged High Street toward home. Her mind lurched on the fragments of understanding that came to her. Mary's moods. Mary's secrecy. Mary's dishevelment on that night. Even changes in Mary's appearance, her plumping. There was no sense of outraged morality in Gabby's shock. She was engulfed by the social consequences, horrified by the voices and visions she imagined. She passed the rank where every evening she took a taxi, climbed to the church and walked with her brisk, hip-swinging style over the long hill to Abbot's Terrace.

Before the house was within sight Gabby was already resolved. She had tidied up her mind as ruthlessly as she tidied the details of her business. Harry was no longer that milkman. He was a celebrated athlete. Gabby rearranged her mind as she would rearrange a room's furniture for convenience and ease. If Mary loved the boy as she said, had given herself to him for that reason, if it was what Mary wanted, Gabby would fight the world for her happiness. Her high heels clapped fiercely on the pavement, her handbag swinging as Mary swung hers. They would have to marry immediately. If they went to another suburb for the ceremony, Gabby could say that Mary had been secretly married for months. The bedroom on the sunny side would be best for the nursery. Gabby was filled with protectiveness. Her Mary was going to have a baby.

It wasn't much more than thirty minutes since Gabby Charlton had walked stunned from Dr. Pitt's office. In that time she had altered the prejudices of a lifetime to suit her daughter's need. At the front door she took a deep breath and entered.

In the last days before the Crystal Palace International, Bill Persons eased the torturing schedule. For a month Harry had been attended by an audience as he worked each afternoon on the Royal Park track. Hagerty, the Club coach, had said, "How does he take it? How can a man command his mind and body like that?" In a trance of concentration, Harry had been running four fast miles, four half miles, quarter miles, hundred-yard sprints, and long jogs broken by a half hour's calisthenics and light workouts on the weights.

Bill Persons said, "When the work stops the tension will hit. Don't let it worry you. The tension will be part of your power."

Persons took a room at the Red Lion over the last days. He and Harry went up the West End for a musical and played uproarious games of golf with hired clubs.

Persons had gone to look at a pump the Soho disposal stores had got for him out of a scrapped submarine. "A lung for the mountain," he called it. Harry had come in from the milk round, showered, eaten and gone home to his room to rest.

"Telephone, Mr. Hayes." Mrs. Withers tapped her fingernails on the door.

"Hullo, Harry? Is that Harry speaking?"

He could not place the gay voice. For a moment he thought it was Mary.

"This is Gabby Charlton, Harry."

"Oh, how are you, Mrs. Charlton?"

"I wonder if you could give me a few minutes this afternoon."

"Oh, yes," he said, uncertainly.

"Just a little chat. Shall we say the boutique, at about five?"

Harry stood in his room looking out the big window. What could she want? He lay down to think about it. His time clock began to tick. He raced toward the mark of three minutes fifty-five seconds.

Gabby had barely argued when Mary insisted that nothing must be said to Harry until after the race he was preparing for. There were no limits to the comfort Gabby wanted to give Mary. She would do or say nothing that would cause Mary upset, but that did not alter Gabby's private determination. The very idea made her toss her head. The very idea that the boy's convenience should be considered above her daughter's and for the sake of a wretched footrace. It made her think again of Harry as a milkman.

Before five o'clock, Gabby hurried her last customer out, sprung the lock on the front door and went to her smart, chintzy office and opened the cocktail cabinet. She poured a large sherry and smoked an infrequent cigarette, rehearsing herself and listening for the door. When the bell chimed she stubbed out the cigarette, looked quickly in the mirror, smoothed her hands on her hips and then swung out, smiling gaily.

"Harry," she said intimately, drawing him in by the hand.

"How good of you to come. Let's go to the office, shall we?" She gestured about her. "I suppose you feel like a bull in a china shop. I've never understood why pretty things make men go to pieces." . . . . "What can I give you?" she asked, standing at the cocktail cabinet.

Awkward, Harry said, "Nothing, thank you, Mrs. Charlton."

"Oh, do have a sherry, it's so much more sociable."

"Just a small one, then."

Gabby gave him the glass, sat him down, took one of the little gilt chairs herself and crossed her long legs expertly.

"Mmmm, that's better." She sipped from her glass, looking at Harry mischievously. "Well now, you naughty boy. What have you got to say for yourself?"

"How do you mean, Mrs. Charlton?"

"Come now," Gabby chided in a mockery of sternness. "The cat is out of the bag."

She cocked her head and waited, while Harry grasped for understanding.

"I'm afraid I don't follow."

"We've been having high jinks, haven't we? You and I have to put our house in order."

Harry looked for somewhere to put his glass. He was lost in these riddles, the coquettish looks, the evident tension in Mary's mother. The last months and the next few days were too present in him.

"Look," he said in sudden impatience, "I don't know what you're getting at, Mrs. Charlton."

The altered tone, the sudden authority in him, surprised Gabby. With a spurt of impatience herself, she said coldly, "In very plain words, young man, my daughter is pregnant. You've put her in a nice position. Is that clear enough?"

He had been in his hard, clean, free world. So much so that for a minute the words had no meaning. While he labored, Gabby went on.

"Mary did not want you to know because she didn't want you upset before this race thing. She's not very responsible at present. You had to know of course, and there it is."

He said, "I'm sorry. I didn't know. I'm sorry."

Because he was so obviously stricken, gulping his throat, Gabby became effusive.

"You have both been very naughty. Though it's not the end of the world. We have to get organized before the little stranger arrives, don't we?"

"How is Mary?" Harry had to ask.

"She's been worried out of her wits. It appears to me the child has been more concerned for you than she has for herself. Really! You men! Now, the first thing to do, immediately you have finished this running business, is go and see her. Let her tell you about it herself. Then we will have a conference. I've a big house. We can fix up quarters for you there. Mary will need my help when the baby comes. After that we will see."

He was pounding as he did before a race, his breath catching. For a minute he steadied his thoughts, beat back the confusion, ordered up the calm he needed. He rose from the frivolous gilt chair and looked down at Gabby.

"How long—how long has she been pregnant?"

"About three months, the doctor thinks."

"Tell her not to worry."

Gabby put her glass on the cocktail cabinet, smoothed her hips, looking at him coquettishly again.

"Really." She wagged her head. "You children. What fixes you get yourself into. Now that is over, shall we have the other half?"

"No, thank you. I'll be going. Don't worry, Mrs. Charlton."

"Worry?" Gabby laughed and tossed her head. "It's too late to worry, dear boy. What you and I have to do is quickly get down to business. That child of mine is too starry-eyed to think for herself."

"Tell her it will be all right. I'm truly sorry. Can I phone you on Monday?"

"Why not just pop in? Why don't we all have dinner together? We will keep it as a surprise for Mary."

He was too swamped to resist. Obediently, he nodded.

Gabby walked him to the door. "See you Monday then, about seven. Oh, and good luck in your race thing."

The desolation that shook him was not for Mary Charlton, himself, the unacceptable idea of marriage, the force of the shock. It was for Bill Persons and the impossibility of facing those blazing, transparent eyes.

28

HE HAD lain on the bed and fought his battle, eyes blindly fixed on the ceiling. The will so painfully practiced was invoked now. Mary's pregnancy, the consequences, his swirling emotions, were pressed down and willed away. He struggled back toward where he had been. His face was as dead as stone when he fell violently into sleep, as spent as ever on the track.

The great tungsten floodlights had been switched on at 8:30, glinting the tubular steel, concrete and cantilevered roof supports that bent in tension like a grasshopper's legs. There was seating for 12,000 with 4,000 under the cover of the free-flying concrete roof. The curving amphitheater of the stands was more than usually full. The Invitation Mile would star the great African runner, Keino, and the Silent Man, as the newspapers sometimes called Hayes.

The International had opened with the pole vault at 7 P.M. and was running late. The mile had been scheduled for 8:50. Bill Persons waited at the tunnel let into a wing of the stands. It worried him. The delay could be fretting. As usual, he had ordered Harry to spend the day alone, to take a jog in the morning, to time his arrival at the stadium. Persons strode back and forward checking his watch, more than usually agitated. In twenty-four hours, Harry had gone off peak. The fine tension, the collected power, the vibrant, controlled expectation, had blunted. The dulled eyes worried Persons most. He couldn't account for it. He was sure he had not overtrained the boy. That was the mistake made by others. He couldn't have overtrained him because it would have been like overtraining himself. He would have felt it in his own flesh. He knew that body as surely as he did his own.

When he saw Harry, tall and grave in his club blazer, holding the familiar Globite case, it was as though Persons watched himself walking toward himself.

In the dressing room, alone in a corner, Persons worked on Harry's leg muscles. He looked better than he had yesterday; there was more life in his eyes. But the stubby probing fingers could read the tension. Others watched, kept clear as they had learned to do.

"Over there, that's Harry Hayes. Keep away, for Christ's sake, or Persons will take your head off."

There was laughter and chatter across the room in a group about a figure Harry could not see. A scarlet cap pitched into the air. It reminded Harry Hayes of something. The group broke and moved noisily to the tunnel. A tall Negro, chewing gum, wore the scarlet cap.

Harry shot his hand to Persons' shoulder. "That's Keino. Isn't that Keino?"

Persons glanced. "Yes," he said.

Under his fingers the calf muscles locked as hard as cramp.

"Who else, Bill? Who else is running?"

"Nobody. What's the matter with you? There will be nobody out there except you and me." Then more persuasively, "Relax, lad. You know what you can do. There's not a man in Britain tonight who can touch you. Remember how it was the first time? You've come a long way since then. We haven't begun yet. Who's Keino? There will be only one man out on that track tonight. Young Harry Hayes, running wild."

Harry leaned his head on the cold wall and closed his eyes for a minute. The fingers that kneaded him gentled. He looked down at the square impassioned face.

"Yes, Bill. Nobody else out there. Just you and me. No Keino, no stands, no anybody."

"Nobody. Just you and I running over the top of the world."

Harry closed his eyes again. The tension bled away.

"That's it. Just relax now. They can wait for us. When we go we will take our time down that tunnel, moving free and easy. When we hit the field we will take one long look, one deep breath and then we spring like a tiger."

Harry was smiling, his head back. Persons kept his hands on him. He checked his watch, heard the amplifiers announce the placings for the 10,000-meters. Now, it was time.

A great shout had greeted Keino's introduction. The African took off his famous scarlet cap, prancing and waving at the stands. The Australian, Cory, on his last European tour, was given a veteran's reception. But it was Hayes they waited for, Silent Harry, the Iron Man of Britain. Colmant, from Manchester, acknowledged the rowdy calls of his special supporters. The spectators were loud in the released impatience of their waiting. This was what most of them had come for. The long-legged African, his cap sparkling in the flooding white light, was on the inside, Harry Hayes next, Colmant and Cory outside them. As the starter raised his pistol the stand drew its breath. Then Colmant broke, startling the others off balance. A big "Aaah" went up in the stands. It was unusual to break from a standing start. Colmant was dazzled by his company. Sweat started on the runners' faces. Their pulses pounded as they concentrated. Raggedly, they lined up again, bent for flight, striving for calm, full lungs. Again the starter raised his pistol. Again the quiet beat down on the arena. On the pistol's report the spectators gave their breath in a roar. In the first few strides of bunched, colored shirts, Harry Hayes had gone to the front.

The false start had upset him. He struggled to order the time clock that ticked in his head, waiting for the regular rhythm that would beat out the pace and the laps. It had come, and he was settling to it when Colmant drove past and pulled away. When Harry reached for him, Colmant fought back. As they went past the time-keeper for the first lap, the Manchester runner had been overhauled.

The loudspeaker announced the time. First lap, 50 seconds.

Persons grimaced. "What's wrong?" he whispered. "It's too fast. What's wrong with your clock?"

They were into the back straight again. Harry knew he had overrun the first lap, was willing himself to settle when he sensed the challenge at his shoulder. Again, his concentration faltered. Colmant would run himself out. He would burn up. But it wasn't Colmant who went past; it was the veteran Australian, Cory.

As the half-mile neared, Cory increased his pace and the distance lengthened between them. Fear hooked in Harry's belly. What was wrong? His timing must be wrong. An experienced man like Cory wouldn't overrun the half-mile. He was going away. He was opening too big a gap.

"Time for the second quarter, 56.5 seconds."

Harry Hayes was going after Cory as they turned away from the stands. The Australian could not hold the pace. He was falling back as though Hayes was hauling him in on a line.

In the roll of sound from the stands, Bill Persons stood with his face screwed in anguish. They were trying to use Harry up. They were trying to kill the Iron Man. He shouted uselessly into the roaring excitement.

"There's nobody there, lad. There's just you and me. For God's sake, there's nobody there."

The bell rang for the last quarter. Time, 2 minutes 57.8 seconds.

In the back straight Harry Hayes was running free. He had lost all sense of timing. He was crying inside him for the peace that had not come, closing down his mind for the effort that would take him into the country which never failed him, the country where the others could not live. He was in the home straight when he made the reach inside him. He was in the home straight when Keino leveled and flung off the scarlet cap. While the panic clawed and the pain vised, shooting thunderbolts through his body, Harry Hayes reached again and again into the empty will of his reserves. Keino was in front, the enormous, perfectly paced stride flying him toward the tape. Keino was in front, his undisturbed rhythm drawing him farther and farther away. Harry Hayes had gone to pieces before he crossed the finish. Beyond the tape he jarred cruelly on legs that had stiffened to wood, head banging on his spine, arms clawing at nothing. Then he pitched over and lay writhing.

In the roaring, gasping stands, where she had sat alone in pride and love and secrecy, Mary Charlton cried out, her hands bent in horror to her mouth.

The clear sky had returned to moonlight. The great tungsten flares had died. It was the way Persons had wanted it at last. There was nobody in the stands. There was nobody on the track. There was nobody there except him and Harry. The first-aid men had done what they could, helped with glucose and stimulant.

One said, "He just about run himself into coma. He hasn't had any sickness, has he?"

Persons shook his head, too fierce to speak, while he worked on Harry's stomach muscles and pulled the blanket about the twitching body.

"I've seen most of his runs. There must be something wrong when an Iron Man like Hayes goes down for the count."

The press had paid more attention to the fallen hero than they had to Keino, grinning again in his scarlet cap. He had won in 3 minutes 56.2 seconds.

Bill Persons was too absorbed to dismiss the reporters. Photographers triggered their flash guns. There was both mourning and satisfaction for the ruin of Bill Persons' Iron Man.

When Harry Hayes could struggle to sit and focus his eyes, Persons was on his feet, dangerous and impossible again, striking at cameras, pushing the reporters back.

"Get to hell, you vultures. Get to hell and leave us alone."

They had gone at last, looking back, their voices instinctively lowered. Against the trees that bushed on two sides of the stadium, Hayes and Persons made dark patches in the thin moonlight on the barbered green field.

Something had happened. Somehow he had lost the boy and the boy had lost himself. Now that his concern was gone, now that Harry's strength was returning, Persons felt his anger. He would want to hear the reason for this. It had been there, in the palm of his hand. They had fêted him in Sweden, accepted his own terms for Harry's tour. Now the red carpet he had won for them would be a mockery. His Iron Man had fallen apart.

"How do you feel?"

Harry took a few steps, his face clammy gray. "I'm all right."

He still did not know what had happened, could hardly bear to ask. A light burned in the dressing-room tunnel. There was not another figure to be seen in the stadium. It was eerie and frightening.

"How long was I out?"

"Long enough."

"Forgive me, Bill. I went for it but there was nothing there. I switched to the second tank and it was empty. I couldn't stop the black coming down. There was nothing there. It had gone. I don't know."

He hung his head, the tears of defeat and frustration and exhaustion running on the gray, expressionless face. He looked again around the dark stadium that frightened him by its emptiness.

"Keino?"

"Yes."

"By how far?"

"Far enough. Come on, you're getting cold."

Harry walked silently and weakly toward the tunnel, his head down, holding the blanket about him.

A masseur had waited in the dressing rooms, having a drink with a few officials and organizers. An official had just asked "Shouldn't one of us go out there?" when Harry and Persons emerged from the tunnel. The coach and his beaten champion were eyed uneasily.

The masseur said, "I waited on, Mr. Persons. Thought he might have had the cramps."

"Thanks. A rub wouldn't hurt. Go on," he said to Harry. "Get showered and have a rub."

"Like a drink, Bill?" an organizer called.

In the lofted rooms with their sticky smell of liniment, warm from hours of steaming showers, Persons stood brace-legged and dangerous, drinking whisky. They had told him "Bad luck" and ventured nothing more, finding other subjects to talk about in the constraint of those pale eyes.

Harry Hayes had gone to dress when the caretaker banged up the tunnel with his torch and keys.

"Mr. Hayes is here?"

Persons said, "What is it?"

"Young lady wandering about in the dark out there, trying to find him."

"What young lady?" Persons asked.

"Didn't say, sir. Seems to be in a bit of a state. She was out near the gates when I came across her. Wants to know if Mr. Hayes is all right."

Harry Hayes had joined them, holding his Globite case.

An official said, being cheerful, "One of your fans, Harry. There's been a lot of inquiries." He looked at his watch. "She must be keen."

"Tell her to go to hell," Persons said and turned away.

The caretaker sniffed and looked uncomfortable. "Fact is, when I say she's in a state, she's in a state. I don't think she's a fan. It's more like she might be a friend or a relative."

Harry's voice was low and shaky, his eyes pinched. "What does she look like?"

"A proper young lady. Very well dressed, with this long, straight blond hair they wear nowadays."

"Tell her to go to hell," Persons said again and put his glass down.

"It's Mary."

Persons heard. His head whipped round, eyes burning. "Who's Mary?"

"Mary Charlton."

It meant nothing for a time and then as Persons remembered, his pale eyes widened and blazed.

"That letter. The girl that wrote that letter?"

Persons swung on the caretaker. He shouted, "Kick the bitch out of the stadium." They were all frozen. The caretaker began to speak. Persons pushed at him. "Get away. I'll kick the bitch out myself."

He rushed toward the tunnel. He was almost at the exit when Harry caught up, had to pull on his jacket to stop him. Their voices echoed and banged on the walls.

"Bill, don't. Bill, stop it."

Persons whacked at the hands holding his coat. "Are you mad? Let go. What do you think you're doing?"

"Leave her alone."

"Leave her alone? I'll kick the bitch over the stands."

Harry said, "Bill, you can't. She's pregnant."

Persons stopped. He stood stupidly in the echoing tunnel. Stupidly he asked, "Pregnant?"

"Yes."

"Pregnant? How would you know?"

"By me, Bill. Pregnant by me."

Persons whispered, "By you?" He closed his eyes.

Harry Hayes could say nothing, his face masked.

Persons said, mumbling, "All this time, it's been her? Ever since that letter and before? Behind my back, against everything we've been doing, that girl? You've been going to that girl?"

"No," Harry said desperately. "It's not true. Only a little while. Only when my mother died. Bill, listen to me."

Persons gripped Harry's throat, the square, stubby fingers shocking him against the wall of the tunnel. Persons had his lips back; there was no facing his eyes.

"That was it. You betrayed us. You betrayed it all for a girl. That was what happened out there tonight. That was why you ran like a cur."

Harry pulled at the inflexible arm, the blackness about him again.

"Judas," Persons hissed. "Judas, Judas, Judas."

Harry was sliding when Persons let him go. He spat once at Harry's face and then rushed out of the tunnel.

In the dressing rooms one of the men said, "Wonder what that was all about?"

"Who knows, with a pair of weirdos like that?"

They began to clear up.

MATHEW C. KAVERLY . . .

29

THE BOMBAY congress of the nineteenth Olympiad had broken up in confusion. Members and delegates packed their bags like men who felt that their outlines had blurred. The presentiment that something had happened beyond them, a difficulty in accepting Santa Anna's election, haunted leave-takings, hollowed voices, made a need to be quit of each other. Only Mathew C. Kaverly was happy, humming "It happened in Monterey."

"A great victory, a great victory, Hans," he told the gray-faced Chancellor, lumbering about in the room, leaning over the balcony to watch the departing members.

"There go the Russkies. There go the French. I hope they've packed their damn honor."

Stein could feel the cables in his pocket chill his skin through the cloth. "But the height, Mathew. There's going to be trouble about the altitude."

"Bah. The altitude. Those are losers' squeals. You heard what Dr. Sánchez told them."

"That's only one opinion, Mathew. Hardly disinterested." Stein took out the folded cables. "I want you to read these."

"Contrary opinions?" Kaverly asked.

"Yes. Niskanen says there will be those who die."

The old man whooped. "Those who die?" he asked incredulously.

Stein nodded, biting his lip.

"Those who die? The fittest young men and women in the world?"

Stein nodded again.

Kaverly began to shake—his almost noiseless laughter. There was a heavy cigarette lighter on the table. He took the cables. "You're a nervous cuss, Hans. You know who start up things like this?"

210

Stein tried to tell him the cables were in answer to his own, stopped, shook his head.

"The damned politicians, that's who. And this is what I think of them."

Kaverly clicked the lighter and held the cable forms while the yellow flame leaped along the edges.

In the months after Bombay Mathew Kaverly kept absorbed in his desert command post. The teleprinter link with Olympic headquarters in Lausanne was more than usually busy. The altitude controversy had amused him to begin with. "Losers, weepers," he had advised Stein in a message. "When they stop hurting it will blow itself out." But that had not happened. The national committees and the sports federations were beginning to signal unease. When Stein teleprinted a suggestion that he should visit Santa Anna and make his own judgment as a medical man, Kaverly quickly agreed.

A helicopter met Stein at the airport. He had been three weeks in Santa Anna and wore a seersucker suit unwisely bought there. He had washed the suit in his bathroom washbasin according to his thrifty habits. His customarily pale face and the gaunt angular body in the cotton washed of its filling were an unmistakable reminder of scarecrows. He carried a small bag with personal possessions and a large square suitcase that packed a collapsible bicycle ergometer he had pedaled doggedly in his hotel bedroom.

Kaverly waited on the helicopter pad. There was little warmth in his greeting, his eyes screwed against the sun. The edge of his temper sharpened before he had taken Stein's hand. The Chancellor was wearing what Kaverly knew to be his stubborn look.

After an early dinner with his sister, they sat in the garden under the looming mountain in the long, tender colors of evening. Stein had carried a black leather diary from the house. He smoked the strong cigarettes he favored, his long fingers brown with nicotine stain, expelling the smoke away from Kaverly. The bird music piped softly.

"Well," Kaverly said, "the damned jackals are out."

Stein said, "There's an enormous resistance, Mathew. We've never had a problem like this. The English press is up in arms. There's a movement to demand a change of venue."

"Demand?" Kaverly clamped his jowls. "Nobody makes demands to the IOC. Don't talk to me about demands."

"There's no good of being stubborn, Mathew. I can be stubborn too."

Stein opened his diary. "I'm going to read some notes I made. There aren't matters of opinion. These are observations carried out on myself."

Kaverly picked up a handful of gravel, firing the stones on his knuckle. He said nothing, appeared to take no interest. Stein watched him and then began reading.

"May 11, the day I arrived: Took a brisk walk in the afternoon. Needed a noticeable effort on inclines. Difficulty sleeping that night. May 12: Pulse at rest 85 beats a minute against a recorded 65 at sea level. After brief exercise on the ergometer, pulse read at 100 to 102 per minute."

He waited for Kaverly's comment, then continued. "May 13: Whistling in the ears, a sensation of being full up. Nervousness, chafed lips, dry nose. A pulse jump 48 per minute after mild ergometer exercise."

Kaverly growled, "No wonder. Those damned cigarettes you smoke."

"May 14: Complained of being unwell to hotel doctor. After physical examination altitude sickness was diagnosed. Instructed to cut out smoking—"

"Ha!" Kaverly shouted.

"—and alcohol. Advised to drink as little liquid as possible. To walk up and down stairs slowly and minimize exertion. Meals to be light and easily digested. Symptoms of distress continue. May 25: Rate of pulsebeat increase cut by half after exercise on ergometer—"

"There you are," Kaverly said. "It's in your own damned notebook—rate of pulsebeat increase cut by half." He dropped the handful of gravel and aimed a thick finger at Stein. "If you can acclimatize in two weeks, puffing on those poisonous things, the athletes are not about to have trouble."

"The rate of increase was cut by half, Mathew. It was still way above normal. The physiological changes that occur during acclimatization are still only partly understood. In thin oxygen the lungs have to work harder. This means a fall in the carbon dioxide level. Blood acidity is reduced. The kidneys are affected. I'm not pretending to be qualified on these matters, Matthew. But I'm heartily afraid of cardiac difficulties in the 10,000-meters and the Marathon."

The bird music stopped. The old man had his head down, brooding. In the silence they could hear Miss Kaverly's voice, calling for Karl in the house. He put his fingers in his mouth and blew the piercing whistle. The birds began singing again.

212

Kaverly said, "It's a plot."

Stein did not understand. "Plot?"

"Of course it's a plot. I beat them in Bombay. All those damned politicians. They're after me now. They're trying to discredit the IOC. Why do you think they've all started yapping at once? How many times have they tried to get me?"

He began to fill, his neck reddening.

"Those jackals. They think that if they make enough noise I will run. But it's Mathew C. Kaverly who is president of the last true International." He had begun to shout. "We will see which of us runs, do you hear? We will see which of us runs."

Stein looked palely away, down the trees filled with invisible birds. He turned another page in the diary. "I made a study of a number of case histories, Mathew. There is one here on a Santa Anna boxer."

Kaverly reached over and slammed the book shut, rose and stood over Stein.

"There's as much medical opinion on my side as there is on the side of the jackals. More. I haven't wasted my time. I've got a pile of it inside. I knew you'd arrive here with your damned jaw on your boots. You've never had much stomach for fighting, Hans. I didn't choose Santa Anna. I wanted to go to black Africa. But I forced Santa Anna down their throats to keep the IOC clean. Do you want me to stand up and say we were wrong? Give them the chance they want to discredit us? I'd see them in hell first, if Santa Anna were halfway up Everest."

Primly, Stein said, "I hope to God you're right."

"And if I'm not?" The old man breathed hoarsely. "Whose side will you be on, Hans?"

Stein said, distressed, "It isn't a matter of sides, Mathew. It's a matter of clinical risks."

"Sides," the old man bellowed at him. "Right against wrong. Black against white. It's a matter of sides, do you hear?"

They said no more. The cigarette in Stein's hung hand grew an unbroken gray ash. His knobbed knees and shoulders humped the seersucker that drooped about him. He didn't have the strength to contend with this man who had so often been right in the past. Once I was strong, he thought mistily. Why is the gift of certainty given to one man and withheld from another?

"Mathew, Hans," Miss Kaverly called, "your chocolate is ready."

Kaverly turned to the house. "You go in. I'm going to play the fountain."

Stein was very tired from his journeying. His pulsebeat was still unsteady. He took a pill and fell quickly asleep. In his room the old man climbed onto the adjustable bed and turned the knob to make himself comfortable. There was a television screen in the ceiling. He flicked across the channels, holding the remote control, hoping to find a Western. Grunting with satisfaction, he turned the knob to raise his pillow.

On the screen nothing moved in the streets. The townspeople peeped from behind blinds. A shopkeeper in a white apron hurried inside and slammed the door. The five hard-looking men on horses were watchful and silent, riding past. In the sheriff's office Gary Cooper took a shotgun from a wall rack. . . .

They had reason to want him gone. He had made a power of his presidency. When the Hungarian team had been stranded on the Danube, in the flame and shells of the uprising, it was he, Mathew C. Kaverly, who had arranged a truce and got them to the Melbourne Olympics. Single-handed he had united the German teams as the omen and hope of their divided homeland. "Kaverly squared his broad shoulders and set his square chin which is full of character," a German paper had written. "Our attitude on your flag is the same as on the name of your team," he had told them. "One team, a German one. One flag, a German one. If you can't agree what emblem should go on your colors, then I'll decide for you. The emblem will be five white rings, the symbol of Olympic peace."

And so it had been. They had carried that flag at Rome. When Sukarno forbade the Israelis to compete in the Asian games, it was he who had kicked Indonesia out of the Olympic movement. He would unify North and South Korea yet. They had already agreed on a joint flag. A white flag this time, with five rings in color. He had disciplined Spain, Holland and Switzerland when they threatened to withdraw as a protest to Russia over Hungary. He had forced through the recognition of Red China. The United Nations had been unable to do that. Given time, he, Mathew C. Kaverly, would tear down the bamboo curtain, let in the light on eight hundred million souls.

The old man moved heavily on the bed, breathing hoarsely with excitement. The jackals had always yelped. It was he who had got it all done. Kings shook his hand. Brezhnev had given him more time in Moscow than he had given the English Prime Minister. He had nineteen decorations locked away in the safe. . . .

Blam! The horse reared. The man in black pitched out of the saddle. *Blam!* Gary Cooper threw himself down behind a water trough. Bullets screamed in richochets. Another man fell. . . .

Kaverly wriggled on the bed. He thought of Stein's pale face. He guessed that Stein had sent for the cables he had got in Bombay. Stein was weakening. He would have to keep an eye on Stein. . . .

The townspeople came out on the street. Stood over the sprawled death. Gary Cooper holstered his revolver. He turned his back and walked slowly away, alone.

The station announcer said, "Tomorrow's weather will be mostly rainy, with sunny intervals. Wind from the southeast with—"

"Rubbish," Kaverly shouted, and switched off the remote control.

KAVERLY HITS OUT AT SANTA ANNA CRITICS

The New York Times had given the old man's press release a two-column caption. He read the clipping, grunting, and tossed it into a teleprinter bin with the others.

He was goaded now. The darts aimed at him had begun to hurt by accumulation. They had slowed him as the picadors slow a bull, loading him with stings to bring his head down. Stein continued to worry at him on the Lausanne teleprinter, taking fright at shadows. The old man had waited, dangerous with contempt. In time he would identify the conspirators. He only needed to know where to charge.

He had traveled a part of the year, as he always did, in his capacity as IOC president. Santa Anna had welcomed him as a hero. He had exhibited himself as a target to the national sports federations, to start the jackals out of cover. But they yelped in France if he was in Germany. They yelped in Germany if he was in Britain. If he declared himself in France, cries were raised at home.

Stein had said, "It's not only the danger, Mathew. The low-altitude countries don't have equal opportunity to prepare."

"Read that," the old man ordered, producing a photostated report from his jacket. "That's the report by top authorities. Read that." He banged a thick finger on the paragraph he had underlined. " 'Six weeks is all any athlete will need to acclimatize at Santa Anna.' I'm sick to death of all the rubbish being written. There are the facts. Read that."

The old man had reason to believe in the report. Responsible medical opinion was divided. Research teams from three nations had taken guinea-pig athletes to Santa Anna and declared their satisfaction. He had read from the report on television. He had circulated hundreds of copies to the world press. He had taken to carrying it with him everywhere. There were copies in his desert command post, copies beside his bed. An English newspaper had called him "Mathew 'Read That' Kaverly."

As the Bombay conference receded into the past, there was a limbo in which the Olympics were forgotten. The world had harder issues to worry it. Then, as the appointment in Santa Anna neared, trickles of attention ran again, joined like raindrops on glass. The world which had harder issues to worry it appreciated the distraction. National prides and national prejudices looked ahead to a different conflict. Magazines published travelers' notes on Santa Anna. Attention was drawn to athletes who might wear their countries' colors. The thousands of officials and selectors whose importance was identified with the great International, became loud in committees and gave nothing away to each other. Governments took dutiful notice of the public stirring and Prime Ministers and Presidents presented cups and had themselves televised and photographed.

As national interest inspected itself and grew jealous of prestige, those who wished to make excuses beforehand and those who were truly concerned raised their voices. The IOC had made the decision for Santa Anna despite the clear warnings announced at Bombay. The Executive Board had influenced the membership on the conference floor. Mathew C. Kaverly used the Executive Board as the accomplice of his petulant will. The old man put out more copies of his famous report.

He had turned seventy-seven. He was six years younger than that on public record. But the sap had begun to wither in him. He felt it on cold desert mornings as an oppressive chill in his marrow. He felt it in the burden of tiredness that long air journeys left on him for days. He felt it under the shock of attack as a craving for understanding. Pride had been his wife and strength his celebration. In the Wall Street crash he had been no less ruined than friends who had jumped from windows. But he had been fortified by an athlete's disciplines, protected by the strength he cherished. This was the gift he could return to the young, the pride and joy of accomplishment. The young would need it in a world of gutless goals. The young would need it in a world of gray faces. He could not live without a reason. The Russians had entered the world's community when they carried their first Olympic flag. Given time, he would bring in China. He was already more than halfway.

There had been nothing on the Lausanne teleprinter for days. Kaverly had told Stein that he wanted no further communication unless the business was urgent.

He was putting up a hydrogen balloon in the garden when the bell that signaled an incoming message rang. The old man went to the command post and stood sullenly over the ticking machine.

The message said: "Mathew C. Kaverly from Dr. Hans Stein: Have had a worrying letter from Commander Rostrom. Believe you should accept an immediate copy. Shall I transmit?"

Rostrom was president of the International Sports Federations. A worrying letter. The old man's breath began to hoarsen. Rostrom. He had not thought of Rostrom. Rostrom had never mattered. Kaverly had cut Stein off when he last called, had broken the message and ordered him off the line. He wouldn't be back for nothing. The old man fumbled, giving Lausanne the go-ahead. He leaned on his knotted forearms, his breath blowing. The teleprinter began its chatter.

The Chancellor
IOC
Mon Repos
Lausanne

Dear Chancellor:
1.   The IOC has seen fit at its congress in Bombay to approve the application of Santa Anna to stage the current Olympic Games.
2.   Comprehensive reports from eminent medical authorities show that there is an element of risk to athletes in endurance events should they compete at Santa Anna's altitude without being properly acclimatized.
3.   As the cost of proper acclimatization will, for many athletes, be prohibitive, we urge that the Executive Board urgently consider moving all endurance events from Santa Anna to a sea-level site.
4.   If the Executive Board feels it is unable to do this, then the undersigned federation secretaries, acting with

the full approval of their committees, give notice that they will have to consider recommending to their affiliated national organizations that their members decline selection for Santa Anna.

The machine chattered away, pushing up the paper, printing the names of the letter's signatories. Kaverly felt the old, missed power rise from the knuckles he clenched on the table, charge up his arms and fill him. His jowls reddened with blood. There were twelve of the world's twenty-one federations registered in their secretaries' names. He stood like that in the disconnected silence, his heavy old head bent to the glassed-in message. It had been almost too long, the waiting. When he could, with one finger, he stamped out CALL YOU LATER. The teleprinter remained mute. He pulled up the rolled paper, tore it off, sat to read the message again.

"—the undersigned federation secretaries, acting with the full approval of their committees, give notice that they will have to consider recommending to their affiliated national organizations that their members decline selection for Santa Anna."

The old man's head sank into his shoulders. A misery and loneliness washed out the defiance of at last having something to fight. His head began to weave.

"Not my boys," he mumbled. "Not my boys."

He could fight the corrupters. It was for the young people that he spent his fortune and strength, to keep the last true International clean. It was for them that he had armed himself with the power to scourge the forces of self-interest. For all the young men and women who would discover themselves in the joy of achievement for its own sake. For all the young men and women freed of the politicians' barricades when they met to know and respect each other in the brotherhood of pure sport. If they abandoned him, if the lie-tellers used the young— The great white room with its polished, ticking instruments jumped and began to blur. The first wave of a migraine crashed behind his eyes, spun his stomach with nausea. The old man pushed himself up.

"No!" he bellowed. "It won't be!"

He staggered, the message clutched in his hand, lumbering aimlessly in the command post, bumping on the tables and cabinets.

Three days later, Dr. Hans Stein was handed a teleprinter message at IOC headquarters. It said: Chancellor from President: Arriving Lausanne soon. Take no action Rostrom letter. Kaverly.

Stein paled. He had already made a deal with Rostrom. He had to. If the press had got wind of an athlete's revolt it would have blown the IOC to glory.

Mathew C. Kaverly landed unannounced in Geneva. The migraine had been a bad one. In his weakened condition it had hurt him. He wanted to rest from the air journey, build up his strength, before he saw Stein. There was sun on the lake. The rakish, sparkling-white steamers that carried commuters and trippers hardly left a wake on the polished water.

When the old man alighted from the taxi at the Hotel Central Bellevue, the doorman was quick to tell a porter. The manager and the assistant manager hurried into the foyer. Mathew Kaverly was conducted by them both to his customary fifth-floor suite. There was no formality about passport or signature at Reception. The guest book would be carried to Mr. Kaverly's rooms when he was established and rested.

It was three in the afternoon. The old man had not slept on the aircraft. The weakness the migraine had left was soothing rather than distressing. He was emptied, almost at peace, as is a man who has discharged his passions in violence. The familiar rooms, the familiar view, the familiar welcome, had comforted him.

The sleep that had for so long escaped him began to creep through his blood. He did not dare to believe it but it invaded him steadily. He nodded and dozed, was only jerked to attention by the sudden fall of his head. Quickly, before it went away, only stopping to slip off his shoes and jacket, the old man lay on the bed and pulled up the quilted cover.

The telephone woke him. The manager wondered if Mr. Kaverly would dine in his suite or wished for his usual table. It was seven o'clock. He had slept a dreamless four hours. The old man felt clearer and harder than he had in a long time. He lay on the carpet, did twenty-five push-ups, flipped over and did twenty-five sit-ups. Breathing deeply, filling himself, he unbuckled his wristwatch and undressed. The gray that had scarcely touched his head had invaded the matting on the big, humped shoulders and chest. He would call Stein now. There was no need to wait.

He showered, wrapped himself in a towel, and lumbered out to the balcony and looked over the lights twinkling away to Geneva. The cool breeze braced him, dried out the dampness on his skin. He would pull the mat from under Rostrom.

The hotel secretarial service had called the Mon Repos headquarters, had been put on to the Chancellor at his home. A clerk rang from the desk to announce that Dr. Stein was on his way up. Stein was also familiar at Hotel Central Bellevue. He walked across the square to its coffee lounge every morning.

The door was open, waiting. The old man was in a chair, reading the dinner menu.

Stein rushed in, already anxious, his hand out. "Mathew, you should have let me know, so that I could have sent the car for you."

"I wasn't sure of the flight." The old man looked at Stein over his reading glasses. "Are you still losing weight?"

"A little, perhaps. I had a touch of influenza. You look well enough, Mathew."

"That's because I stay away from you doctors," the old man said meanly. "You had better sit down and have a cigarette."

Stein pushed at the packet with his long, stained fingers, and blew the smoke away from Kaverly. He said nervously, "I called you on the printer yesterday, but got the shut signal."

"I had business in New York. What did you call about?"

Stein puffed the strong, acrid-smelling smoke. "I had a talk with Rostrom."

The old man put his reading glasses away. "I thought I advised you to take no action on that."

"We met before I got your message, Mathew. I had to do something. If he had leaked that ultimatum to the press there would have been an uproar."

"Ultimatum." The old man snorted. "That was no ultimatum."

Stein said, "I assure you, Mathew, that is the way Rostrom sees it. However, we managed to reach an agreement." He corrected himself. "Well, not an agreement—I couldn't do that on my own authority, of course. But Rostrom is prepared to make a compromise that would leave the IOC undamaged."

He knew that he had expressed himself badly, waited miserably for the old man's anger.

"We have to face it, Mathew. In the present climate of opinion he had us against the wall. Criticism from the press is one thing. Criticism from the athletes, a no-confidence vote like this, is something that has never happened."

There was no blowup. Kaverly folded his hands on his lap. "I see. And what might this compromise be?"

Stein said, in a rush, "It solves all our problems, Mathew. We move the endurance events—nothing else, just the endurance events—to San Bernardino on the coast. Santa Anna has plenty of building time. Why, we could make the Games that much more attractive for the visitors. There's lovely country around San Bernardino. It's only the endurance events we move. Everything else stays on the heights. Now, the IOC makes the announcement. We can say this alternative always existed, that we waited to explore all available medical information first. Rostrom guarantees that the federation's letter will remain in confidence. Everybody will be happy. It will be the end of this whole worrying business."

The old man's jowls splayed on his collar; his chin lay on his chest as though he slept. The crisp, boyish hair was all the anxious Chancellor could see.

Stein put out the French cigarette in an ashtray, poked another from the packet beside him. Kaverly said nothing.

"Rostrom was very reasonable about it," Stein said, making himself sound cheerful.

The old man looked up, studied Stein. "Rostrom was reasonable, was he? Rostrom!" He got up and began his lumbering walk out to the balcony where he stood a while. "You're a bloody fool, Hans."

Stein knew he had paled, summoned his bad nerves. He had decided that he would not allow the old man to move him. If he had to declare himself at last it would be here, now, on this issue, on the judgment he had made.

He said calmly, "Thank you, Mathew."

The old man too was calm. He spoke as one might to a difficult child. "Hans, can't you see through this? This is the thin edge of the wedge. How long have the federations been trying to get into the IOC? For how long have they been trying to get the casting vote on the Olympic venue? Don't you see that if we back down now it is as good as admitting they've found a formula for blackmail? They take us over. The twelve signatures on that letter—did you study them?"

Stein had not studied them. He said uncomfortably, "I don't see that it has any relevance."

"Don't you? There were twelve signatures on that letter. Twelve out of twenty-one. And, Hans, every last one of them represented a professional sport. Cycling, boxing, running, wrestling—all the money games. The drug takers, the fixers, the gamblers. You see the pattern now? If they become an influence, amateur sport will be dead in ten years."

Stein waved his hands. "No, Mathew. No, it's no good. You see a plot in everyting. Let us get back to Rostrom—"

"Rostrom!" the old man interrupted. "Rostrom is nothing. What is he? A retired Commander in the American Navy who used to organize recreation. A paid administrator living out of a filing cabinet, worrying about his parks. Rostrom is a monkey up a stick. Rostrom will come down to anyone who offers him a banana."

Stein said, "I don't know, Mathew. You confuse me. But none of this alters the facts. Rostrom has a right to be concerned. He has been more than reasonable about this."

"Rostrom is in Geneva," Kaverly said.

Stein was surprised. "How do you know?"

"I had him contacted from New York. He is expecting me to call this evening. I am going to ask him over now."

"Look, Mathew. I've made up my mind. I've made a decision about this."

Kaverly handed him the menu. "Make a decision about that. I'm going to have the duckling."

Stein could feel his certainty waning. He was disorganized by Kaverly's gentleness, the strange softness even in his movements. He was disturbed, too, about the matter of the signatures on Rostrom's letter.

He said, "What are you going to say? You've got something worked out. What are you going to offer him?"

"Something to eat," the old man said.

"What?"

Kaverly popped his eyebrows, smiling. "I'm going to offer him something to eat. I'm going to offer the monkey a banana."

They were talking over coffee when Rostrom was announced. The old man had been greatly excited by Stein's news that an encouraging reaction about Olympic participation had been received from Red China. Kaverly had organized two confidential approaches early in the year: one through the International Red Cross, another through a Canadian delegation in Peking to discuss grain contracts. His ruling at the Melbourne Olympics that Nationalist China should parade as Formosa had been a successful diplomatic stroke.

Rostrom was fiftyish, with spiky, short-cut hair and a Navy blazer. He had the appearance of a man happy to ignore his sagging belly and chins for the pleasures of eating and drinking. He was flushed now, fuzzy-eyed, needing to make an effort for important company. He had expected nothing more than a telephone message from Kaverly, an appointment for next day, and had forgotten even that over a gay dinner.

Rostrom said, "Well, sir, it's a privilege to meet you again." He offered the old man a hearty Naval handshake. Kaverly barely touched his fingers.

"And the good doctor?" Rostrom asked. "How are you this evening?"

Stein said, "Well enough, Commander. And you?"

Rostrom turned ingratiatingly to Kaverly. "A good trip, I hope, sir. When did you get in? You brought fine weather. We've been splashing about in the rain, you know."

Kaverly said, "Take a seat, Rostrom. Coffee?"

"I don't mind if I do." Rostrom's native accent had been reconstructed by what he believed to be winning English habits of speech.

The little cup looked like a thimble in the old man's lumped fingers. Because Rostrom waited for him, because the power in the big, heavy body was a palpable thing, his position and reputation an enforcement in the other man's mind, Rostrom needed the support of the coffee to occupy his attention. He had already got what he wanted from Stein. But being in Kaverly's private company was unnerving. He tried to think of something to say; the silence had become a menace. He glanced at Stein, who was poking at a cigarette packet.

"This letter of yours," Kaverly began.

Rostrom put his cup and saucer on the arm of the deep chair he sat in. "Yes, the letter. Well, sir, we are all squared away there. The good doctor and I had a long talk about that. I'm sure my federation will be happy. Yes, I think we can say that we are all squared away there."

"Do you?" Kaverly said. "The Chancellor and I have reviewed the position. There will be no change of site at Santa Anna."

Rostrom looked with shock to Stein. "The good doctor and I—"

"You mean the Chancellor?" Kaverly said softly.

Rostrom's flush deepened. He pulled himself up in the deep chair and looked to Stein for help. Stein, however, was staring up at Kaverly.

"I don't understand," Rostrom said. "I thought the matter

was closed. Surely, it's in all our interests to put an end to the current controversy."

Kaverly said heavily, "It is in the interest of the IOC to reject blackmail."

Rostrom pushed himself up by the arms of his chair, knocking over the cup and saucer. "Just a minute, sir. I mean that's going too far. Dr. Stein, I ask you. Let me remind you, sir, I do have an official position. I mean, this is going too far."

Rostrom was bewildered and angry, further confused by the brandy he had drunk over dinner and later in the bar. The importance of rank, which had eluded him in the Navy, he now enjoyed as the federation's president. Even Mathew C. Kaverly owed him that recognition.

The old man smiled at him, almost friendly. "Sit down. I haven't finished."

Rostrom said, his voice jerking, "I prefer to stand."

The old man gave Stein's pale, pained face a wink as he turned to put down his coffee.

"You know the rules, Rostrom. The IOC, and only the IOC, decides the venue of the Games. If we gave the decision to the federations, they would auction it to the highest bidder."

Rostrom began his protest.

The old man wagged a thick finger at him. "You have reminded me that you have an official position. Let me remind you that your official position is as a paid administrator. What your federations will thank you for is money."

"We represent the athletes. My position—"

Kaverly interrupted, "Sit down, man. You must not be upset by plain talking. I've got a proposition for you."

Rostrom sat down.

"For eight years the federations have been pressing for a bigger share of the Olympic gate. We are ready to give it to you. The organizing city takes eighty percent. The IOC and the federations split the twenty. Wouldn't it be a feather in your cap if Santa Anna agreed to a sixty-forty basis?"

Rostrom was trying to think, to avoid the pressure of the big old man who insisted on standing over him.

"That's not the issue, sir. The issue is the venue."

"Ah," Kaverly said, "yes, the venue. Not the altitude, Rostrom? The venue, eh?"

"No," Rostrom said, "I meant the altitude."

"Let me tell you, Rostrom, you can forget about that. You

tell your federations from me that if they make a fight on that issue, I will expel them."

Stein said, "Mathew!"

"Forty percent, Rostrom. Forty percent of the gate, plus forty percent of ten million dollars."

Both men gaped at Kaverly. He popped his eyebrows at them and waited, smiling.

Rostrom said, "The gate plus ten million dollars? Ten million?"

"Ten million dollars," the old man affirmed.

Stein was on his feet. "But that's impossible. Where would ten million come from?"

They were all standing.

"From Pay Television," Kaverly said. "I made the deal in New York on my way here. You want to be a hero, don't you, Rostrom? There it is. Take that back to your federations."

Rostrom began to speak.

Kaverly took his arm, walked him across the room. "Think on it, Rostrom. Telephone me at headquarters tomorrow. Good night." He pushed the stunned man through the door.

Rubbing his hands, lifting his eyebrows, Kaverly watched Stein.

"Mathew! You'll never get it through the Executive Board. It's against everything."

"No it's not, Hans. Think of the money we'll be able to distribute in the backward countries. Playing fields, equipment, athletic scholarships." His voice rose and boomed. "Only the IOC is empowered to sign a contract like that. Rostrom, the federations, all those monkeys up sticks—I've got the bananas, Hans. They will have to eat out of my hands." He shook Stein by his bony shoulders. "I've beaten them again," he bellowed. "They thought they had me. I've beaten them again."

30

THE WASHINGTON winter had been severe. The State Department buildings wore the curling morning fogs like clouds of worry.

In the time since Bombay much had altered for Bob Schultz, but gently. He had continued to lose his hair, gently, and now brushed it more urgently forward. He had returned to the Bureau after the Sixty-third Congress as romantic as a hero, a swaggering raider and coup-maker in the plowed furrows of diplomatic routine. Gently he had handled his brilliant success and gently affirmed his authority. He was known and marked in high places. The dashing conception of Operation Gold Medal had been an enjoyed after-dinner story in State Department confidences. The right-wing revolution in Santa Anna had been blocked according to plan. The money to finance the economy had been acquired according to plan. The wildly unlikely project had misled every professional judgment by continuing, almost willfully, to go according to plan. From his new office next to George Cole's, Bob Schultz kept the watching brief on the rebuilding of Santa Anna.

Harvey Tonkin returned to Washington on leave at the end of eighteen months in India. He stayed in his old apartment with Schultz for a racketing two weeks. The apartment which had been awesome to begin with was now Bob's familiar home. He was upset by the disorder that Harvey brought with him and was kept awake by his parties. Scott Reynolds visited and Bob Schultz found it hard on his nerves. The Indian conspiracy delighted Harvey. He could not leave it alone. He kept asking Scott how he felt about the Games going to Santa Anna, and advised Schultz that one day he must visit him in Bombay. Harvey and Scott reminded each other of the visit to Sardar's palace and wondered what had become of Luba Ivanova.

Harvey would say, "This Luba Ivanova was on the Santa Anna delegation about the Olympics. But old Bob doesn't want to hear about that. We boring you, buddy?"

If he had been drinking champagne the little man would collapse in unexplained laughter.

"After this race Scotty had up in Udapair, this race with the horse and Sardar driving a sports car, old Scotty here almost got barred from American athletics. Sardar had to straighten it out. What was his name, that IOC president, Scotty? No good asking old Bob. Bob wouldn't know anyone like that."

"Mathew C. Kaverly," Scott said. "It wasn't all that funny. If Sardar had not been on the Board, I could have been in bad trouble."

Harvey would ask Schultz, "That a name you ever heard of, buddy? Mathew C. Kaverly?"

He would lean back shaking, while Schultz sweated and Scott Reynolds looked puzzled.

With his new authority Bob Schultz was hard on Harvey that night, cold in his anger and apprehension. He had waited in his own room, not sleeping until Harvey's party broke up.

Harvey said, "I know, old buddy. I know. It's just that the whole thing gets to me. There's old Scotty with no idea you've been anywhere near In'ia. Don't know we got it all fixed he's going to Santa Anna. When I think about it—"

Harvey began laughing again. Bob Schultz had slammed the door.

After Bombay, Schultz had met once again with Lance Dobson. The CIA man's knowing watchfulness was as unpleasantly obvious as ever.

"Well, how are you?" Dobson had stood jiggling his hat and appraising the new office as though he had come to make an inventory.

Schultz had contacted Dobson on George Cole's advice. The loudening outcry about Santa Anna's altitude had caused speculation outside the Bureau. Cole wanted the speculation smothered. In his high-backed swivel chair, the favored window behind him, Schultz had made a telephone call, after nodding to Dobson, widening the distance between them until Dobson's mocking scrutiny was spent.

When he was ready, Schultz said, "Sit down, Dobson. What do you hear?"

The CIA man had been in contact with Conrad Carson, the Chancellor's assistant in Lausanne, his pipeline into the IOC. Dobson took a plain brown envelope from his inside pocket and pushed it across the desk. The pages inside discussed a future shipment of beef between persons unnamed. It said there would be no alteration in the destination of the beef although a possibility existed that some of the heavier carcasses might be off-loaded at the port of entry. It said the Chairman entirely ruled out any other changes in shipping plans.

Schultz remarked, "This isn't dated."

"It's now. I telephoned you as soon as we got it."

Schultz put the pages in a drawer. He had not been over-concerned, but neither he nor Cole wanted untendered rumors that might hold up the intricate Santa Anna financing.

"Well, that's it. Thanks, Dobson."

Dobson looked at his hat and very deliberately pushed in the crown and placed it upside down on his head. Schultz stared at him. Dobson half closed his eyes and did nothing.

Schultz asked coldly, "What's that for?"

"It's my other hat." He sat there, looking ridiculous.

Colder yet, Schultz said, "What do you mean?"

Dobson took his hat off and replaced the crease. "Has it

227

occurred to you to wonder why there has not been one complaint from the Russians, from any of the Communist countries, about the height at Santa Anna?"

"I haven't followed it," Schultz said. "This Bureau isn't interested in athletics, Dobson."

"No? Well, we *are* interested in my shop."

"If that's your other hat, you can wear it somewhere else."

Dobson said, "To continue: the reason the Russians are not complaining is that they couldn't be more pleased. All the Communist athletes go into the services. They're state-subsidized professionals."

He waited and smiled at Schultz's irritation.

"You can see what I mean, can't you? The Communist countries already have their teams at high altitude. They will keep them there until the Games. They can't be inspected. When they come down they will run all over us. Very, *very* bad for American prestige."

Watching Dobson, aware of his dislike, Bob Schultz felt a sting of worry. "Isn't that a matter for the IOC?"

"It is," Dobson said. "A lot of people, in a lot of places, want those Games down off the heights. Heavy carcasses will be off-loaded at port of entry."

Schultz knocked on the drawer holding Conrad Carson's report. "'A possibility' is the wording. I've read Mathew C. Kaverly's press statements. You and I know enough about Kaverly to know he won't be pushed."

"We pushed him in Bombay," Dobson reminded him slyly. "He's about to be pushed again. The sports federations have presented the IOC Executive Board with an ultimatum. The Chancellor agreed a few days ago to transfer endurance events to San Bernardino. It's wrapped up. There's nothing Kaverly can do."

Schultz jumped ahead in his mind, calculating what this would mean to the Santa Anna operation. He thought again of the report in his drawer.

"Just a minute. There's nothing about that from Carson."

"Carson doesn't know yet."

If money had to go into building stadiums on two sites, unproductive money for State Department purposes, there would be trouble. The Inter-American Development Bank was watching the spending of every dollar. They had laid down priorities for it. First, the deepwater harbor. Next, communications. If they had to build stadiums on two sites, it could mean a second Olympic Village, the need for a second hotel development. Schultz had been running on the smooth rails of success. Now he saw the tracks ahead leap and buckle. The comfortable certainty went out of him like wind. When he looked up, Dobson was watching him lazily. For Dobson's purpose he had already stripped Schultz of his new office, the swivel chair, the importance of the big window.

Bitterly Schultz asked, "Why are you telling me this? You could have let me run into it head on."

"I could have done. But that's my other hat, isn't it?" He put it on. "Another thing, Schultz. What kind of information are you getting out of Santa Anna?"

Schultz was too rattled to pretend. "How do you mean?"

"You have been checking through Whit Monk at the Embassy, haven't you?"

"That's right."

"You would be well advised to use our Department. That's what it is there for, you know."

Schultz felt another shock coming. "Why? Is there anything wrong down there?"

"Your money's leaking. It's hay in the sunshine for everybody. There are contractors on that operation who have never put up an umbrella. The Castroites are working up a national demonstration. Millions for the Olympics, nothing for workers' housing. They are mixing cement down there that wouldn't hold up to ice a cake."

Schultz stood with his knuckles on the desk. Surely the advice he received from the Embassy could not be so wrong.

"How do you know? Whit Monk is working on this full time. He knows the country. He's been there for years. Whit Monk is working directly with Bueno. The Inter-American Development Bank has had its own men in Santa Anna. You've got to be wrong about this. Whit Monk—"

"Whit Monk is being led by his nose. He believes what he hears from Bueno. You guys have backed the wrong horse in Santa Anna. Bueno hasn't the guts to handle this. He's an idealist. He has beautiful thoughts. What you need down there is somebody who will go in and bloody a few thousand heads."

"Why are you telling me all this?"

"Maybe it's my two hats," Dobson said. "You held up well in Bombay. I don't want to see that operation crack. We pulled off a neat trick down there."

"Is this a matter of CIA report?"

"Not yet. It will be eventually."

Schultz made a last try to turn it into rumor, something Dobson had heard, something planted by Pisarro to mislead and obstruct. Something even from the Bureau, or out of Inter-Americas because he had brought it off because it had gone according to plan.

"This could all be rumor. It's too wide of our information. We get stuff like this every day, Dobson. Half our job in these Departments is to distinguish fact from fiction. Where do you get off to be so sure?"

Dobson got up. He considered a moment. "It's no rumor. It's no fiction. After Bombay they made me Santa Anna expert." He smiled whimsically. "Matter of fact that's my third hat. See you, Schultz."

Long after he had gone, Bob Schultz stared at the uncomforting blank of his door. "My third hat." Dobson was running a Santa Anna operation.

Schultz began to sweat. He would have to get on to Whit Monk. He would have to do something, get in first, before CIA filed a report.

Before Schultz could do more than urgently cable Whit Monk, Dobson's advice was brutally confirmed. On the Santa Anna heights one wing of a hotel, nearing completion in the shell, had collapsed, killing seventeen workmen and injuring twenty.

SUNNY

Australia

31

THE AUSTRALIAN AMATEUR Athletic Association's championships had been fixed for Australia Day in Melbourne. The publicity had announced: AMERICAN MIDDLE-DISTANCE STAR TO RUN AT 4A'S CHAMPIONSHIPS.

Scott Reynolds boarded his Qantas flight at San Francisco after a long, gay lunch. At midnight he would be over Honolulu. At 7 A.M. he would touch down in Sydney and change for the short flight to Melbourne.

Dr. Liz had given him a pamphlet before he left. It was captioned "Climatological Data for Melbourne" and had been issued by the Commonwealth Bureau of Meteorology for the 1956 Olympic Games. "You might care to read this, Scotty. It will give you some idea of what to expect." She put her hand out. "Best of luck."

Scott had taken her hand and then leaned forward and touched his lips to her cheek. "Goodbye, Dr. Liz. If you ever come out of your laboratory, that will give you some idea of what to expect."

Scott watched the stars hung in their limbo, his head turned pointedly to the window. He had no wish to chat further with the old gentleman beside him. To be suspended in the heavens, watched by the unblinking stars, encouraged introspection. It was freakish that the earth should curve like this, miles high, in a seeming absence of movement. It was as freakish as he was freakish.

After his tour of India, Scott Reynolds had worked a hard track season. Before it ended there was no doubt about his claim on Olympic selection. Two years after the Bombay conference, in the rising concern about Santa Anna, the track coach spoke to Scott in his office.

"The Medical School is looking for guinea pigs. One of the ethical drug houses has subsidized a research unit to investigate"—he followed the words of a bulletin on the desk with

231

his finger—"1: Evaluation of the relationship between physique motor performances and man's capacity for work. 2: An investigation of the relationship existing between selected physique measures, general motor capacity and athletic performance. 3: The effect of high altitude on athletic performance."

Scott said, "What does it mean, coach?"

"It means ten dollars a day during the winter vacation, live in. You might learn something that will be useful. You want I should recommend you?"

"Like you said, I might learn something."

The track coach wrote a note, sealed it and addressed the envelope. "Take this to the Admin block at the Medical School."

"Thanks, coach."

"My pleasure, Reynolds. You've turned in a great season. I hope you learn something."

The jet had darkened into silence and sleep. A few seat lights gloomed. Scott Reynolds remained turned to the night in his window. Yes, he had learned something.

The research unit was well endowed, well staffed, well equipped. Dr. Ernest Murrow headed it; he had a reputation as a philologist. Murrow was assisted by Dr. Elizabeth Adamson, two physicists and two physicians. He addressed his track men, field men, swimmers and weight lifters by prefixing G.P. to their names. The G.P. stood for guinea pig. It was the doctor's contribution to the noisy good humor. After his successful season, Scott Reynolds was accepted as the unit's star.

Liz Adamson was a new graduate, still unused to being called Doctor. She was tall, attractively angular, with a body that invited attention because it was so uncertain of itself. The young men she worked with were bantering with Dr. Liz. It did nothing to soothe her graduate nerves. It amused them to disconcert her.

Scott had reported to the laboratory to work on the bicycle ergometer. Liz Adamson told him to pedal for five minutes; the bell in the electric timing clock would mark the periods. She emphasized that maximum effort was needed and fitted the nose and mouth pieces that measured the passage of air through the lungs.

Liz scribbled on her clipboard and made her voice short. "Again," she said, "this time with maximum effort, if you please."

Scott bent again over the handlebars. The bell rang. He leaned back breathing deeply through his nose, a gray pattern of sweat growing on the chest of the track suit.

Liz Adamson checked his heart rate.

"Shall I go again?"

Liz Adamson noted figures on the clipboard, her pen a little unsteady. "Why did you join this unit, Mr. Reynolds?"

Scott gave her his winning smile. "I heard about the lady doctor."

Liz Adamson's voice shook. "If Dr. Murrow had been making this test I wonder if you would have tried to take advantage of him."

Scott was surprised. "What do you mean, Dr. Liz?"

"I mean that you're loafing. Your heart rate didn't go above 165. If you had been delivering maximum effort it would have been 185, perhaps 200."

Scott said, "Steady. I was thrashing this thing as hard as I could."

"You were not. Next time you can work to a metronome. If you don't take this unit seriously, I suggest you stop wasting our time and yours."

She left Scott sitting on the ergometer in the crowded equipment of the laboratory. He pushed his hair back.

"What does she want? Blood?"

In the next month, Scott Reynolds worked regularly on the ergometer, paced by the metronome. One of the physicians took the test.

Dr. Murrow was pushing his medical team as hard as he pushed his guinea pigs. The new semester was approaching. He laid his glasses on the desk and rubbed his eyes.

"Well, Doctor, that just about winds it up, as they say."

Liz Adamson handed him a file. "I wonder if you'd have a look at this first."

Murrow put his glasses on. "G. P. Reynolds," he read. "Can't this wait until tomorrow?"

"It's the new analysis, Doctor. I'm not very comfortable about it."

Murrow raised his eyebrows and began to leaf through the file. "Maximum heart rate after exertion, 165 to 185. That's dramatically low."

He turned the page. "Ventilation, 209 liters a minute. Are you sure of this?"

"Yes, Doctor. Four checks have been run on it."

"What's his body weight?"

"Sixty-seven kilos."

Murrow pouted his lips and looked pleased. "G.P. Reynolds must have a magnificent pair of bellows. I can see what's worrying you. Such a wide variant from the mean will distort the average result figures, is that it?"

Liz Adamson shook her head. "No. That can be provided against. I've been wondering about his blood count. The red count is seven million."

"High," Murrow said, "but not excessive. What are you getting at?"

"I'd like permission to run more tests, Dr. Murrow. I'd like to keep checking his red count and do a physical examination."

"Go ahead. I don't know what you expect to find." Murrow looked at his watch. "I've missed Perry Mason again," he said sadly.

For the next month, at three-day intervals, Liz Adamson took blood samples from Scott Reynolds and passed them to Pathology. Because she had been mistaken about him and remembered it hotly, she made herself relax with Scott.

He told her, "If I'd known I was to be a blood donor I'd have held out for a bonus."

When the close association of their full-time work ended with the winter vacation, the research unit gave a party for the guinea pigs. Dr. Murrow smoked the huge, bent pipe the athletes had presented to him. Late in the evening, he tapped Scott's shoulder.

"If you can tear yourself away from my assistant, G.P. Reynolds, I have something to tell you which may be to your advantage, as they say." He picked up a bottle of beer. "Bring your drink."

In his office Murrow sat on his desk, plump and happy, swinging a leg. "G.P. Reynolds, you're a very unusual young man."

"Oh?" Scott laughed. "I didn't think you'd notice, Doctor."

"No frivolity, G.P. Reynolds. I repeat, you are a very unusual young man."

"How is that?" Scott asked more carefully.

Murrow pointed his pipe and held it there while he drank from a laboratory beaker. "Nature, G.P. Reynolds, has taken unusual trouble with you. In your case, nature, as they say, has put herself out."

Murrow sucked on the pipe. "Do you understand me?"

"I'm damned if I do," Scott said.

"How shall we put it? Your heart. You know what a heart is, G.P. Reynolds? Your heart is super-efficient. I would guess that, in common with many top athletes, your heart in weight and mass greatly exceeds the norm. All serene about heart?"

The doctor suspended his pipe and sucked hard at the beaker.

"We leave heart and proceed to ventilation. Ventilation is the volume of air the lungs can handle. In physical effort, the muscles burn great amounts of oxygen. Your lungs, G.P. Reynolds, are so constructed that you would have made a famous hog caller. I would be surprised, and as a scientist nothing surprises me, as they say, if there are ten men in America at this time"—Dr. Murrow checked his watch—"which is eleven minutes after nine, who could return a ventilation figure like yours."

Scott Reynolds felt the need to sit down. He held his glass untouched. Lines formed on his smooth tanned forehead.

Murrow said, "I see we reach you, G.P. Reynolds. We now leave lungs and proceed to blood. In physical effort the breathing of a large air mass is useless unless the lungs extract oxygen and, more importantly, diffuse the oxygen through the red corpuscles so that it can be carried to the muscles. In your case nature has again been prodigal. Your red cell count is abnormal. In fact, G.P. Reynolds, venturing into the world of the general practitioner, which is a world I happen to abhor, it would be my diagnosis that you have a mild case of polycythemia."

The doctor concentrated his pug features on Scott Reynolds.

A little shakily, Scott asked, "A mild case of what?"

"Polycythemia. An abnormal count of red cells. Newborn babies sometimes have it. People living at very high altitudes often get it by the process of adaptation to environment. Do you find this a dry argument?" Murrow took another pull at the big beaker.

While he steadied himself, Scott Reynolds sipped his drink. "Is it dangerous in any way? This high red-cell count?"

"I don't believe so. You might keep an eye on it over the years. Let me make a guess. I would say that athletic success has never come very hard to you."

"No," Scott said, considering, "I don't suppose it has."

"Have you congratulated yourself on this?"

"Well. I don't know, Doctor."

"A little humility becomes us all. In my case my wife insists on it. In your case, G.P. Reynolds, you have the somewhat unfair advantage of being somewhat of a freak."

Scott Reynolds said, "Jesus."

Dr. Murrow was busy burning matches, lighting his outsize pipe. When it was fuming again, he asked, "What is the lesson in all this?"

"Apparently, that I am a freak." Scott said, disturbed.

"No." Dr. Murrow pouted his lips. "No. A track star you may be, Reynolds, but you lack the scientific mind. The lesson in all this is that you are favored by nature, as they say. You don't compete in an athletic event on the same terms as your competitors. You are an oxygen trap. Ergo: Choose an event in which oxygen is the consistent prerequisite for success and reap the benefit of eternally aberrative nature."

Scott was leaning on the back of his chair, his party gaiety gone, trying to take it in.

Dr. Murrow adjusted his glasses. "I see that aberrative nature preserves the wonder of balance. In your case, G.P. Reynolds, the extravagance of physical endowment is evened by a certain lightness of gray matter. In my case, I am as you see me, balanced in the opposite direction."

The doctor looked at the empty beaker and belched. He said, "Let us return to the muscle men. I am sometimes convinced that if I flexed my brain and the transfer could be made, I would be capable of astonishing athletic achievements myself."

Dr. Murrow got down off the desk. "You don't follow?"

Scott shook his head.

"In a word, G.P. Reynolds, the Marathon. The Marathon for Santa Anna. At that height, the farther you go, as they say, the farther you should go to the front."

Scott waited and thought for weeks before he went out to run the Marathon. In athletics, traditionally, the Marathon divided the men from the boys. Psychologically, it was not Scott's event. He had been unable to settle to the mile because he recoiled from the crushing effort. His temperament was suited to the middle distance where what he now knew to be his freakish physiology had given him a brilliant season. But looking ahead to Santa Anna caused him depression. Ron Clark, the Australian wonder, was touring the world, tearing up record after record. Keino of Kenya would exchange altitude for altitude when he put on his spikes at Santa Anna. On the books, Scott could not expect to do better than a Bronze Medal. When Mathew Kaverly had chewed him out in Bombay about the frolic at Sardar's palace, he had reminded Scott that the meaning of athletics was not in winning, but in competing. The answer to that was, horseshit. He needed a Silver Medal at the worst.

Scott had run eighteen miles of the Marathon before sore calf muscles stopped him. Because he had been afraid of it, his time was not remarkable, but it had not hurt. In a rush he knew he could run the Marathon. The certainty raised goose-flesh on him like a fright. At Santa Anna, where normal lungs and blood would gasp and faint for the thin oxygen . . .

The big jet had been letting down for half an hour. The long spread of aluminum wings sparkled like silver. The passengers were bright with anticipation, trafficking from their seats to wash and shave, changing into clean clothes. The cliffed coast stood up out of the Pacific. The tremendous spread of the city seemed to be knitted everywhere by waterways. Scott finished his coffee. The notice to fasten seat belts flashed.

The international flight had arrived as punctually as a train. The Qantas kangaroo hopped on the tail planes of other parked aircraft. Scott had to tune his ear to the strident Australian voices. In the casual, efficient bustle, he relaxed and felt at home. He had a half hour to wait for the Melbourne connection and decided he needed breakfast.

The man was small, tanned, with waving gray hair and a vivid sparkling expression. Scott glanced at him when he sat at the table and then returned to the menu. "Orange juice, cereal and two boiled eggs," he told the waitress. "Will there be any delay? My flight leaves in a half hour."

"You'll have plenty of time, sir."

The waitress poised her order pad at the other man.

"Orange juice, cereal and two boiled eggs," he said in a grotesque imitation of Scott's accent. "Hurry it up, dear. My flight leaves in a half hour."

Astonished, unsure whether to be offended, Scott stared at the other traveler.

The man kept his face straight and then shouted with laughter. "You're Scott Reynolds, aren't you?"

"Yes, that's right."

"Welcome to Australia, Scott. I heard you were coming in this morning. I'm Percy Cerutty."

Scott's even, white smile widened. "Good lord! I've read some of your books. It's an honor to meet you, sir."

They shook hands.

237

"You can cut out the sir business," Cerutty said. "Call me Perce. You're in Australia now."

Scott Reynolds and Cerutty traveled to Melbourne together. The world's most controversial trainer of athletes, great maker of Australian champions, had put his flight forward to welcome the American runner.

That night, while the officials of the Australian Amateur Athletic Association, who had arrived late at the airport to receive their visitor, telephoned wildly about Melboure, Scott Reynolds and Cerutty were sitting over dinner at Cerutty's training camp in the bush and sand dunes at Portsea.

Cerutty had said angrily, "That's like those 4-A people to be late. I've been telling them for years that they're behind the times. Come down to Portsea with me. You can have a bit of a run on the sand tomorrow and we'll take you back on Monday morning."

There had been no resisting him. When Scott went to bed that night in a hut tiered with bunks, Cerutty directed him to a berth against the roof in a corner. A hand-printed notice was tacked to the bunk, near a ladder.

"The Landy bunk. Four world record breakers have slept in this bunk. They were Landy, Stevens, Halberg and Elliott."

Scott said, "That's far-out company for me to keep, Perce." He inspected the bunk critically. "I don't think it'll take my length."

"The best men in the world have slept in there," Cerutty said. "D'you think a god gives a damn if his bunk's a few inches short?"

The little man who looked and talked like a prophet had drained Scott more than had the journey. Uncomfortable in the short, rough bunk, he fell asleep in the lull of waves breaking.

The 4-A championship opened on an unseasonably drab day which by afternoon had turned to whipping rain and wind. The storm blew in and out within twenty-four hours as deliberate as an act of malice. All spirit had left the athletes and spectators by midafternoon. Scott Reynolds ran his race in indifferent time, against indifferent opposition. The officials, who had not forgiven him for going to Portsea with Cerutty, were further disgruntled by the weather. Scott shortened his Melbourne visit at the suggestion of two sporting journalists—one English and one Australian—with whom he had been convivial at a party.

Laurie Rounder wrote a column for the London *Daily*

Globe, "Round Sports with Rounder." He was in Australia to report Britain versus Kangaroos Rugby League tests. Rounder had a particular interest in the 4-A championships. The *Daily Globe* was to sponsor an international athletics meeting at the Crystal Palace late in summer. The newspaper was hunting the world for crowd pleasers, to appear in the invitation events. Rounder had already decided about Scott.

"That film-star profile," he told his Australian colleague, "will bump à few hearts on the telly." Laurie Rounder had looked after Bob Jenkins when the Australian reported the test in Britain. It was his turn now to look after Rounder. Scott was invited to join the pair on what the Australian advertised as "a bit of a bash."

Scott had got to bed the worse for wear after a round of the King's Cross strip shows and a midnight supper in a celebrated club. He and the Englishman had been instructed by Jenkins to take a Palm Beach bus to the Seaforth post office next morning. The Australian would drive up through French's Forest to collect them. They would surf, join Jenkins at home for a barbecue lunch and in the afternoon visit what Jenkins sentimentally described as a scene of dying Australiana.

Riding out of Wynyard on the bus, Laurie Rounder said, "This dying Australiana thing Bob was so secretive about—if you feel as bad as I do, it's probably us."

The rollers had come in tall and green on a hot day unspoiled by wind. Laurie Rounder had ventured waist deep into the seething white spume, turned and sat with the children while the Australian shot the slopes and encouraged Scott in his efforts. They were refreshed and eager with curiosity when Jenkins passed the waterskiing lake and parked off the busy, bushy road. There was nothing to see there.

Jenkins was pleased with his surprise. "Come on," he said, grinning. "Split up a bit. Don't get too close. Just act natural and follow me."

They walked into the hot bush, crossed the creek on a fallen tree and pushed through the shrubs and the long grass.

32

THE SHORT, mild winter brightened imperceptibly into spring. The gum trees in French's Forest tipped themselves with early green and sparkled in the glassy sunshine. The gray-green seas that had rolled through the Heads steadied and deepened to blue. Surfboards appeared on the coastal beaches; yachtsmen shook out colored sails.

When he heard Sunny come in from the factory, running the shower, Big Jim Harcourt opened two cans of beer and carried them down the steps. He sat on the bed opposite the reconditioned television set.

Sunny came out of the tiny bathroom in a towel.

"Have a drink."

Sunny took the can, pleased. "What's this for?"

"The bloody drought's broken. I'm starting up the game second Sunday from now."

Harcourt studied Sunny. He prodded the towel. "You're getting fat. You've been out in the paddock too long. Starting tomorrow morning, it's you and me for the roadwork. Gus Drake's got another boy he wants to run against you. Old Gus is still sore about that two hundred quid we took off him last summer."

He prodded Sunny in the stomach again. "That'll have to come off. You're as fat as a pox doctor's clerk."

Sunny had thickened and strengthened as he grew into manhood. The deep chest and diaphragm had quilted with muscle. He had bought a bicycle and pedaled the eight miles to and from the factory.

Gilmour had clipped an article by Percy Cerutty, and had passed it to Harcourt. "There you are, that's Cerutty's diet for Herb Elliott. Those egg flips and brandy you have been pouring into Sunny go in one end and out the other. Half the time he's sitting on the crapper. Wake up to yourself. You don't give a man the diet they fed that greyhound."

"Why not?" Harcourt demanded. "He bloody well runs like one." But he folded the cutting and put it in his wallet.

There had been another party for Sunny on the birthday Father O'Malley had given him. Sunny had started technical classes with another young apprentice of Gilmour's.

"Ask some of his classmates," Gilmour had told the other boy. "I have spoken to Sunny but he's a bit shy about it. You're not too proud to speak up for him, are you?"

"It don't worry me," the boy said, "as long as they don't reckon they'll wind up with a snake sandwich."

Gilmour spoke to Harcourt about it: "Some of the kids from the Tech are going to turn up. It will break the ice for Sunny. I am laying on the keg. You can lay on the steaks."

"What steaks?"

"We're having a barbecue."

Harcourt was unenthusiastic. "You're going to get everybody's back up, the way you favor Sunny."

"Never mind about that," Gilmour said. "You just lay on thirty or forty rump steaks."

"You're bloody well mad. I'm not laying on any thirty or forty rump steaks."

"Yes you are," Gilmour said. "I know how much you've made out of Sunny." He squinted at Harcourt. "And never mind wondering where you can get them wholesale. Some of those kids at the Tech reckon they'll wind up with a snake sandwich."

"We've got a tailspinner," Big Jim Harcourt announced. "He's going to spin for the tail." He shuffled notes into his shirt. "Know any of this lot?" he asked his ring keepers.

"Yeah, one's a reporter. Been here with Gus."

"Twenty-five oners to see him go."

Gus Drake was sitting at the back of the ring, busy backing the tail. He was to have run his new boy against Sunny that afternoon and had arrived to cancel the match. Summer flu had put his boy to bed.

"Ask Gus if he can okay the other two. We want twenty-five quid in the center," he called, "twenty-five oners to see him go."

Scott Reynolds and the Englishman got the hang of the game and were making small bets in concentration.

"A quid he heads them," Scott offered, and winked at Jenkins. The American accent attracted brief attention.

Jenkins was laughing. "The Yank's got a quid for the skull," Jenkins called, making it worse for Scott. "Get set with the man who broke the bank at Las Vegas."

In the latening afternoon, Big Jim Harcourt handed over the game to a ring keeper and stood back, drinking from a can of beer. Gus Drake walked over, counting a heap of crumpled notes. He got himself a beer from the cardboard carton and punched it with the rusty opener that hung by a string from a tree.

Harcourt said, his eyes on the game, "Had a good run, did you?"

The beady little bookmaker took a drink. "You know who that Yank is, don't you?"

"Yank?" Harcourt said. "What Yank?"

"Behind you. The pretty boy. The one laughing."

Harcourt took a long look over his shoulder. "What's he doing here, if he's a Yank?"

"Jenkins, the sports reporter, brought him. He's Scott Reynolds, an American runner. I picked up a few quid on him at the championships in Melbourne last week."

"That a fact?" Harcourt looked again at Scott Reynolds. "He any good?"

"He's not Ron Clark, but I'd make a book on him."

They stood drinking and watching the crowded ring, the polished pennies twisting and flashing in the sky. Harcourt drained the beer, crumpled the can with his thumb and fingers and tossed it behind him on a rusting pile. He dug an elbow into Gus Drake's skinny ribs.

"Why don't we match this Yank against Sunny?"

Gus Drake got beadier, looking up at Harcourt. "He'd eat Sunny. He's a track star."

Harcourt tapped his nose. "How many of this mob would know that?"

They studied each other in the hot, singing bush.

Gus Drake decided and shook his head. "How would you make your book? There's no way. Most of this mob would back Sunny."

"That's right." Harcourt tapped his nose again. "I couldn't make the book, but you could, Gus. I could go a bundle on Sunny to make it look good. We could split her down the middle afterwards."

Gus Drake cocked his head and got beadier. "Where would that leave me? If they found out about the Yank, they'd crucify a man."

"It would all be in the way we put it over," Harcourt persuaded. "We can tell them he's a runner. We don't bloody well have to go into detail."

Gus Drake plucked at his ear. It was too good a chance to miss. He said, "Right. It's on. But if there's any strife, you front for me. I couldn't go two rounds with Whistler's mother."

Jenkins said, "Come on, Scotty. Think of the story it will make when you get back to the States. A match race at a two-up game against an Australian aborigine."

Scott grinned undecidedly, looking up the firebreak. The novelty of the setting excited him. The idea was wild enough to be attractive.

"What would I run in. I couldn't run barefoot on that."

"What size shoe do you take?"

"Nines."

242

"My sandshoes would fit you. I could nip home and be back in half an hour."

Gus Drake had taken Bob Jenkins aside again and then walked off to wait.

"What did he say?" Scott asked Jenkins.

"There's thirty quid in it, Scott."

Scott put up a hand. "Whoops," he said. "I'm a lily-white amateur."

"Gus knows that. He makes his living out of athletics. Gus says he will bet you the thirty you can't jump over his hat."

"What?" Scott shook his head, laughing with them.

Gus Drake waited, intent on a brier bush, sliding beady glances at them.

"I saw a tennis amateur win two hundred quid jumping over a suitcase in his hotel bedroom," Jenkins told them, still laughing.

Scott said, "I don't know. It's a very tall hat."

"Thirty quid, Scotty. It would give us a bash for your sendoff. You ran against a horse in India, you told us. How about this for an encore?"

"Over what distance?"

"Three miles."

"Wouldn't a mile do?"

"Gus wants you to be at home. You'll probably walk the last mile."

In the odd surroundings, with the Australian waiting for him so eagerly, the cries of the gamblers added heat to the temptation. Scott looked again up the long, still break in the tangled scrub to the high, clear sky, to the faces turned to him. His blood lifted. He wanted to run. He banged Jenkins between the shoulder blades.

"Right, buddy. Bring on the hat."

Scott Reynolds had stripped to his bathing trunks. The nipped waist, the flat chest, the long, cultivated muscles, the practiced way in which he moved to loosen and warm, discouraged the gamblers. They watched him shake hands with Sunny, smiling and curious, taller by a head than the brown-armed boy in a cotton singlet and football shorts. Harcourt announced the American, and Gus Drake offered three to one against Sunny. Some of the regulars who were ahead on Harcourt's dark horse accepted the odds.

Gus Drake took some anti-American money but the mood of the gamblers was wary. Big Jim Harcourt judged his time and then stepped noisily into the ring to take three hundred

243

to a hundred on Sunny. The two-up players winked shrewdly at each other and counted notes off their rolls.

"This bloke's red-hot," Harcourt told Sunny. "For Christ's sake put on a good show. If you let him get too far in front the mob is likely to cut up nasty. He's a track runner—the rough going will hold him up—but if you don't make it look good there's going to be a bloody great scream. How do you feel?"

"I feel good," Sunny said, relaxed and smiling. "He talks just like the fellas on television, don't he?"

The big group of men moved to the start, excited anew and noisy.

Gus Drake said anxiously, "Remember, you've got to front for me."

"Dry your eyes. If we're lucky the Yank will break a fetlock."

Bob Jenkins had signed them in at the local Returned Service-men's Club.

"This is a club?" Scott said as Jenkins showed them the bars, restaurants, carpet bowls and clattering poker-machine alleys. They took a table in a lounge with a glass wall through which they had a view of the beach and the late surfers and board riders. "It looks more like a Miami hotel."

The journalists looked away when they caught each other's eye. They were uncomfortable for Scott. He was still sweated, the blond hair clotted on his forehead.

"Get this into you, Scotty," Jenkins said, lifting his glass of iced beer.

"Well, that was a surprise, wasn't it?"

"How do you mean?" Jenkins asked.

Scott laughed. "Come on, you don't have to be kind. I can take it."

"Well how could you expect to run on broken country like that?"

"No." Scott shook his head. "That wasn't it. That boy is good, darned good."

"You led him all the way, didn't you?"

"That was the funny thing. He started behind me and just stayed there. When I pulled away in the second lap he just pulled away with me."

"Go on, Scott. If you had put the pressure on, he would have been nowhere."

"No," Scott insisted again, "I can judge timing. He gave

me such a surprise that I was really running in there. Those last two miles were fairly fast."

Laurie Rounder said, "Yes. I took a check. It wasn't much outside your time in Melbourne, making allowance for the rough going."

"You sure?" Jenkins could not believe it

Rounder nodded and glanced at Scott. "That little chap, whoever he is, could perform respectably at any first-class meeting in Britain. I think perhaps Scott would agree with me."

Jenkins was still incredulous. "What do you say, Scott?"

The American was a little chagrined. "If Laurie had the watch on us, he would know. That boy's a dark horse."

Jenkins slopped his glass. "It's funny you should say that. That's what they call him at the game. Harcourt's dark horse."

Rounder asked thoughtfully, "What do you know about him? Has he appeared as an amateur?"

"I've no idea. Gus Drake gave me a tip that they were running match races with an aborigine. He thought it might give me a kinky par, but he wasn't there on the day I went along with Gus."

Rounder opened his notebook. "How did you say his second name is spelled?"

Laurie Rounder flew out the following Saturday evening. Scott Reynolds had returned earlier in the week. He had accepted the Englishman's invitation to appear in the *Daily Globe's* International. Scott saw it as the opportunity he needed to establish himself as a contender for the Santa Anna Marathon. If the guinea-pig unit was right about his physiology, if nature had given him an edge, he could make his claim on the American selectors where it mattered, in the headlines of the British sporting press.

Laurie Rounder collected his hand luggage and prepared to join the mill at the International Gate. He and Jenkins shook hands.

Before leaving London Rounder had lunched with the newspaper's sports editor. "For three years we've lost heavily on sponsored athletics," the editor had said. "The *Daily Globe* International was your idea. If you don't want it axed you will have to pull something out of the hat. What the *Globe* needs is a crowd pleaser. A personality, somebody we can make copy out of, a circulation builder. Somebody the public are going to want to know about and cheer for."

Rounder said to Jenkins, "Well, then, Bob, I'll leave it to you."

"You're sure about this, Laurie?"

"If he can qualify."

"It's your money, sport. I'll drop in at the game tomorrow and give Harcourt a shock."

Charlie Gilmour's American car was a sign of the prosperity which had overtaken him so unexpectedly. In splashed shorts and bare feet, running the hose on a chamois cloth, Gilmour was ritually bathing the machine when Harcourt braked outside the picket fence. Gilmour was surprised. Harcourt should be at the game. The pace at which the big man came up the drive suggested he had important news.

Gilmour let the hose run into a gutter. "Where's the fire?"

"Never mind. Leave that four-wheeled gin palace alone. I've got something to talk over."

"Why aren't you at the game?"

"I closed her down early. Who's in the house?"

"Nobody. Betty's next door."

Harcourt had to tell and retell the story before Gilmour was satisfied. They sat over the kitchen table, clutching beer cans.

"It's bloody well unbelievable," Gilmour commented.

"It's a turn-up, right enough."

"There's no way it can be a leg-pull?"

"Why should it be? Jenkins was as staggered as I was. The way this Pommy reporter sees it, Sunny will be a novelty. He's going to write an official letter when he gets back to London."

"Can you see Sunny in London? He'd be scared stiff. He wouldn't be able to find his backside with both hands."

"Don't worry about Sunny. That's what you reckoned when we brought him south."

Gilmour punched another beer can. "How will you handle this amateur business? Get him registered?"

"Gus Drake. A few quid in the right direction. Get his application backdated a bit in one of the clubs. Gus knows all the officials."

Gilmour had to get up in his excitement and walk the small kitchen. "I knew Sunny could go a bit. But I never thought he was this good. Sunny in England, a proper amateur. Jesus!"

Harcourt said, "Didn't I tell you? What did I say when he run a photo finish with that truck up at the Alice? That

Yank's supposed to be a champion and he couldn't get Sunny off his hammer."

Gilmour squinted his sandy eyes. "Suppose it is all right. Suppose Gus Drake can get Sunny fixed up. How do we know he will want to be in it?"

"He'll be in it," Harcourt said, "or I'll kick his backside up around his neck where he can wear it for a collar."

Gus Drake and Big Jim Harcourt filled in Sunny's papers on the bar of a beach hotel: name, address, country of birth, date of birth. Harcourt provided the answers.

"Period of residence in present country?"

"About a hundred thousand years," Harcourt said.

"An amateur is one who has never competed for a money prize or monetary consideration . . . or been in any way interested in a staked bet or wager," Gus Drake read slyly.

Harcourt said, "Nothing to worry about there, Gus. I've had his interests protected. Sunny never got a quid out of me."

33

THE HOTEL that Jim Harcourt used had been designed for the commuters who traveled by car to the city. The Beachcomber Bar had murals and sculptures and the internationalizing accents and tones favored by the young generation. When Gilmour came in, Harcourt examined him. Charlie Gilmour still worked on the bench when he had no need to see his suppliers or manufacturers. He wore old-fashioned bib-and-brace overalls in the factory and did not trouble to change when he went for a beer after work.

"You look like a bloody tea boy," Harcourt greeted him. "It gives a man the knock to be seen with you."

"If I was one jump ahead of the demons I might have to get tarted up too." Gilmour ordered his beer.

Harcourt glanced at the bar and dropped his voice. "Listen, Charlie, I've got an idea. I'm going to let you in on it."

Gilmour fluttered his hand and looked as though his beer had soured. "Do me a favor. Don't let me in on it."

"No, listen. This is a beauty. I've got Gus Drake coming any time. I want to get it straight before Gus arrives."

It was simple enough. Big Jim Harcourt wanted Gus Drake to go to England with Sunny. Harcourt knew all about the betting shops that would lay a price on anything from next year's weather to the third World War. He had taken the names of several chains from an English regular at the two-up.

"We don't back Sunny to win. We back him for a place. Nobody outside us knows what Sunny can do. Look at the way he went against that Yank. The Pommies should give twenty to one on him. Another thing," Harcourt said shrewdly. "It will be company for Sunny. It will give him confidence to be with someone he knows."

The size of the scheme boggled Gilmour. "You're mad. It would cost a fortune."

"No, it wouldn't. We could split it three ways. With the air fare, say a thousand. That would give Gus the best part of five hundred to stake. Say he only gets tens on Sunny, or fives even. At fives he would stand to collect two and a half thousand quid."

"If it's that good, why don't you go over?"

"I can't. I've got to run the game. Anyway, Gus knows the trade. Gus would get the right odds."

Gilmour did not know what to say, squinting through the glass to the beach.

Harcourt was excited. "We each of us put up three fifty. It would be worth that, wouldn't it, to have one of our own mob give Sunny a hand?"

Gilmour looked hard at his mate. "You're all heart, aren't you?"

Gus Drake removed his spectacles and returned them in agitation.

"I've never been outside the state, except to lay the odds in Melbourne. I always go down on the train. I get the wind up just watching airplanes fly overhead."

"They're safer than cars," Harcourt said. "Everyone knows that. They've got it down in statistics."

"Yeah, but I don't go much on cars. I can't drive, you know. I always take a train when there is one."

Harcourt got short-tempered. "Well, you can't take a bloody train to England, can you? They can't get the rails to float."

Gus Drake worried about it. "I don't know."

"Look, you're only in for three fifty. We made almost that on the Yank. There are no big meetings coming up here. You could be back in a fortnight, with a Gladstone bag full of money."

Gus Drake worried harder. "But Sunny will be up against

248

real competition over there. How do we know he'll do any good?"

"That Yank was world class. That Yank couldn't lose Sunny, could he? We're only backing him for a place, for Christ's sake."

Gus Drake pushed his glasses. "A man could easily get fives," he said thoughtfully. His eyes got beady.

Big Jim Harcourt relaxed. He winked at Gilmour and called the barmaid.

The small athletic club of which Sunny had been made a member received him in doubt and curiosity. It was much the same as it had first been at the factory. But his shyness was more quickly settled now; he had the support of Harcourt's care and attention. The big man collected Sunny at three each afternoon and took him to the oval to train. Gus Drake bought a stopwatch and joined them, getting beadier and beadier as Sunny's time improved.

"There's no doubt about it," he told Harcourt, "this boy's a natural-born running machine. He can go over any distance."

"They told me up the center that some of these abos would knock out a racehorse. Just watch the way he finishes, Gus. He wouldn't blow out a candle."

"We've got to keep this quiet," Gus Drake worried. "When he runs with the club you'll have to nobble him."

"I'll nobble him." Harcourt promised.

Sunny ran twice with the club in the next two months, entered in the mile. Harcourt gave him his instructions while Gus Drake shot glances over his spectacles.

"Now remember, we're just in this for the exercise. Don't try to make the pace. Most of these blokes could be left behind by a ruptured duck. Just stay in there with them."

"Take it easy, Sunny," Gus Drake worried. "Keep the flaming brakes on."

Sunny laughed. "It doesn't matter to me. I like a bit of a run."

Sunny took second place in both races.

Gus Drake polished his spectacles. "He's got his head screwed on the right way. You've got to give him that."

Laurie Rounder sent Bob Jenkins the official invitation for Sunny to compete in the sponsored International. Jenkins took it to Harcourt. On receipt of a clearance by an amateur club, the *Daily Globe* would dispatch Sunny's air tickets.

Charlie Gilmour sat on the bumper of his big car and rolled a cigarette, watching Sunny pacing on the oval.

"When you ask for a clearance, they'll have a fit. Unknowns don't get invited to Britain. The Athletic Association has never heard of Sunny. This will be another of your big ideas that blow up."

"You'd be just about the most mournful bastard I ever knew," Harcourt said, disgusted. "Tell him, Gus."

"It's all fixed. We didn't say that Sunny has an invitation. We told them you are sending him over to look at the lawnmower business."

"Sending Sunny to London to look at the lawn-mower business?"

"Why not? We said Sunny wanted the clearance just in case he gets a chance to run."

"And you believe anyone is mad enough to swallow that?"

Harcourt looked at Gilmour with great satisfaction. "It's home, you mournful bastard."

The aboriginal stockmen of the Red Center, the great cattle runs of the northern territory and the wild west coast, ride aircraft as casually as cars. In the land of the far horizons the silver glint of wings in the bare blue void is more familiar than the flash of feathers. It was Harcourt's concern, Gilmour's nerves and Gus Drake's ashen apprehension that raced Sunny's pulses. He was more moved by the dash of his new suit and the glamour of the fiber-glass suitcase than he was by the trundling shapes of the jets that rolled and squatted below them on the tarmac. Harcourt and Gilmour had coached him for weeks, traced the route on a map, being careful to dissemble their own excitement. There was no need for worry. England was a notional place to Sunny, neither more nor less real than Sydney had once been to him. The true excitement he felt was because England was close to Ireland, where Father O'Malley had been a boy. That was notional too. The stories the Father had told him about his damp, green home, sitting in his habit on a bench against the wall looking over the stamped red earth to the mission's kitchen garden while the furious eyes of the desert sun went down behind the ranges, were like his own people's stories of the dream-time, a wonder beyond reality.

There were long letters of instruction from the old missionary, wearing on the creases from many readings. Sunny had them in the kangaroo skin wallet which Charlie Gilmour had presented to him.

In the pride of his new suit and shoes, grave with the importance of being addressed as "sir" by the smiling hostesses, Sunny Pintubi watched the moonlight that whitened on the spread of wing in his window. The window seat had been on Gus Drake's ticket. After the shock of takeoff and the climbing turn the little bookie had exchanged places with Sunny. He felt less vulnerable on the aisle and could not see down when his eye caught the window. He was still in his seat belt when the hostess came to offer refreshment. Gus drank a miniature of whisky to wash down a strong dose of sleeping pills and anti-airsickness tablets. The strain of the ordeal had exhausted him. The whisky and the pills pitched him into sleep with the speed of an anesthetic. Sunny Pintubi reached over and removed the spectacles which had begun to slide off the bookie's nose. He sipped his tea, nodding and smiling each time the stewards and hostesses passed.

Somewhere, far below, on the long leg to Darwin, there would be his own red country, the whispering emptiness of the desert out of which he was once carried on an old man's back, lizards tied in his hair. Perhaps Boss Drew would look up and see this star crossing the sky, or Billy Two-Toes, or Mischief. "That old fella generator. Him finish bime-by. Plenty trouble too much." He had not used that talk, even to himself, in a long time. He realized it and it separated him from the boy he had once been. He thought of Father O'Malley and wondered if he had taken his cot outside, under the pepper tree, as he often did in the hot season, with the Army Disposal mosquito net draped from a branch.

It was all so distant and had come so suddenly near that Sunny started and needed to look about the aircraft, to the man asleep beside him, to his own blurred reflection in the window glass in order to reestablish the new identity which often seemed like something imagined or dreamed.

Growing up in the mission and afterwards at Boss Drew's he would have had no occasion to dream or imagine the things that had happened. He had been armed for them because Father O'Malley had encouraged in him his sense of being different. His clever hands had demonstrated his dissimilarity from the other boys. The quickness with which he had learned his lessons had set him further apart. That, and two blue eyes forever reflecting the sky.

The hostess brought pillows. Sunny helped her make Gus Drake comfortable. The cabin lights dimmed. He lay back and wondered at it all.

34

WHEN SCOTT flew into London Airport he had so often told the tale that Sunny Pintubi had become a personal involvement. He had been the instrument of Sunny's discovery. The boy was a stranger to big-time athletics. He would need support and advice.

Laurie Rounder had taken a press car and photographer to meet Sunny at the airport. He had doubts that the young aborigine would be able to find his way to the Kensington terminal. Scott Reynolds rode with them.

Rounder had written in his Sunday column: "Australia has produced many athletes of rare quality but none as rare as the young aborigine called Sunny Pintubi. Sunny is a member of a remote and vanishing tribe whose continued existence in the dead heart of Australia was unknown until a Government patrol stumbled on them in 1957. Discovered only last year, Sunny is here on his first tour. He runs barefoot, with a fluid, tireless style inherited from his Stone Age ancestors. The American track star, Scott Reynolds, who will make his first Marathon appearance in the *Daily Globe* International and who has seen Pintubi run, believes him to be a potential champion."

There was no difficulty in picking Sunny out in the crowd beyond the customs barrier. He stood alone, quite bewildered, bumped and jostled by the pushing travelers.

"He doesn't know what to do," Rounder said.

Scott Reynolds asked, "Shall I call to him? He might not remember you."

They stood uncertainly, Rounder looking in his pockets for a press pass. A small man in glasses appeared and pulled at Sunny's sleeve. The two of them moved toward the long counter.

"It's all right," Rounder said. "He appears to have made a friend."

Scott Reynolds watched, frowning. "That little chap, Laurie. Take a look. Wasn't he—goddamn, he is—that's the chap whose hat I jumped over."

The small hotel in Bayswater was clean and comfortable, run by a West Indian. Rounder had chosen the hotel because he had known the proprietor in his days as a professional cyclist and had his assurance that he would keep an eye on Sunny. Rounder did not want problems. The massive immi-

gration from the colored Commonwealth had made London-
ers touchy.

On the way there, Laurie Rounder had the driver circle
Hyde Park to pass Buckingham Palace and enter Bayswater
Road from Marble Arch. While Rounder identified points of
interest, Sunny Pintubi stared from his window in a strange,
disturbed excitement. He did and did not see the buildings.
He did and did not hear Rounder. The stretched blue eyes
sought unbelievingly for the dark skins mixed among the
white. He saw buses approach and pass, dark-skinned conductors swinging on the platform. At Hyde Park a Negro
steered a pram, smiled at the white girl on his arm. There
were Indians in Bayswater, sitting at tables on the pavement.
Sunny Pintubi was frozen at the window. His chest heaved.
There were no words to the rush of feeling that shook him.

"Hi, Sunny. Wake up." Scott Reynolds smiled and looked
puzzled. "You've been dreaming, boy."

"Sorry, I didn't hear."

Laurie Rounder showed concern. Sunny had scarcely spoken on the journey, had barely answered the formal questions. Rounder was beginning to wonder if his barefooted boy
from the bush might not go to pieces in the welling excitement of a big International. He shuffled uncomfortably.

Scott Reynolds said, still quizzical, "What do you say?
Shall I come by in the morning?"

Sunny smiled blankly at him.

"He wants to know if he can show you where you can
train," Gus Drake said. "We are not over here for our
health."

Sunny had turned back to the window. "Yeah, thanks."

"Eleven o'clock, then?"

"I'll have him ready," Gus Drake told Scott.

Laurie Rounder said, "Well, here we are, chaps."

Scott Reynolds was staying in the Cumberland at Marble
Arch. The *Globe* was paying him top expenses. He and
Rounder had a drink in the cocktail bar after seeing Gus
Drake and Sunny properly settled.

"You're sure you don't mind?" Rounder asked, unconvinc-
ingly.

"Of course not. The kid's good. I owe him something, anyway. I've been dining out on that match race."

"I wonder if he would be any use at the mile." Rounder's
plump, polished face looked sadly at the list before him on
the bar. "All the crowd pleasers I've got are in the middle-

distance events. Do you think he could make a show of the mile, Scotty?"

"Only one way to find out," Scott Reynolds said cheerfully.

"I suppose so." Rounder lit a cigarette and puffed it hard. "Putting these programs together is hell. I've been let down right and left. With the Oympics coming up, the top talent is being as careful as virgins."

"You can't blame them." Scott was thinking about himself.

"I've been building Pintubi up in the column. He's a helluva good copy story." Rounder tapped his offending notes. "If he could make a show of the mile against this kind of weak opposition, it would strengthen the program."

"Give me a few days. I'll let you know."

"I'd appreciate it, Scott." Rounder rubbed his vest and pulled a wry face. "Acidity. Organizing these meetings is hard on the stomach. There are more prima donnas in athletics than there are in Covent Garden." He looked at his watch. "I'd better be going."

Scott Reynolds took an olive and made his voice casual. "Have you had anything definite from Hayes yet?"

"Not yet. I'm giving Bill Persons lunch tomorrow. Well, Scott, I really must be off."

Rounder had been right. With the Olympics coming up, the top talent was getting nervy. Scott could feel it in himself. He had read up on Harry Hayes, discussed him with the coach at the Queens Club. A man who could break the four-minute mile and then come back from failure to set a new British time for the Marathon would be frightening competition. The apprehension which had worried Scott for weeks froze again in his stomach. He needed this win. He had the promise of the football contract, a fat one. In New York the scout had told him, "We know you have got the speed, Reynolds. You give us a Gold Medal, we've got a deal. I don't give a good goddam which medal you take, boy, as long as it shouldn't be for flower arrangements." He just needed to get there, to be up that mountain. Nature had given him a blank check, cashable at 7,000 feet. Meanwhile, Scott Reynolds needed the break of not having to run against Harry Hayes. He would take him, when the time came. At Santa Anna. When the time came, up that mountain, he would take them all.

Four days after Sunny Pintubi arrived in Britain, Laurie Rounder and Scott Reynolds sat again in the Cumberland's cocktail bar. Scott's bags were packed. They were waiting in

254

the press car that was to drive him to Cambridge. Rounder had arranged accommodations there. Scott was going to train for a week in the country; he was in lifted spirits. Harry Hayes would not appear at the *Daily Globe's* meeting.

"Persons wanted the earth," Rounder said. "He is the most impossible man in British athletics. I don't know how he hasn't run afoul of the amateur laws."

They talked about Sunny Pintubi.

"He feels strange, and that's natural," Scott said. "Gus Drake tells me he had never run on a track until a few months ago. He has no idea of timing himself and not much idea of competition. When I ran with him he just stayed with me. It's eerie. He just stays with you, smiling. You know, Laurie, I've been dreaming about it. You know how you dream when you're training? I'm running my race and he's half a stride behind me and I can't shake him off and he's smiling. I tell you, it's eerie."

"What is his best time?" Rounder asked.

"He ran a four-twelve with me, but when we came off the track he was hardly blowing. I had the feeling he would have been there at my elbow had I run a three-twelve or a two-twelve."

"How's he coping otherwise? I mean with his surroundings?"

"As far as I can see he's as happy as a cricket. He's already a favorite at the club. I don't think he has any preconceived ideas about anything. You know? Nothing bugs him because he takes everything for granted. I tell you, Laurie, I've never seen anybody move like that kid. In the book he does everything wrong. He hardly lifts his feet, his arms dangle, but he goes over that track as though he's floating. He gets along like a goddam ghost."

Scott's voice was almost exasperated. He noticed it and glanced up into Rounder's surprise, unpuckered his forehead and gave his golden-boy smile.

"You see? He has got to me."

"Apparently he has. But four-twelve is a useful starter, Scotty. Particularly if he didn't seem to be trying."

"You get somebody to work on him, Laurie. Put him over that mile until he drops."

Sunny breakfasted with Gus Drake each morning at nine o'clock. He was up and out hours earlier to ramble Hyde Park or ride the buses. He always waited for a bus with a colored conductor. The authority of the uniform and the obedient white passengers moving down the aisle were wonders to him. The manager of the hotel was another wonder. Sunny had never conceived of a dark-skinned Boss. Often, after Gus Drake had thought him asleep, Sunny would leave his room to sit in the foyer. Most of the guests were interested in him. The manager had pointed out the pieces about Sunny in Laurie Rounder's column. Once the manager got out an album of photographs of himself as a professional cyclist. Sunny told him about the mission, about the wide red country, his job in Gilmour's factory. The manager asked his own questions and looked thoughtful at the answers.

At the club Sunny had run to please Scott Reynolds. When Scott left for Cambridge, Sunny ran to please the old athlete Rounder had hired to coach him. Gus Drake accompanied them to the club, pushing on his glasses and looking worried.

The thermometer was up and climbing. The weather forecasts had warned of a heat wave. Gus Drake included the possibility among his calculations. What the Pommies called a heat wave would be an autumn day to Sunny.

The old athlete said, "The boy is obliging enough and there is no doubt he is fast, but he has not got the winner's instinct. He does not concentrate, Mr. Drake."

Walking back to the hotel, Gus lectured Sunny. "We are not over here for our health. You've only got another week. Get stuck into it. If Big Jim were here he would kick your backside up around your neck for a collar."

"Don't worry," Sunny said, hardly listening.

Gus Drake flicked his eyes. In ten days Sunny had changed. His awkwardness, his initial difficulty with people, survived as a charming shyness. He had become more remote, more assured. Gus Drake had no interest in the causes of the change, only in the effect. He would have given a racehorse he intended backing the same quick fix of attention had it come into the saddling paddock in a lather.

The Press Officer at Australia House picked up the reference to Sunny on the *Daily Globe*'s sporting page. He had worked twelve years in London and had never heard of the Pintubi. When Gus Drake and Sunny got back one day from the club, the Press Officer and a photographer were waiting in the bar. A cut of Sunny looking startled was circulated to the nationals with a sensational story about the last of the lost people. Most of the newspapers carried it, to Gus Drake's alarm and Laurie Rounder's delight. Rounder capped this windfall with a lead par of his own. The wire services cabled the reference to Australia. Big Jim Harcourt saw it in the afternoon press and advised Gus Drake in a letter to get up off his skinny backside before Sunny shortened to odds-on.

Gus was having his own troubles. William Hall, the world's biggest bookmaker, had answered his telephoned inquiry and set out the procedure by which business would be accepted. William Hall expected a detailed letter together with a check for the wager. William Hall would then quote the odds. On receiving the gambler's letter of acceptance, he would mail a voucher establishing the bet. Wins would be paid by check. Gus got very beady about the complications of the system. His rule was cash on the nail.

The hotel manager was amused when Gus questioned him about the firm.

"If you can't trust them, Mr. Drake, you can't trust the Bank of England."

Gus had no intention of trusting the Bank of England. He looked again at the letter and pushed his glasses. "This mob wants my money down before they have even quoted a man the odds. They can get stuffed, for mine."

The West Indian said, "You should try one of the gaming clubs. Mr. Rounder could introduce you. That way you could deal with your bookmaker direct."

"Do they pay off in cash?"

"Any way you want it, Mr. Drake."

Gus Drake, through Rounder, became an overseas member of a gaming club off Curzon Street. He had £500 to stake. He tried for tens and accepted sevens that Sunny would win his race or place second. The bookmaker would not consider a third-place bet with only nine entrants in the *Daily Globe* mile. He had never taken a wager on athletics before and had checked the odds with Ladbroke's. His clerk had inquired about Sunny Pintubi from the editors of *World Sports and Athletics Weekly*. Nobody knew more about him than the pars Laurie Rounder had published in his column. There was no record of an Australian aborigine having ever performed on the track. *World Sports* knew of a mixed blood named Perkins who had played professional soccer with a northern club. Outside that the only thing aborigines were known to do was throw the boomerang. Envelopes containing the £3,500 and £500 were locked, at Gus Drake's insistence, in the gaming club's safe.

Under the eye of his coach, accompanied by Gus Drake

and his stopwatch, Sunny worked all day on the track and in the gymnasium. In the early mornings and the evenings he rode on the buses and took long wandering walks in the streets and parks. Gus Drake suggested a bus tour on the advice of the old coach, who thought Sunny needed rest and entertainment. The tour included lunch at The Prospect of Whitby on the Thames in London's East End. Captain Cook was said to have slept there before sailing to discover Australia. In the afternoon the tour visited Westminster Abbey. Gus Drake bought a postcard of the historic monument and mailed it to Harcourt. The postcard read: "Got set for sevens. Sunny OK. This is Westminster Abbey, a bloody great shearing shed full of dead Pommies. Yours, Gus."

The *Daily Globe* International was held on a burning-hot day before a record crowd, to the gratification of Laurie Rounder, his editor, and the newspaper's chief accountant. There were two collapses in the Marathon by the Welsh and French entries, abscribed to the heat by one and to English cooking by the other. Scott Reynolds won his Marathon undistressed in a time not much outside Harry Hayes's recent British record. The coincidence that both athletes had switched successfully from the explosive events which first established their reputations was seized on by the English press. The handsome American made an impressive appearance on Eamonn Andrews' Sporting Roundup on ITV Television. Scott Reynolds explained his choice of the Marathon by gracefully complimenting the brilliant new crop of middle-distance stars and modestly suggested that they were making the competition too hot. Andrews told his audience it was his bet that Harry Hayes and this great American sportsman would wear their countries' colors in the devastating test of character and stamina to be expected next year at Santa Anna.

Over Scott's deprecating smile, a blowup of Sunny Pintubi breaking the tape filled the screen. The commentator's voice continued: "And now for the track surprise of the year. The winner of the *Daily Globe*'s Invitation Mile, the Australian aborigine unknown, Sunny Pintubi. I had hoped to have Sunny here in the studio but unfortunately it could not be arranged in time."

Laurie Rounder had seen to it that it could not be arranged. Sunny's run had flummoxed them all. His attraction as a drawing card had worked too well. The romance of his background, the story of the "lost people," had snowballed in

258

London's press. The *Sunday Globe* was laying out an exclusive on the Pintubi and had urgently cabled Australia for photographs and copy. Sunny was tightly under wraps. He and a protesting, excited Gus Drake were at that time being whisked by Rounder to a hideout in Brighton.

Forty-eight hours after the *Daily Globe*'s meeting, Charlie Gilmour sat on a box in the sunshine outside his factory and opened the afternoon paper. He had been dispirited all day. There had been no cable from Gus Drake, which told its own story. Harcourt had been short and gloomy on the telephone. Gilmour did not mind the loss of his subscription. He deserved that, letting Big Jim talk him into another harebrained scheme. He was worried for Sunny. London would have scared him stiff. Gilmour resolved that when Sunny got back he would have things out with Big Jim. There would be no more of this match racing at the two-up game. Sunny was his apprentice and as smart as a whip. He deserved to get a fair go. When Sunny got back, Gilmour would lay down the law to Harcourt.

Gilmour came up off the box as though he had been rocketed. His eyebrows rose into his hair. He could not believe the newspaper. The pages began to shake and rustle. AUSTRALIAN ABORIGINE WINS INTERNATIONAL MILE AT LONDON'S WHITE CITY.

And underneath in black type: **Who is Sunny Pintubi?**

Gilmour turned, almost falling off the box, and rushed into the factory, waving the paper and shouting. The startled men on the benches could not understand. Gilmour got desperate. Still shouting, he ran to the black power box and threw the main switch. The machines died, screeching. The alarmed staff backed away from their tools.

Gilmour waved the paper. "It's Sunny. He won! He won, for Christ's sake! It all here in the paper."

Gus Drake at last spared a thought for the syndicate. Harcourt got his cable late the next afternoon while he and Gilmour sipped beers for their hangovers and grinned idiotically at each other.

The cable read: HOME AND HONED FOR SEVENS COLLECTING FROM THE POMMS TOMORROW YOU LITTLE BEAUTY. GUS.

In the Brighton hotel where Laurie Rounder was sweating out a background story on Sunny for the *Sunday Globe*'s exclusive, and wondering how he could plausibly explain how he had come across him in Australia, a farewell letter and a package were received from Scott Reynolds, who had accepted an invitation to appear in the Irish Championships at the Dublin Stadium. The package contained a tape. Scott had rerecorded it from one he had cut in the commentator's box during Sunny's race. He had intended it for the entertainment of Dr. Liz and the others in the guinea-pig unit who had enjoyed the story of his match race Down Under.

Gus sent the tape registered express airmail to Harcourt, and noted the cost in his expense book.

As the players came in from the firebreak and the log bridge across the creek that Sunday, they would have taken flight had it not been for the reassurance of Harcourt's beaming presence. The trees around the stamped ring were hung with loudspeakers and a technician was squatted in earphones over an outsize tape recorder. Cardboard cartons of frozen beer were beginning to sop their sides as the chill went off the cans. It was Harcourt's treat. He and Charlie Gilmour had learned the tape by heart. This broadcast was for Sunny's supporters.

The technician's voice droned. "Testing. Testing. This is Station Harcourt testing from French's Forest and up the Creek."

Harcourt said, "You'll be up the creek if you don't pull your finger out."

The loudspeakers hummed and settled. Muffled voices spoke indistinctly from the background. There was a cough. Scott Reynolds spoke in the flat accents of the American Midwest.

"Hi there, Sunny. Sorry I missed you in London."

Harcourt shouted, "This is it. Settle down."

Scott's voice continued: "This is a copy of a tape I cut at White City. The shouting you will hear over the last quarter is me, boy. They almost threw me out of the box. Give Gus my best wishes and Bob Jenkins, if you see him when you get home. All the best to you and to Australia. I have a feeling we will meet again. That's about it, Sunny. All the good luck in the world."

There was a click followed by silence. Muffled voices cut in again. Then came the assured, professionally pitched tones of the White City commentator. The crowd of gamblers froze into silence, their heads tipped in concentration.

"They're coming out on the track now for the mile event. First out is the champion Alan Hanson, in No. 1. The champion always wears No. 1. No. 2 is Neil Miller, once Britain's second-fastest man, but who has not found form this season, John Batton, an Olympics finalist, Alan Reeve of Longwood, Keithley and Meadows, the Yorkshire boys, McCrystal, and finally the two invitation runners, the American, Gypson, and the Australian, Pintubi. Pintubi, making his first appearance in this country, runs barefoot. He has not the form of the British boys, but he may make the pace while he lasts. And they're off the first time. Hanson being careful not to get boxed in. Batton in the lead, then Reeve, McCrystal and the others in a bunch. Pintubi moving out wide. He had better not stay out there if he wants to finish the distance. The first 220 yards gone. Batton still leads, Hanson nicely placed. Back of the bunch are Gypson and Pintubi. Oh, a big box-up there. Pintubi took a bit of a bump."

The gamblers stirred, caught each other's eyes. Harcourt's big fist squeezed on the beer can.

"Coming up to complete the first lap it's still Batton, Reeve, McCrystal, Hanson, Keithley. Time is 60.4 seconds. There is Pintubi, still last. You can say one thing about this colored Australian. He has a wonderfully smooth style. It's completely unorthodox but he gets length in his stride by the flexibility of his hips. He seems to float over the ground."

"You float 'em, Sunny," a gambler shouted.

"This modest start emphasizes the British boys are more interested in winning than breaking records. A place is at stake in the international side for the Empire Games. The will to win or finish is vital. Oh, another box-up at the back there as Pintubi makes a move to go through. Oh, he's been bumped again. The Australian seems to be fed up with the crowded going at the back and is trying to break clear. Batton is still in front of McCrystal and Reeve. Batton taking it easy. Quite relaxed. Time for the half mile, 2 minutes 4.3. Interesting how this race has developed. Hanson is in control, careful not to get boxed. Now the field is bunching as the runners try to place themselves. Nothing spectacular so far. These men are running tactics against each other rather than trying for a fast time. Six yards would cover the field now. There is a lot of bumping going on. Oh, there goes Pintubi again. A bad bump that. This is obviously an inexperienced boy. He doesn't know how to get himself placed."

In the bush the men shifted and growled, forgot the race had been run and won.

"Look at this! Pintubi is stretching out, reaching for the leaders. He is determined to get clear of the bumps he has

261

taken. This is it. The last quarter. You will hear the bell and there's going to be an explosion. There it goes. Batton now in front, Hanson has not yet made his move. Now Batton takes a nasty bump from Hanson. Oh, he's lost his stride. This is as much a fight as a footrace. Reeve has gone to the front. Hanson, the champion, is trying for the inside position and can't find it. Here comes Pintubi on the outside, flying. He has kept out of the ruck and it's paying off."

The bush filled with shouts. The men were on their feet. The technician screwed up the volume. Harcourt's thick red neck ran with sweat in the creases. Scott Reynolds' excited voice jumbled on the commentator's English accent.

"This is remarkable. Hanson has been bumped again. You can't run a finish like this. Oh, oh, here comes Pintubi running clear. The Australian aborigine just might steal this race. If he does it is the British boys' fault. They have wrestled their way through this mile. Look at this! Pintubi has struck the front and is just hanging. He has turned to look back as if he doesn't know what he is doing out there. Behind him the field is battling. They are rucked in so tight I cannot place them. And it's Pintubi! It's Pintubi to win the wrestling mile! Pintubi first, Hanson second, Batton third . . ."

They tossed up their hats and beer cans, banged each other on the back. The commentator continued to discuss the race.

"There he is, the barefoot boy from the bush. He is standing to be photographed, showing little sign of distress. The man embracing Pintubi is the American, Scott Reynolds, winner of yesterday's Marathon. Reynolds met the aborigine unknown during the Australian championships early this year. . . ."

35

LAURIE ROUNDER had forwarded the invitation. He wrote fluently in French and often contributed features to the prestigious *Paris Équipe*. The paper was giving a party for the touring Australian rugby team and wanted Sunny there on the night. Gus Drake made the trip because Rounder offered to escort them on the Golden Arrow. Gus calculated that taking the boat train would be that much less distance to fly.

At the party, among the friendly accents of his countrymen, offered drinks he could not identify, dazzled by his reception and the alcohol he did not know he was drinking, Sunny at last felt the wonder of success, momentarily freeing him from the inhibitions of a lifetime. When the boisterous, roistering footballers offered to take Sunny out with them on the town, he was too clouded, too dazed, to establish the sudden lift of panic.

"We will see him back to the pub. Here, Sunny, get this down you."

There was cruelty as well as curiosity for this abo who had made the headlines. Confused, heavy-eyed, Sunny was bundled into a taxi.

It was all blurred, an undertow that washed him from bar to bar on the jostling, pimp-ridden streets around the Moulin Rouge. The Australians were conspicuous in their blazers, remembered from other tours, and the girls hurried out to greet them, contending shrilly for attention with the touts offering strip shows always just about to start.

The fixed smile was a mask on Sunny's face, the reeling impressions as uncertain as a dream. Intent on their debauch, scrumming down in the bars, violent toward complaint or protest, the tourists lost interest in Sunny. Occasionally they remembered him.

"Give us a corroboree, Sunny. How about the dance of the sacred mosquito?"

Or, more meanly, "Send him back to the pub for his boomerang."

An official, veteran of other Paris visits, led the players to a narrow street off the Boulevard de Clichy. The building had been a small hotel. The reception area had been converted into a bar with a long zinc-topped counter, plastic-topped tables and padded seats. Girls lined the benches, most of them young and pretty. Lurching, shouting for service, the Australians sat at the tables, calling self-conscious jokes to each other, eyeing the suddenly excited girls. A waiter hurried with trays of beer. The girls crossed giggling from the bar. Sunny sat smiling his fixed smile, dazed and uncomprehending.

Soon, from a corner, a young man shouted, "We want an exhibition."

Self-consciously, their laughter edged, others took up the cry.

"We want an exhibition. We want an exhibition."

Confidence grew with the chant. They banged their palms on the tables, grinned at each other proudly. The waiter caught the madman's nod and hurried into the street. When he returned, the two elder women with him nodded gravely to the men as they crossed the bar.

A porter in a green apron showed the crowding men into a

big room on an upstairs floor. A tatty screen in one corner hid the bidet and washbasin. A huge, old-fashioned bed dominated the room. Thick velvet curtains, faded and dusty, shut out noise and light from the street. Sunny stood against the wall, feeling sick. He was puzzled to be in a bedroom.

The younger woman was blonde. Quickly, dully, her eyes blank, she undressed and lay down on the bed. Her companion took off her shoes, tucked her skirt in her suspender belt and reached into her handbag. She got up on the bed, holding the artificial penis between her thighs. The dreary, hopeless, poignantly desolate performance and patter began. The mother-and-father way. The German way. For this the blank-eyed blonde gave a Nazi salute. The church way. The blonde turned and pretended to pray.

The room quietened. The men moved uneasily, avoiding each other's eyes. Sunny stared in roaring shock at the naked flesh of the white woman.

Much later, downstairs, when the most sensitive had drunk themselves back to cynicism, the party began to rouse again. Strong-voiced and confident, the Australians bawled their songs, called for more beer, rose to dance between the tables to the gay French recordings. Sunny's mind continued to reel on the image of the blonde's naked flesh.

The girls were businesslike now, fearful of the prospective alcoholic impotence of their escorts. Willingly and unwillingly the men were persuaded upstairs.

Sunny was beyond knowing or caring when a girl took his hand. In the room she asked for money in broken English and with the French gesture for *l'argent*—the greedy rubbing of thumb on fingers. He handed her the francs he had been given at the party. He had no idea of their value, or why she wanted the money. It could have been for the drinks. He was beyond understanding anything other than that he had seen a white woman naked, that she had revealed herself to an aborigine in blank unconcern and uninterest. When the girl felt for him she was shocked and then angry when he tried to strike her away. It was the wide red country under the river gums, and the old gin was grinning with broken teeth at him. He fell back on the bed as once he had fallen when the wild fella's spear seared his temple. It was the blonde on the bed who came to him now and he started up in guilt and terror. The girl was examining the badge of his difference and shame, a tiny, puzzled smile on her face. Horrified, Sunny stared back.

Then the girl looked up at him. "Good for girl." She smiled kindly. *"Comprenez?* Ver' good for girl."

It was to be a long time yet before Sunny accepted and understood, and by then he was an established man with the courage to ask a girl to marry. But he was freed for it in that crude minute in a bawdy house in Paris. There are no barricades that cannot be crossed; all insuperable difference is imaginary. Out of the barren lust of an exhibition and the egalitarian interest of a whore, Sunny Pintubi became armed with a truth he would never have found in books.

An hour before the flight was due, Harcourt and Gilmour waited in the visitors' lounge, uncomfortable with impatience. Harcourt had eaten two dozen oysters and a grilled lobster for lunch. He was full of food and beer, had switched to whisky because it was easier to get down. Gilmour's appetite was small and the sparkling Burgundy had made him charitable.

Harcourt hiccoughed and rumbled. "What do you say now, you mournful bastard? Who's been right all along? Who was right back there at Drewie's, that first time?"

Harcourt had not let up for a week.

Gilmour blinked his sandy eyes happily. "You've got to be right sometime. I've heard of perpetual motion machines. What you've got is perpetual notions."

Harcourt took an indigestion tablet. "Sevens," he said, with satisfaction. "The first thing you're going to see come through that gate is old Gus staggering under a Gladstone bag full of money."

When Gus Drake and Sunny did appear, Big Jim Harcourt could see nothing clearly. He and Gilmour were jostled out in the push of reporters and photographers.

The interest of the press in Sunny Pintubi far exceeded a winning athlete's attention. He was an aborigine. He was a Pintubi. Two blue eyes reflected the sky. His membership in the obscure amateur club had not been forwarded to the national executive when the press carried the story of Sunny's White City win. The executive had disclaimed knowledge of him when the newspapers rushed their inquiries. Sunny Pintubi was a mystery, without origins. Bob Jenkins kept his own counsel. He was preparing an exclusive, "The Sunny Pintubi Story," having the same trouble Laurie Rounder had in avoiding the truth about the match race on the firebreak. Jenkins and Rounder had been in touch by telephone, agreeing on the story between them.

The changes in Sunny made by the month could not withstand the confusion. His ready smile was tired. The reporters jostled and picked at him, noting with curiosity the refinement of features, the soft, waving hair, his clothing, the fluency of his speech, the lightness of his skin.

"Where do you come from, Sunny?"

"What's your club?"

"Where have you run before?"

"Are you a Pintubi?"

"Are your parents alive?"

"Where do you live, Sunny?"

He tried to answer, fright and shyness rising to thicken his throat. His eyes searched for support, found Harcourt and Gilmour. In panic he pushed toward them.

Little Gilmour caught Sunny's face and stiffened. He tugged at Harcourt's sleeve. "We've got to get him out of here. He's had it."

Harcourt watched stupidly for a moment as Gilmour tried to get through. He was stunned by the reception. Neither of them had reckoned on this. It was worse now as others crowded, curious about the disturbance. Harcourt roused to follow Gilmour. A photographer, reaching up a heavy camera for an overhead shot, brought it down hard on Harcourt's new hat. The photographer's mumbled apology choked as Harcourt straight-armed him. The big man charged in, red to the hairline, as he did into trouble at the game.

They were on the harbor bridge, clear of traffic. Gus Drake clung to the jump strap, still shaken by the scene at the airport, and peered down at the sunlit water, grateful to be safely home. Charlie Gilmour, too, was tense, his sandy hair streaming in the wind. Harcourt had taken his hat off and rubbed the lump on the side of his head. Gilmour kept glancing at Sunny in his rear-vision mirror. "Did anything like that happen over there?"

"There was a bit of excitement when Sunny won," Gus Drake said, "but nobody went up the wall."

"How does it feel to be home, Sunny?"

Sunny smiled weakly. "It feels good."

On the long, free run through French's Forest to the beaches, Harcourt began to laugh.

"What's tickling you?" Gilmour asked.

"That bloke with the microphone. He must have had his feet tangled in the cord. When I yanked on it, he came clean off the floor."

266

Harcourt turned and gave the two in the back a big grin. "You little beauty," he told Sunny.

Harcourt wanted to stop at the first pub now that they were clear of the city. Gilmour told him he was taking Sunny to the factory. The boys had got in a few cold cans for a welcome.

In this familiar place, among his workmates, it was as though he had not been away. The crowded events, the foreign sights and sounds, began to ebb and disappear. Sunny was at home, knew it now and felt the flood of his old identity. Their unaffected pleasure in him was as subtly altered as he knew himself to be. There was a difference now, a dissembled respect in their jokes and banter. Sunny relaxed. His tiredness left him. He sat on a bench with a can of beer and answered their questions, slowly and gravely at first. He began to hear the words he used like another voice explaining unanswered things to himself. His eyes shone. There was wonder in his face. He almost forgot them as the old difficulty with words solved itself on his tongue.

Gilmour watched closely. "That boy has changed," he told Harcourt.

"Yeah." Harcourt wasn't impressed. He was anxious to get down to business with Gus.

They took off their coats in Gilmour's office. Gus Drake punched a new can.

"That's the first decent drink I've had in a month," Gus said. "That warm English beer tastes like panther's piss."

"Well, Gus," Harcourt said, luxuriating, "tell us how you got set."

Gus told them about William Hall and his introduction to the gaming club.

"Didn't I tell you, Charlie?" Harcourt shouted. "I said they'd have to get up early to put anything over old Gus."

Gus coughed and pushed his glasses. He had some trouble with his voice. "There's something else."

Harcourt waited. It couldn't be better than it was. Gus edged around the desk. He coughed again and took a pull on the can, flicking a glance at Charlie Gilmour. Harcourt's big smile stiffened, waiting.

"Like I said, you've never seen anything like this gaming club. These Pomms operate in a big way."

"Yeah, yeah," Harcourt said impatiently.

"When I went to collect I had to stand a few rounds. That's the way they do things over there. I got a bit full. You know I can't drink. They were pouring these brandies into me."

Harcourt untipped his chair. "Yeah?"

"Well, I got pretty full. They were all pulling a man's leg about Sunny winning by a fluke. That's what they said in England. They called him the barefooted boy from the bush."

Harcourt and Gilmour had heard that on Scott Reynolds' tape.

Harcourt had come forward in his chair. Gus Drake's glasses slid down his nose. His naked eyes were rolling in anguish.

"I got full. All these Pommies were giving me the needle and I made this other bet."

There was an eternity of silence. Harcourt's chair screeched on the floor as he turned imploringly to Charlie Gilmour. His voice was strangled.

"Bet? Bet? This other bet?"

"I took five to thirty-five hundred that Sunny would make Olympic selection."

"You did what?" Gilmour managed.

"They were needling me," Gus almost cried. "I got full on all these brandies. I saved our stake. We're still in the clear. I just got full and made this other bet."

Harcourt's chair was reversed. He had been sitting astride it, leaning over the back. He tried to walk over it.

"You skinny little bastard."

Gilmour grabbed at Harcourt.

"I'll kill him!" Harcourt shouted. Gus Drake ran back and forward, keeping the desk between them.

"Steady down!" Gilmour shouted. "He's still got the stake money."

"I've still got the stake money!" Gus Drake shouted. "Don't let him touch me, Charlie."

As the Australian season lengthened to its close, interest in Sunny dwindled. He had appeared in three late meetings for two seconds and a third against strong to indifferent opposition. The press had exhausted the romance in his background. It could not support his disappointing performance. The sporting pages hinted that Pintubi lacked the stuff of a trier. The times he ran varied bewilderingly. The Australian character would be fierce for a trier who lost. There was only dismissal for a winner who would not try. What could you expect—he was an abo, after all.

There had been the mission and his life had begun there, because he had no true memory before it. The old man of the lizards and the land that sailed spinifex and sand to the sky were as unreal as Father O'Malley's haunt about the damp, green place of Ireland. In the hutments and rough buildings around the stone church, where the loud bell rocked in its tower, he had laughed and run with other children his age, and hidden from the bigger boys' bullying. There were parrots there; after the rains berries and flowers grew in the hills. The ghostly white-barked gums with the dust washed off their leaves shaded the rock holes that filled in the riverbed and the old mission truck splashed there to cross when it made the journey to fetch supplies. Around the mission in their wurleys of bark and scraps the adults sat on their legs by the cooking fires. The children cut little spears and imitated the men when they tired of the mission tucker and went hunting for kangaroos and euros. Sometimes his playmates would be gone, disappeared overnight, wurley empty, cooking fire cold, on a walkabout with their parents.

Sunny had no family, had no tribe. Sunny had Pintubi skin. The mission was his family. Father O'Malley was his parent. His country was as far as he could see.

In the years between Sunny's meeting with Harcourt and Gilmour and his being pitchforked into public curiosity, the cruel and lonely confusion that sometimes rose in him like a shriek had been tried against and won against behind the solitary defense of his smile. His hands had helped him. He was realized by his power with machinery, released by its dispassionate acceptance.

The pride grew in him as he worked and studied and ran on the firebreak for Harcourt. He had been given a dictionary at night school because the cheerful young teacher had noticed his difficulty with words. The words came to him and stayed. At his sheltered place on the headland above the breaking waves, Sunny composed sentences, encouraging the new words, whispering them on his lips, as absorbed and satisfied as he was when he worked over the parts of a motor. As fluency and understanding took root and grew, the range of his thoughts grew with them.

So his pride grew and changed him, and alongside his pride confusion multiplied. He saw no other black faces. There was nobody to share the burden of difference. He had never heard tell of a dark Boss, never imagined that such a thing could come about. There had been no preparation for the revelation that struck and possessed him in England: the black man with the pram and the white girl, the bus conductors in the authority of their uniform, the manager at the hotel giving orders, the dark faces in the street, in the bars and restaurants, the dark faces driving big cars.

It was not altogether an accident that he had won the race in the great stadium. He had been pushed to the front by panic but he had been pushed by the revelation that sang inside him too. He was as good as they were and as free. There were dark Bosses and such a thing could be. In front, he had faltered for a moment, but then it was over, he was safe.

Sunny Pintubi had not survived the return to the country of his people. He had not survived the meaning of the reporters' questions, the freakish image of himself he saw reflected in their patronizing eyes. There were no dark faces smiling in the streets.

Bob Jenkins had published his article about Sunny. He had brought a photographer to the factory for a shot of Sunny at work. A few days after the story appeared, a letter came addressed to the factory. The notepaper was headed Student Action for Aborigines. A pamphlet was enclosed. The secretary of Student Action asked for an appointment with Sunny and congratulated him on his success.

That night Sunny Pintubi lay on his bed, eyes to the wall. The pamphlet was crushed in his fist. A box of black type on the second page framed facts. The black type sailed again and again through his brain.

> There are 450,000 aborigines in Australia.
> The death rate of aborigine children is twice that of white.
> Only 2% of all aborigines reach third year high school.
> The Aborigine Welfare Board reports only 19 houses built, 43 under construction, 4 bought in Sydney.
> There is only one aborigine university graduate and four undergraduates in all Australia.
> Segregation of aborigines is general in country towns.
> The Constitution of Australia states: The Parliament shall . . . have the power to make laws with respect to the people of any race other than the aborigine race, in any state, for whom it is deemed necessary to make special laws.
> Aborigines on cattle stations are exploited as cheap labour.

Sunny did not answer the letter or call the telephone number given him. Early and late he trained on the oval. An old athelete on the club committee had offered himself as a coach. The Student Action for Aborigines wrote again, and again after that. One Saturday morning Sunny did telephone. He dressed carefully in the afternoon and took the bus to the city.

They met in a coffee shop, four young men and two girls. The students were regulars there. They used the place as a club. The awkwardness and shyness which had altered to reserve stiffened Sunny's hands, haltered his tongue, as they sat him down and took seats around him. They called gaily for the waitress, introduced Sunny to the manager and staff, to the other students who entered. There was no condescension cooling their eyes. Sunny was a hero to them, his gravity more effective for that. The girls told each other how much more handsome he was than in his photographs.

But he did not understand when the big blond boy talked about the death of Albert Namatjira, how he had died in heartbreak in spite of his fame, after he was jailed for giving his tribal brothers forbidden liquor. He did not understand when the big blond boy spoke discreetly about the aborigine ghettos. Sunny had not learned that word. He did not understand when the big blond boy talked about the Freedom Ride the students had made earlier that year. They watched his face and waited.

He did not understand the reference, but he understood the meaning and wings beat in his stomach as they had done when he first saw the dark faces from the car window in London.

"You can help us, Sunny, to help your own people. You know what Australians are like. A champion jockey or an athelete like you has more pull than a prime minister." They laughed experimentally and waited. They could see by his struggling face that he did not really understand. He was one of the most sophisticated aborigines any of them had met; he was exactly what the student movement needed. But somewhere, somehow, the guts had been kicked out of him.

It was spring when they told him, all prepared with excitement. Chicker said, "Sunny, we're going to take the bus out again."

The girls quietened, watching Sunny, their eyes big with admiration.

"What bus is that, Chicker?"

"The old Freedom bus, Sunny. We're going to do another ride. Are you going to be in it?"

Sunny's stomach crawled and he knew why and hated it but could not will it to stop. For something to say he asked, "Where are you going?"

"A place called Morelands, up the north coast. There's a big settlement there on the river."

He tried hard to be casual. "I wouldn't be able to get away. We're pretty flat out at the factory."

"We need you, Sunny," a girl told him. "You've got a name. You know, you can be an example."

"She's right, Sunny. You could take a leave. From what you've told us, Gilmour's on our side. You know what they say about abos being hopeless—you're one of the examples that prove them all wrong. We're going to make this the biggest Ride we've done. With you along it will hit every paper in the country."

Sunny tried to steady his whirring thoughts. "I'm pretty sure I couldn't get away," he said, licking his dry lips.

Charlie Gilmour looked at the ground, scratched his sandy hair and whistled through his teeth with worry.

"I don't know, Sunny. It takes the wind out of a man's sails. I don't know about things like this."

"They'll only be away three or four days."

"I don't give a stuff about that—you can take a month if you want it. But a thing like this, getting mixed up in politics. You might get filled in. A bottle over the skull. Anything might happen."

Sunny said softly, "It isn't politics, Charlie."

Gilmour paced the office, head down, fists jammed in his overall pockets. "I'm buggered if I know what to say. Never buy trouble is my motto. You'd be sticking your neck out. You're going like a house on fire at the Tech. What do you want to upset things for?"

"Maybe to help somebody else like me to go like a house on fire."

Gilmour lifted his head with shock. It was the most self-conscious remark Sunny had ever made. Gilmour coughed with embarrassment. "Um," he said and rocked on his heels, wondering what to say next.

Sunny waited quietly.

"Have you mentioned it to Big Jim? He'd be likely to blow a gasket."

"He's not my boss. You are."

It was getting worse for Gilmour. He blinked at Sunny, realizing with another shock the force that had been building in him. He had a momentary glimpse of Sunny as he had been, wiping his hand on the step at Drewie's the night the generator broke down. The memory gave Gilmour what he needed.

"Father O'Malley," he said with relief. "That's the thing to do. Write to the Father about it."

"If it's all right with the Father, will it be all right with you?"

"Anything the Father says is OK by me. You write to him. If the Father reckons you should go ahead, you go ahead. I'll fix it up with Jim."

"I wasn't worrying about him," Sunny said. "I just wanted to get it straight with you."

When Sunny had gone Gilmour puffed his breath and got a cold can from the refrigerator. He walked about, drinking the beer, taking blind looks out of the office window. It was getting hard to keep up with Sunny.

They met at the Beach Hotel early on Saturday evening. Harcourt had just closed his book on the afternoon's racing and was satisfactorily on the right side of the ledger. Gilmour had approached the subject nervously.

"The old Father wrote him a letter as long as a newspaper. It had instructions about everything except how to button his fly."

Harcourt said, "He's likely to come back with a creased skull. It might knock some sense into him." He did not seem very interested.

Gilmour was frankly surprised. "You think it's all right, then?"

"Why not? If he wants to be the only black beatnik in the country, that's his lookout."

"The newspapers will probably get onto it."

"Good luck to them."

Harcourt dismissed it and called for another round. Gilmour continued to be surprised. He concluded that Sunny had finally made an impression on his mate.

36

THE ABORIGINAL encampment was outside the town at a railway bridge over the river. They had built hutments of rusty, holed galvanized iron, split petrol cans, packing cases, oddments of canvas. The aborigines drew a government ration, had no civil rights, worked at odd jobs in the town. Slumped in cast-off clothing, their totemic laws forgotten, the songs and legends of the dreamtime only remembered by very old men, the aborigines of the river towns lived like blowflies on the white man's trash heap.

Because they had always been there as an eyesore and trouble, the townspeople accepted the blacks as another environmental handicap, like the hills that interfered with everything. Their flat, flaring nostrils, the alien cliffs of their brows, the dark, muddied eyes that slithered away from meeting the whites' glances, the gray-black scaling of arm skin and leg skin, their hot, animal stench—all conspired to stifle pity or guilt. The Whites only remembered them when drink got into the camp through somebody's charity or profit —for then bloody battles were fought or white women frightened in the streets.

A charge of prejudice would have offended the river town citizens. In their egalitarian Australian way they wanted one man as good as another. But the blacks, you had to know them. You couldn't get through to the blacks. The Aborigines' Protection Board had a school for their children in a Quonset hut on the river. The truant officer was always chasing the children. He got no help from their parents, was baffled by the multiple tribal namings which made identification a puzzle. A child might attend the school for a month or a term, when he felt like it or was made to. Then his family would move to another camp, to cut cane, pick fruit, dig potatoes, until the old man got five or ten pounds in his pockets and came by a bottle of rum. You couldn't get through to the blacks. See how they live? Take a look at them. Animals wouldn't live like that. In the old days the pioneers used to bait them with poisoned flour. *They* couldn't do anything with them.

The sooner they die out the better . . .

Go and see how they live . . .

Try and get one to work. . . .

The town knew the Freedom Riders were coming. The editor of the Morelands *Echo* had been asked by a Sydney paper to telephone a story if anything violent occurred. There was uneasiness, and irritation. The men talked about it over their beers in the Returned Servicemen's Club, their open-necked shirts sticky with the heat. Observations were made in the shadowed billiard room where the proprietor took starting-price bets on the Sydney races and dribbled cigarette ash on his waistcoat. The young men reckoned that those flash city bastards could use a belt buckle in the teeth, and made dangerous faces for each other. Nobody thought much about the abos. The anger had other reasons.

"We don't try to tell them what to do. We pay our own way, mind our own business. What do we get in return?

Taxes to build more Sydney skyscrapers, criticism and low prices. It's enough to make a man do his block."

Morelands muttered itself to sleep that night, aggrieved and resentful, the jealousy of provincials. . . .

It was late when the Freedom Riders chose a motel and marched in. The night clerk was a dark Italian. He had been uncertain about Sunny Pintubi when the others presented him defiantly. The lobby was empty. There was no staff about to advise. The night clerk signed Sunny in. He was uneasy, but gave himself comfort. He had never heard of a blue-eyed aborigine.

The Freedom Riders sat on each other's beds, drank canned beer and talked about tomorrow. They planned to picket the Morelands swimming pool.

It was early morning when the old bus turned off the Sydney-Brisbane highway and made a rush at the hills that stockaded the town. The bush was full of singing, the slopes as dark as jungles with the growth of banana plantations. Like the dotted colors on a butterfly's wing, the green was shot with the red, blue, and yellow of the plastic bags that protected the hands of fruit from the calling birds. Weatherboard houses, painted in pastel shades, were front-stilted against the hillsides. Their windows glinted in the sunshine.

The bus felt its age, climbing the hills. It had already had one rebore too many. The young people shouted to help it along. The bearded driver concentrated, shifting down through the gears.

The big man in shorts and singlet, driving a heavy truck clamorous with milk cans, had made his pickups from the platforms outside the farm gates and was heading back to the railway. It was hot in the cab and he was sullen with hangover, sweat starting and running on his forehead. The old bus was straddled on the narrow road, grinding away at the hill. The truck driver held his hand flat on the horn, waited for the bus to pull over. Oily smoke blew in clouds against his windshield. He held the horn down, hardly hearing it himself over the banging milk cans and the roar of the bus. Cursing, he changed gears, pulled in behind the bus, hooting into its deafness. The bus ground on, keeping its snail's pace. There was a lot of hill up ahead.

In the truck, the driver silenced and hardened. He followed the bus, keeping its pace as though he were resigned. His lips whispered. The road widened toward the top of the hill. The truck driver had waited for it. He pulled out and slammed his foot down, collecting the next gear fast. With his offside wheels leaping and banging in the rough, the milk cans dinning behind him, he drew up with the bus, leaned across to shout curses. The bus windows were full of faces, looking back startled at his. Then he saw the Freedom Riders sign. He stared stupidly for an instant. This is what had kept him up late, drinking, talking about it at the club. His brawny, brown arms pulled on the wheel, his expert eye flicked ahead, judging. The bus had gone off the road as far as it dared. The bearded boy was fighting the wheel.

"Sort this bloody lot out among you." The truck driver had the lead of them now and pulled the heavy vehicle across the road. The bus went off the verge, crashing down saplings. In slow motion it rocked from one set of wheels to another, slid into a tree, metal crumpling, glass bursting, and stopped there tilted to one side.

Up ahead the truck driver slowed to look in his rear-vision mirror. His beefy face was pale. They hadn't gone over. It might be all right to hog the roads like that in Sydney. Still, a man had better have a bit of a story when he got into town. The truck driver didn't want any trouble with the police sergeant.

The manager of the swimming pool hurried out of the Town Hall and crossed the shady square. The few children in the water at this early hour were ordered out, into their clothes. The manager locked the mesh gates and hung up the POOL CLOSED FOR CLEANING sign. The Mayor, who was also undertaker, had brooded importantly before he made the decision. Nobody wanted trouble. The less these beatniks had to go on, the better.

The young people in the bus were tense and silent as they came within sight of the town. None of them had suffered more than a cut or a bruise, but they were still shocked from the violence of the accident. Sunny Pintubi's fists stiffened on his knees. They turned, winked and smiled, put their thumbs up for him. It would be harder for Sunny.

"Here they come, the bloody no-hopers."

One of the rowdies picked up a house brick, braced his legs in preparation.

"Here they come. Get ready."

The brick exploded so loudly on the bus's good side that the driver pushed for the brake. He thought a tire had blown. The bus was skidding to a stop in the dust that edged the asphalt when the smoothed river stones and knotted sticks

276

banged against the metal. They could see the men below them, laughing and shouting as they threw. The bus shot forward, pulled away. The rowdies scrambled up the slippery bank, their hands full. In front of them the students saw other heads appear above the road. As their tormentors stood up, the girl behind the driver shouted into his ear.

"Go for them, Chicker. Take a run at them."

In the banging, lurching bus, the driver accelerated, went into the dust, his nearside wheels risking the drop. The old vehicle clattered through the missiles as the outraged faces in the windshield plunged hurriedly back down the bank. In the sunken river delta, bemused figures picked themselves up among the thistles. The Freedom Riders were looking back, roaring with needed laughter, clapping the driver on the shoulder. He blew an insult on the horn.

The old bus had been to other towns north and south of Sydney. Little had happened. It was to be different in Morelands.

When the battered bus pulled into Central Square to send a deputation to the Town Hall, it was surrounded before the students could organize their placards. Tomatoes burst around the door as a committee member prepared to step out. As the mob built up, fired by the young men who had been humiliated an hour earlier, charges and countercharges were lost in the rising clamor. The bearded student was trying to draw attention to the crumpled metal where the bus had hit the tree. It was on the far side, away from the angry faces. Eggs began to burst with the tomatoes. The men in the bus dropped the placards and pushed to the door. Hands reached up for them, pulled them out. They went down, clubbed by punches, scrambled up, order forgotten, backed against the bus, swinging viciously. In the distant corner of the square, a constable and a sergeant sprinted out of the police station. The sight was too much for the shopkeepers and citizens who had kept their distance across the street. Men, women and children streamed toward the riot. The one black face backed against the bus was lost in the struggling. He tried to hit out, to lift his heavy arms. When had an aborigine struck a white man? The enemy aimed their punches at him. The police were pushing and clubbing through to the bus when Sunny struck his first blow. He looked into the man's eyes, measured him; his arm seemed to travel forever. The nose smashed. Sunny felt the bone grind and flatten against his knuckles. The bright blood spurted. The ruined face stared in disbelief at the black man.

The batons stopped it. The burly police clubbed impartially at heads and shoulders, stamping their heavy boots on feet and ankles, hooking with their elbows. Blood spattered the bus, the dusty cement, ran in the sweat on faces and chests. The students doctored each other, leaned gasping for breath against the bus.

"All right, who's the leader here?"

The medical student straightened.

"I am, Sergeant."

"Get all your blokes in a line. Get the girls into the bus." The sergeant studied the townsmen rounded up by the constable.

"I suppose you're proud of yourselves. There's going to be a few sorry faces when I sort this lot out."

When he turned to the Freedom Riders, the Crowd's attention went with him. The students had given as good as they got. The sergeant thought they had done well, for city boys. He was about to chase the black away when he noticed his good clothes, the way he stood resolutely with the others. The sergeant's face hardened. He pushed back the blue peaked cap on his balding head. This was something he wouldn't stand for—bringing in blacks to stir up trouble.

He said, heavy with policeman's menace, "This chap with you?"

"Yes," said the medical student.

The crowd began to edge closer, whispering to each other.

"You brought this man into town?"

"He's one of us."

Sunny stood still, his eyes over them at the hot blue sky above the pepper trees.

"You," the sergeant said. "What's your name?"

"My name is Sunny Pintubi." The voice was broadly Australian, but deeper, thicker, more sonorous.

The sergeant began to point his baton and stopped. "Sunny Pintubi? Are you *the* Sunny Pintubi?"

The medical student called, "There's only one of him, Sergeant."

At the sergeant's back their voices rose. Sunny Pintubi . . . I've seen him on the telly. . . . Who is it? . . . Sunny Pintubi. . . . That abo with them is Sunny Pintubi.

The sergeant scrubbed his cheek with the baton, uncertain for a moment. "Why does a man like you want to get mixed up in this?"

278

Sunny dropped his eyes to the sergeant. His soft voice carried on the waiting. "It looks as though someone should, doesn't it? That pack of dingoes didn't give us much of a go. It was five to one back there."

Somebody called, "Watch it, mate."

In his soft, carrying voice, Sunny said again, "You could have given us a fair go."

The sergeant snapped his cap down. "All right. Down to the station with the lot of you. Come on. Get moving. The rest of you, break it up. Clear out, or I'll have you all in the cells."

In his office the sergeant gave the Student Action leader a mug of strong tea. He had the facts of the matter. The battered bus was evidence enough.

"All right," he said, "you can take your deputation to the Major, but that's it. You're going to get yourself into proper trouble one day. If I were your dad, you'd get the point of my boot up your backside. Those girls you've got with you —the constable said one of them had to get her head stitched."

The student started to speak, but the sergeant put his hand up. "Don't propaganda me. If you knew how much trouble the police have out at the blacks' camp, you'd know you're barking up the wrong tree. I want all of you out of town in an hour."

He checked the tin alarm clock on the shelf.

"Now, I'm warning you. If you and your bus are here at midday, you'll think the bloody roof has fallen in."

The sergeant paused at the door. "Is that fellow really a Pintubi?"

"He was found in Pintubi country."

"I thought they only came across the Pintubi six or eight years ago."

"That's when they put the first patrols in."

"Something's funny there. He's got blue eyes."

"Yes. Nobody knows about that. He was only little when they found him."

The sergeant said, satisfied, "There are no blue-eyed blacks. That Sunny, he's got white blood somewhere. It sticks out a mile. You don't see them like him down at the camp."

They shook hands and the sergeant opened the door.

"You're doing the right thing, not bringing charges. It would only make bad feeling. Our lads don't mean any harm. Now remember, boy, I want to see the back end of that bus going up the road in an hour."

As the Freedom Riders stepped out, their cut faces bathed and taped, a group was collected under the peppers. Trays of tea and sandwiches had been sent from the cafés to the girls in the bus.

As the students marched across the square toward the Town Hall a boy ran up.

"Can I have Sunny's autograph?"

The police escort smiled and nodded. As they halted, other children who had watched ran up with books and pencils.

"Good on yer, Sunny," a loafer called.

Other voices rose.

"Bare it up 'em, Sunny."

"Good on yer, mate."

The student leader shook his head ruefully. "Would you believe it?" he asked the others. "There's no two ways about it, we're a weird mob."

The bus came down off the balding hills, twisted through miles of dark, exuberant green. The bellbirds tolled and hopped again on slopes spattered with colored plastic. Cabbage-tree palms and crimped ferns crowded in the pocketed hollows. Extravagant blossoms and passion-fruit vines clambered over doorways and carports. The breeze of the Pacific sharpened, drying the tackiness of cloth and skin. The sea shone and winked in glimpses. Green rollers curled and thumped into white spume that spilled up sandy inlets. In the battle-scarred bus the Freedom Riders dozed, the girls' heads on the men's shoulders. Sunny Pintubi's cheek was cushioned on a towel, his face turned to the broken window and the coastline.

Are they my people? I don't know them. They don't look like Arunta or Wailbri. They don't look like the old man who brought me in and died.

I remember you, ghostly old man, dead lizards tucked in your hair. I remember our lizard tucker. I remember other faces more ghostly yet than yours, old man of the lizards. Our country was as silent as the sea and I remember it. Our country was as wide as the sea, with spinifex sailing on it. I can taste the dark smoke of spinifex fires. There were waves like the sea, no-more-little-bit waves of sand, tall, longa sky, plenty-high too-much.

He wasn't my father or grandfather. Just an old man of my "skin," he told them. I rode on his back. There was a good place. We stayed there, found bushes with sweet flowers on them to suck.

Are they my people? Skin of a blue-eyed Pintubi? Long time ago that white man of mine been sit down with Pintubi skin.

"Don't use that blackfellow talk, Sunny. Remember, you're part white. You're years older than these other boys, mentally."

Father O'Malley.

None of us understood when he spoke about the cool, green place of Ireland. You never did get home, Father. Shade of dead men got no country. All-a-same level when dead. Heaven-talk-talk, rubbish fella.

"Sunny, speak properly. You want to make something of yourself, don't you?"

And Father Keen, smiling.

"This is Sunny Pintubi. We call him Father O'Malley's blue-eyed boy."

Grandfather or great-grandfather, the white man who haunted his life? He had been blue-eyed. There was nothing more of him. Just two blue eyes reflecting the sky.

"You've got good blood, Sunny. Always be proud of that. The men who pioneered this great wilderness with God's help were men of strength and courage. The saints be praised, your ancestor might have been an Irishman like me, riding to school on a cart in County Cork."

Father O'Malley had named him.

"See how he looks now, the little chap, with a few months of the good food in him. With those big blue eyes and a smile on his face that would set an Orangeman dancing. Sunny it is, and that will be his name. We will call him Sunny the Pintubi."

I don't know why I feel nothing. When I hit him his face broke up like rotten wood. His eyes couldn't believe. His eyes were blue, like mine. I've wanted to hit one, often enough. I don't know why I feel nothing.

Those kids with their autograph books.

Sometimes you can't make sense out of anything. . . .

37

THE RIOT at Moreland was reported in the press and on radio and television. Sunny Pintubi, the unknown mission boy who had beaten Britain's best, was being talked about everywhere again, his failures quite forgotten. Members of the clergy were moved to write letters to the editor and the Guild of Australian Writers issued a statement, as remarkable for its pomposity as for its ignorance, deploring the aborigines' condition. A prominent Labour politician referred to "Moreland's morons" in a speech, and praised Student Action. A prominent Liberal politician accused the Labour politician of exploiting the tragedy of civil strife, and a prominent Country party politician declared himself absent from home when his secretary announced that the press wished him to make a statement.

Mae Harcourt gave afternoon teas and called Sunny to be introduced when he had showered and changed from work. Big Jim Harcourt waited and listened, noncommittal about everything.

In all the months since Sunny's return from England, Harcourt had not given himself peace about the £3,500 which had slipped through their fingers. He had brooded about it as a loss. When the pain of that dulled with time he began to brood on it as a five-to-one bet. He forgot the figure of £3,500 and thought about £17,500, which troubled him much more than five times as badly. Charlie Gilmour had dismissed the bet as forgotten. Other Australian athletes had recorded times which Sunny could not hope to equal. An aborigine, in any case, would never get selection to represent Australia in the Olympics. But Harcourt had not forgotten. He had brooded on it and schemed on it and moved it about in his mind. He had felt a signal of instinct about the Freedom Ride. And congratulated himself on it now. Sunny was becoming a minor celebrity. Anything he did would attract special notice. The quick Australian response to the underdog that fights had weighed in on Sunny's side. Harcourt decided to break his silence with Sunny. He had not been seeing much of Gilmour and resolved to put that right. When he had worked it out a bit more he would have a word with Gus Drake.

They met at the Beach Hotel. The memory of his awful error had been harder on Gus that it had been on Harcourt. He could hardly take a drink without suffering a reaction.

"I'll get straight to the point, Gus," Harcourt told him.

Gus listened, his head bent, glancing from the side of his glasses.

"There it is, then. We go back to our original stake and use it to put Sunny into full-time training. The way I see it, the publicity he's getting just might give us the inside run."

"I've been thinking about that," Gus said, getting beady. "One of the 4-A nobs reckons Sunny should switch to a better club this season. He says he'd like to see an abo on the team."

"He said that?"

"Yeah. I've been feeling my way around a bit."

Harcourt got excited. "When was this?"

"A couple of months ago, at the football."

"Why didn't you let a man know? There could be seventeen and a half thousand quid in this."

"Don't wake it up," Gus said. He polished his glasses. "There's only one way to handle this, you know. We'd have to get Cerutty."

"Cerutty? You mean send Sunny to Melbourne?"

"There's no other way. We've got only a year. There's nobody in the world like Cerutty. If Cerutty will take him on, we've got a chance."

Harcourt looked sick. "We can't get Sunny to Melbourne. He's got this apprenticeship. He goes to night classes."

"Up the apprenticeship. Up the night classes," Gus said.

"But Charlie. Charlie would blow his bloody stack."

"Up Charlie," Gus said. He watched Harcourt.

The big man shook his head. "It's not on. We've got to work it some other way."

"There's no other way. It's Cerutty or nothing. I'll buy out Charlie's share."

Harcourt slowly turned and looked down on the little bookmaker. Gus shifted uncomfortably.

"No, you won't. If Charlie's out, I'm out."

"Seventeen thousand five hundred," Gus said.

Harcourt shook his head. "If Charlie's out, I'm out," he said softly.

Gus pushed his glasses. "You straighten things out with Gilmour. I'll look after the rest of it."

Harcourt drank silently until another thought struck him. "How about this altitude problem the papers have been writing about?"

"Cerutty has got an answer to that. He calls it tidal breathing. It's a way to use more of your lungs to get more oxygen aboard. It might mean a bit more pull with the selectors. Cerutty claims he can train his boys for height without taking them above sea level."

Harcourt thought again. "I don't know about this. But I'll give it a fly with Charlie."

"Seventeen thousand five hundred," Gus reminded him.

They had met on the day of enlistment and marked each

other for mates by those inescapable insights of judgment common only in war. They had survived the desert derbies and the Kokoda Trial and a lot of things worse and better, including twenty years of marrying and getting settled. Harcourt had not fathered because Mae was barren. Gilmour's wife had lost a son in childbirth and the next year Betty had needed a hysterectomy. Each in his own way shared Sunny as they had shared so much else, and each in his own way was bonded to him. Harcourt knew the best and worst of Gilmour, and Gilmour knew the best and worst of Harcourt, and they had learned it truly and all the way through. Each was stripped to that rare place where at last there is no pretense, peeled skin by skin like an onion. They were mates and they did not have to talk about it or think much about it either.

When Harcourt put the proposition to Gilmour, his usual confidence failing him, the two men came closer than they ever had been to splitting up forever.

The big man had flinched before the violence that had shaken the wiry body of Gilmour, whose eyes were suddenly as red as a ferret's in their sandy framing of lashes. Harcourt had seen Gilmour go like that and use the bayonet, and keep using the bayonet, when Mick Drew took his wound at Tobruk and fell and hooked on the wire.

Harcourt had left in a shaken rage of his own and got drunk at the R.S.L. Club.

Gus Drake telephoned the next week.

"It's all off," Harcourt said. "Charlie won't be in it. It's not fair to the boy."

"How about us?" Gus squeaked. "There's seventeen and a half thousand quid going begging."

"It's no good. Charlie won't be in it."

"But I've got Cerutty. I've been on the blower. He said he'd be interested to see how Sunny goes."

"It's all off."

"But listen here," Gus said.

Harcourt listened. "It's all off, Gus. I'm hanging up."

The Freedom Ride to Morelands and the shock of what had happened, the crashed bus, the violence, the white face that had buckled and smashed on his fist, the children crowding for his autograph under the pepper trees in the square, the cries of "Good on yer, Sunny" from the very loafers who had pelted them, changed Sunny Pintubi again. He was not alone now, and the explanations which had stayed misty and

284

distant while he struggled for them came faster and easier and often now out of the mouths of others.

He went to Mass because the local priest had called and the Catholic instruction which had been a dreamtime story like the Arunta myths he had heard, focused for him and assumed a meaning. The identity shaped by fragments, touched, came together and locked. A door knock to raise money for aboriginal welfare set an historic precedent. Sunny was wanted at the launching.

But everywhere and with everyone he was "Sunny Pintubi, you've heard of him, he won a big International in London." Or: "Oh, the runner. How are you, Sunny?"

When the athletic season opened and the sporting press speculated about the coming Olympics, Sunny Pintubi's name was hopefully mentioned as though the disappointments of the previous season had no consequence or had not occurred. Charlie Gilmour saw these reports and had a pang of uncertainty. He had gone up the wall about Harcourt's wanting to exploit the boy for money. He had got red-eyed and had not thought past that. He had never considered that Sunny could be Olympic material or what that could mean for better or worse if the likelihood truly existed. It stayed in his mind for weeks as a worry. Gilmour's tradesman's pride in Sunny, his own secret that one day Sunny might take over the factory, had become more of a self-indulgence that he himself understood.

Gilmour had other bothers that would never have occurred to Harcourt. All that had happened to Sunny was Gilmour's responsibility. It was becoming more than he could cope with. Sunny would still be at Mick Drew's or somewhere else, anyway on his own ground and among his own people, had Gilmour not let Harcourt talk him into bringing the boy south.

That had probably been the first mistake and it worried Gilmour as his own. Sunny still avoided the factory urinal; that was another worry. What kind of brand had the wild fellas put on him?

Mick Drew wrote sadly: "I don't know what to tell you, Charlie. You've given him a chance, that's all a man can do. He will have to work it out as best he can."

Sunny did work it out. He got there without anyone's help and was ready with it when Gilmour had to talk about his worry. The factory had closed.

"Wait on a bit, will you Sunny?" Gilmour had asked earlier. Now he punched a can of beer. For a week Sunny had been coming to work carrying his training gear in the flight bag he had saved. It was this that caused Gilmour to unburden.

"I see you've started training. I thought you had given that up."

"I almost did."

"Wouldn't you be better off spending the time with your books?"

"Yes, I would," Sunny said.

Gilmour put up his eyebrows. "Yes, you would? If you feel like that, what in the blazes are you doing it for?"

"It's hard to explain," Sunny said steadily.

Gilmour studied the bubbles that pushed out from the triangular hole in the beer can. "It's got to do with the Freedom Ride and all the rest of that, hasn't it?"

"Yes," Sunny said.

Gilmour turned his face away. "You've got to be an athlete because it isn't good enough just to be a tradesman, maybe even foreman here in the factory—that's it, isn't it?"

"Yes," Sunny said.

There was a silence between them.

"When I was a kid," Gilmour said, "there was pride in being a tradesman. The old dad was a fitter and turner."

"I'm going to be a tradesman," Sunny said, "but I've got to do this other thing too."

"You feel they'll pay you no attention, otherwise?"

"It's not only that, it's for me, too, Charlie."

Gilmour turned his back. "How do you mean?"

"It's for me, too. It's how I feel."

"I don't get you."

"It's the only way I can be as good. When they know it, I will know it, too."

When Gilmour was able he said, "Just a minute, I'm going for a leak."

He did not need a leak but when he came back he moved fast and his sandy eyes snapped.

"How would you like to really get stuck into this thing? Take a bloody year off down in Melbourne and train with Percy Cerutty? Cerutty has trained a whole stable of record breakers. We'll get our teeth into this and shake it to death. What do you bloody well say to that?"

Charlie Gilmour delivered Sunny Pintubi to the famous camp among the sand dunes and surf at Portsea. He had laid this down in his terms to Harcourt. Gilmour would deal with

286

Cerutty. When Cerutty was ready, the decision about Sunny would be made between him and Gilmour.

The decision came in a rush. A letter written in the vivid style that the coach-philosopher used in his books. It was characteristic that no attention was paid to Gilmour's possible opinions. Cerutty announced that he was not interested in developing Sunny as a miler or a middle-distance runner, and expected no further discussion about it. He said Sunny was born for the Marathon. He said that until Gilmour next heard from him he was not to write to Sunny or attempt to contact him in any way.

Charlie Gilmour telephoned Harcourt to meet him at the Beach Hotel. In delays at the traffic lights he read the letter again, clutching the typed sheets in one hand, steering with the other. It seemed to Gilmour that Sunny was getting beyond him again.

ROBERT SCHULTZ

Washington, D.C.

38

DOBSON HAD been right. Whit Monk had been led by the nose, by his own enthusiasm and Bueno's wishful thinking. Bob Schultz had made two incognito trips to Santa Anna. The Bureau's economic expert had spent six weeks there, checking progress against expenditures, accepting nobody's estimates. With the Olympic Games less than a year off, Operation Gold Medal was a mess.

Weight had dropped off Schultz; he was haggard with worry. He could not make himself divulge the facts to George Cole. The Bureau's Chief's confidence was too important to risk. If Cole took Operation Gold Medal away, it would end the status which had jumped Schultz over so many heads. He knew of Cole's private concern; there had been heart twinges mentioned in the confidences between them. If Cole took over the operation himself, that would be critical enough. If he handed it back to committee, in order to share the burden, there would not be a man who would lose the opportunity to see Schultz back at the bottom of the table.

In the secret papers across his desk there had been further alarms. Mathew C. Kaverly had made a tour of the Games sites, had immediately demanded an audience with Bueno and threatened a change of venue if the work was not accelerated. Whit Monk had passed on the information because he, too, was frightened now. Kaverly was bluffing of course, but if it reached the press, revived the quietened controversy, it could tumble the house of cards the operation had become.

The second piece of information furnished by Whit Monk concerned a study group sent urgently to Santa Anna by the Inter-American Development Bank. All his life Bob Schultz had been going somewhere, aiming, pushing, grinding. He allowed these reports and the truth of the position to lie in his locked safe while he sought some solution. The reports were dated. For days, in confusion, he tried to find an answer.

Now, if he presented the reports to Cole, with their "Urgent-Secret" codes and the old datelines, there could be no explanation of the delinquency. The patrician gray head would remain bent in the habit of rumination. When Cole looked up it would require no words: Bob Schultz would be finished in the State Department.

Dobson had said it: "You guys have backed the wrong horse in Santa Anna. Bueno hasn't the guts to handle this. He's an idealist. He has beautiful thoughts. What you need down there is somebody who will go in and bloody a few thousand heads."

He was at the end of the limb. It would break before it was sawed off. As is said to happen when a man drowns, Schultz saw the efforts of the past unreel. Shakily, he lifted the classified telephone.

"Dobson, this is Schultz. I want to talk about your third hat."

He got into Santa Anna on the late flight and was sped from the airport on the new road over which the collapsing taxis used to jar and bang. In the hotel, Schultz washed and lay on the bed after eating scrappily in his room. At 10:45 he left the side entrance and walked the darkened Avenida de España to the corner of Retiro Park. A taxi cruised toward the heights, turned, stopped. Schultz hesitated, then walked to the parked car. The part-Indian driver was lighting a cigarette.

Schultz said, "It's hot tonight."

"Sí. It's Bombay weather."

"I've never been there."

The driver reached an arm over the seat and pushed on the door handle. Schultz got in. The taxi turned again on the Avenida and squealed toward the old city.

The house was walled, in the colonial fashion, with broken bottles concreted into the top of the stones. The aged wrought-iron gates were rusted and crooked, needed support to be opened when the driver flashed his lights, illuminating a ruined drive and garden. The driver leaned back and opened the door again. Schultz got out and the taxi moved off, turned into the shrubbery and disappeared. Two ragged men sat smoking and talking softly on the wide cracked steps that mounted to an arched veranda and the dark outline of double doors. A match flared, lighting a dark face, was held and then shaken out. One of the men got up and knocked on the doors.

"This way, señor."

At the end of the hall another dark figure leaned and smoked, the tip of his cigarette beaming. He said nothing, reached behind him and knocked without moving his back from the wall. The door opened. The man hooked his head at Schultz to enter. Three men sat on cane chairs, bottles and glasses before them on a packing case. The boundaries of the room and the lofty ceiling were barely reached by the still, forked flames of the candles. Cigar smoke curled on the musty air, adding an aroma of present life to the heavy, sweet smell of decay.

"Permit me to introduce myself. Colonel García, at your service. May I have the honor to present General Maximilian Pisarro."

The man who had received Schultz was in uniform. A smallish figure in a Palm Beach suit rose from his cane chair and bowed. Lance Dobson rose beside him, nodded and gave Schultz a small smile.

"It is an honor, General."

"Welcome to Santa Anna, Mr. Schultz. You had a pleasant journey, I trust?"

The Colonel pushed a chair behind Schultz.

"Do be seated," Pisarro said. "Can we offer you a brandy?"

When Schultz had taken the chair, Pisarro stood until his aide had given Schultz a glass. When he sat back, the Colonel and Dobson followed.

Deliberately, Pisarro took a candle and placed it before him on the packing case. He looked over the flame and smiled. Because he had been a name more than a person, a symbol more than a name, Bob Schultz could not reconcile the neat, big-nosed face and watchful, dark eyes with the figure whose threat and ambitions had been the cause of all that had happened. A sense of absurdity overwhelmed him. It was as though the past years had been an idiot's game, a mad exercise in notions. What true concern did any of them have with the tedious conflicts of this shabby republic? Schultz neither knew nor cared. He had woven the web like a spider and been trapped in it like a fly.

The beaky face with the still eyes continued to smile over the candle. "How can I help you, Mr. Schultz?"

He couldn't phrase an answer; he was marooned by the candlelight, by this sense of unreality. They waited.

The words were clumsy, not what he had intended: "Inter-American Development Bank is concerned about the corruption down here."

He noticed Dobson wince, the flicker in Colonel García's eyes.

Pisarro was unperturbed. "Ah! Corruption. The South American vice. Are you sure you understand the nature of corruption?"

"We are sure about the loss of millions of dollars, General."

"Granted, granted." The General held up the flat of his small, dark hand. "Permit me to ask you a question. A man enters the Ésmeralda Hotel and finds a wallet containing ten thousand pesos on his chair. What does he do with it, hand it to the desk clerk?"

"Ideally, yes."

"Ah! But if he does that the desk clerk will keep it. The police, perhaps? Ah, but if he hands it to the police, they will keep it. No, Mr. Schultz. If our man is sensible, he will put the wallet in his pocket and hurry home. Let me ask you, what is the man guilty of?"

"Corruption," Schultz said reluctantly.

"No. He is guilty of being lucky."

"And the man who lost the wallet?"

"Ah! He is guilty of being unlucky." Pisarro lit a thin, black cigar. "Do you follow me?"

Schultz stiffened and glanced at Dobson.

"Only the rich can afford to be honest, Mr. Schultz. Santa Anna is a poor country. An American, now, if he is poor, has the hope of being rich one day. Here there is no such hope for the many. Work is a luxury. If one man offers another the luxury of work, he expects something in the way of gratitude. You see, in a country where corruption is the custom, it is merely a custom and no longer corruption. Do you follow? What *you* call corruption, we know as gratitude."

"Are you telling me, General, that there is nothing that can be done about the wastage of money down here?"

Pisarro held up the flat of his hand. "If a father gives his child pesos to go to the market and buy bricks, is the child to be blamed for buying melons? Of course not. The father was once a child himself." The beaky face continued to smile.

Schultz had not come to Santa Anna for this. Pisarro's analogies confused him. "Santa Anna fathers don't trust their children?"

"Ah! Now you follow." Pisarro leaned back, pleased. "If you want bricks, not melons, you supervise. My people need

291

supervision. The strong, Mr. Schultz, supervise the weak to spare them the consequence of their folly."

The three men watched Schultz. Dobson caught his eye and nodded.

"And you can provide this supervision, General?"

"Yes. I can provide the supervision. The accident of the Olympic Games coming to Santa Anna." The General smiled. "This accident, as I call it, can revolutionize our economy. Draconian measures are no longer necessary. You follow? It is important that you should follow me on this."

Schultz was forward on his chair. He had forgotten the oddity of the meeting place, the tubbed candles, the crumbling mansion.

"How would you arrange this supervision?"

"I have the Army, Mr. Schultz. On every building site, a squad of soldiers. Beside every contractor, an officer. On every specification, an Army engineer."

There was no other way. Relief flooded out fear. Dobson would confirm his judgment. The Bureau had not failed Bueno; Bueno had failed the Bureau.

"And the President?"

"The President is in poor health. He suffers from nervous exhaustion. The President could be relieved of his burdens, perhaps accept the chair of the Games Organizing Committee. This great building program could be President Bueno's monument. He would bring the office great distinction."

One last worry had to be nailed. "General Pisarro, there can be no question of violence. The Olympic Games will put Santa Anna in the spotlight of world attention. Any incident, however small, would be disastrous to all our interests."

Pisarro examined the cigar wisping in his womanish fingers. "Ah! You need have no fear. I have already pledged my word to Mr. Dobson. To achieve the ends we all desire, only one guarantee is necessary. This is in your hands, Mr. Schultz."

"What is the guarantee, General?"

"A simple guarantee of noninterference."

"That is all?"

"That is all."

Schultz lifted his untouched glass and sipped the sweet, strong brandy. The beaky face watched him; the eyes, which had been unmoving, were alive and shining now.

"I think I can get you such a guarantee."

"Ahhhh!"

Pisarro's head, with its cropped, dark hair, tipped forward.

292

His pointed chin fell for a moment on his chest. Colonel García breathed noisily, scraping his feet, his gaze stretched at the General.

Pisarro roused. In an instant he had swept up his glass and stood upright. "Permit me to propose a toast."

They rose, poising their drinks.

"To friendship."

"To friendship," Colonel García seconded.

"To friendship," Schultz said.

Pisarro looked over his glass. "Yes," he said, "to friendship. You take my meaning, Mr. Schultz."

George Cole kept notes from his reading. At Bureau conferences he often prefaced his expressed judgments with a quotation that had taken his interest. "The difference between man and animals is that man has learned to anticipate" was an aphorism that particularly pleased him. He used it as a reproof when he thought a proposal shortsighted.

In the months following his secret meeting with Pisarro, Bob Schultz hand-printed the quote and pasted it in his personal file. There would be a reckoning, and soon. To win it he must anticipate every move that George Cole might make. He must get possession of every fact. There must not be a crack or a fault in the structure that might allow his chief grounds to fight. Deliberately, Bob Schultz suppressed sentiment. He reminded himself that Cole was spent, time-serving before retirement, that he carried his fear of death with him like a weight to be lifted each day.

Paper by paper, report by report, Schultz manufactured the ruin of George Cole's hopes for Santa Anna. There were no second prizes in politics. Bueno had failed the test of the unrelenting reality of power. There would be no second prize for Schultz if the Inter-American Development Bank closed its books on Santa Anna. Aiming, pushing, grinding, anticipating it all, Bob Schultz and Lance Dobson built their case.

On an agreed Monday, the CIA status report on Santa Anna went to the head of Inter-Americas. The Development Bank study was put into circulation. On the Friday before that Monday, Bob Schultz had taken six weeks' leave and had been warmly advised by Cole to be sure to have a good rest. He had handed his own personal file to Cole's secretary before leaving, against the chance of its being required. He explained that he would have no forwarding address—he had planned a touring holiday—but would check back from time to time.

Schultz waited an agonizing two weeks. He had gone to stay with his parents. When he telephoned, Cole's secretary told him that there was serious trouble about something. There had been all kinds of upstairs meetings with the heads of Inter-Americas' bureaus. She was sure that Mr. Cole would want to speak to Schultz immediately. He waited in the call box, eyes shut, sweat greasing on his forehead.

The voice was small and puzzled when it came. "Are you there? Mr. Cole said it won't be necessary to bother you."

George Cole forced himself to control the emotion which constricted his chest, filling his veins with fear. The pillbox was open beside him. He sat in the big swivel chair, his head tipped, eyes shut, awaiting and demanding calm. Until these last moments, until the Secretary of State had himself telephoned to make it official, George Cole had believed that his authority and influence must prevail. The bitterness of shock wrenched him. The Secretary had meant to comfort him, recalling shared struggles, taking the trouble to ease his friend, to lessen his sense of defeat by persuasion.

The defeat could not be lessened. It was his and it was merited. He had betrayed the good man, Bueno. The bitter estimate of his own failure was an unendurable reproach. It had been in his hands; he had let it go out of the craven fear of the pains that mocked at his hunger to live. He had failed Bueno and failed the integrity that had been his sternest pride.

Cole opened his eyes and steadied the room, sucked in his breath to relieve the pressure. He had no anger for Schultz, for the contriving he now understood. He pitied Schultz for his lack of moral fiber, the self-interest and perhaps the fear that had driven him into expediency. He had no anger for Schultz because self-interest and fear had become faults in himself. They had conspired in an operation and justified it to secure what Bueno stood for. The operation had changed from a means to an end. To secure the end Pisarro had been justified as the means. Cole closed his eyes again. He was weighted by an unspeakable tiredness. It was over now. Tomorrow he would prepare his resignation, a last futile sop to honor. His wife was having a birthday. It would be a present she would never have dared to hope for. They would move to San Francisco. Get a house near his daughter and her husband. He could see his grandson every day, as long as he lived.

HARRY HAYES

United Kingdom

39

THREE WEEKS after Bill Persons had blundered down the echoing Crystal Palace tunnel and pushed wordlessly past the girl waiting in the dark, Harry Hayes and Mary Charlton were married.

Gabby had found a spacious flat in Hampstead and had rented it for a couple of months in Mary's name. It was a pathetic stratagem. Using the address qualified Mary as a resident. They could be married in the Registry Office there; nobody in Royal Park need know. Harry arranged to take his holidays. After the ceremony they would honeymoon in the flat.

"Who did you have in mind for a best man?" Gabby waited anxiously. It could not be anybody she knew.

There was only one best man for Harry. But that man had not even answered his letters. He frowned, realizing now how solitary he had been in the full world he shared with Persons.

"I don't really know anybody I could ask."

"Oh come, you must know somebody who's been close to you."

The loneliness he tried to submerge came up. "No."

"There must be somebody you've met in athletics. Outside Royal Park, I mean."

"No. You can't make friends with the men you try to beat. Bill taught me that."

Gabby quickly changed the subject.

"There's Alec McBride," Harry said.

"Oh? Who is he?"

"A reporter. A friend of Bill's."

"There you are. I knew there must be somebody."

McBride sat in his corner of the Fleet Street pub and glanced through the evening paper. He had not seen Harry's failure at the Crystal Palace, had been in bed with a cold, although Bill Persons had invited him to share the victory dinner he had arranged. McBride still had the cold, was drinking rum for it and blowing his crumpled nose. He got up almost nervously when Harry Hayes came in.

"You didn't get lost, then? What will you have?" He pulled up another stool. "Sorry I was a bit short on the phone. I was late with my copy. . . . I'd like you to meet Harry Hayes," he told the barman. Other pressmen recognized Harry, drew his attention to nod.

They settled, awkward with each other.

"How is old Bill?" McBride asked. "Still as wild as ever?"

"I haven't seen him for a while."

"Oh?" McBride showed his surprise.

"I'm getting married, Alec."

"What's that? Married?"

"I need your help. I need your help with Bill. This isn't going to be easy, but if you'll listen I'd like to tell you all of it." Harry's voice was shaky.

McBride looked disturbed. "Bring your drink upstairs. There are too many long ears down here."

The registrar was late, although he had given Gabby an appointment. They sat on a hard bench in what once had been the hallway of the old converted house. Alec McBride was dressed with painful care, a new suit draping his big, awkward bones. He tried to be gay for the young people's sake, and for Gabby Charlton's. Gabby was obviously nervous in the austere institutional atmosphere so heartbreakingly different from the ceremonial pomp of the big church wedding she had always planned. She fluttered her hands over Mary's corsage, laughing gallantly to conceal the discomfiture she felt.

The assistant registrar beckoned them in from the odor of pine disinfectant in the hall. The room was big and shady. An oak desk with two chairs before it stood against a window letting on to a small garden. There were fresh flowers on the desk. The room was bare of decoration or paintings. Six chairs lined the far wall. A sign read: ACCORDING TO THE LAWS OF THE COUNTRY, MARRIAGE IS A BOND ENTERED INTO BY A MAN AND WOMAN FOR LIFE TO THE EXCLUSION OF ALL OTHERS. The words remained on Harry's eyes as the registrar led them through the brief ceremony. As the binding documents were signed and blotted, the marriage certificate handed to Mary with the heavy joke that she would take better care of it, the words of the notice remained in Harry's mind. He felt himself to be falling, in the pattern of a dream he used to have in childhood. There was no fear. Just a long, gray, tumbling fall toward something unknown. He kissed Mary, kissed Gabby, was gripped by Alec McBride's hairy hand, heard his own voice and laughter, the registrar's dutiful congratulations, and through it all he was falling softly.

He could drink no more champagne. McBride noticed. Gabby and Mary kissed tearfully. McBride called the car and saw them into it, asked Harry to check for the flat key as Gabby had asked him to do. The big car pulled away into Regent Street. McBride stood for a time, needing the air, his friendly broken-nosed face lit by the brilliant colors of the restaurant's neon.

Even Gabby's finery seemed wilted when he got back to the table. The smile she had worn since morning was still frozen on her face, but she was exhausted by the daylong effort. When she looked up, her eyes were tipsy but she tried again for McBride.

"Well, there goes one small daughter. Have you any children, Alec?"

"I've never married."

McBride lifted the bottle from the champagne bucket and decided against it. He signaled the waiter.

"A large whisky soda." He considered Gabby. "Will you join me?"

"I'm silly enough as it is," Gabby said with a laugh.

"It will do you good. We may as well be tight as the way we are."

"A small brandy, then, with ginger ale."

While the waiter served Gabby, McBride downed his drink and ordered another. He stared about the chattering restaurant with dislike.

Gabby put a hand on McBride's arm. "I do appreciate your support today. Have you known Harry long?"

"A few years. Bill Persons is a friend of mine."

"That man. He sounds awful."

McBride looked hard at Gabby. "What do you know about him?"

"Nothing. And the less the better, thank you. Mary seems terrified of him."

"Bill Persons is a great man. If anything comes between him and Hayes, it will be a tragedy."

"Oh, come," Gabby teased. "You can't mean that. He's only a little coach or something."

McBride shook his head sadly, called the waiter and ordered more whisky.

"Persons and Hayes could be the greatest athletic team in the world. They're not like us. They're bloody mystics. They go out there and challenge mortality. Hayes can be great. If anything gets in the way it will kill him. They're not like us," he said again.

McBride waved for service.

"You're an attractive, competent, courageous woman."

"Thank you, sir."

"You know what you need, don't you?" McBride told her, drunkenly, sadly.

Gabby Charlton gasped. Her eyes snapped wide with shock. She had not heard the word for twenty years. Suddenly her thoughts jolted to Mary. A thrill went through her body. She knew she should slap the sad face that now smiled at her gently. She knew she should rise and sweep out. She knew she should say or do something. She could not get her breath.

"I had a funny feeling when we met. I was trying to place you. It came to me a few hours ago. You're Mark Charlton's wife."

Gabby found her voice. "How on earth did you know that?"

"We actually met a few times, when the world was gay, at press parties. Mark used to keep a photograph of you on his desk. I was his sports editor on the old *Chronicle*."

Gabby had both hands on the table, surprised out of the shock that had burned her cheeks. "Good lord. What an extraordinary thing. How would you remember?"

"You were very beautiful. Besides, I never forget anything. It's a great handicap." McBride took a drink. "I'm a Celt, you know. I see things. I see trouble for those kids. It makes me sad. I often get sad. When I get sad I drink big drinks. Tell you something else. When I drink big sad drinks I sometimes get angry and hit people." He sprawled a hand over his crumpled nose. "That's how I got this. Hayes could be great. They're not like us. If you're naughty to that boy, if you stand in his light, I'll have to come down to Royal Park and spank you."

Gabby's breath went out. She could not even summon up a sense of outrage to help her. She could only sit and stare.

"Where was I?" McBride asked. "Ah, yes. The reason I get sad is that I feel for people. It's a great handicap, like not forgetting things. You need company tonight. If you like you

298

can come back to my place and I'll make us some coffee."
He waited. "Well?"

Gabby felt faint. She had drunk too much. The din of the
orchestra hurt in her head. "Where do you live?"

"Jermyn Street. I've got an attic in the millionaire belt."

Gabby gave up trying to think. "Would you continue to
drink there?"

"On my own, yes. With you, coffee if you prefer it."

"In that case," Gabby said, reaching for her things, "it
would be an act of mercy."

Gabby had arranged the honeymoon flat on the previous
day, had decorated the rooms with flowers. Her radio had
played softly through the long wait, had startled Harry when
he opened the door while they looked in, as shyly as if they
had no right there. Mary hurried through, found a refrigerator ready with food, peeped at the bedroom and came away,
her breath fast.

"Well, here we are."

Harry could think of nothing to say. He sat down and
loosened his tie, pressing fingers on his forehead.

Anxiously, Mary asked, "Have you a headache?"

"No, it's not that. I think I'm drunk, Mary."

"Poor Gabby. She has tried so terribly hard."

He looked up at the catch in her voice, rose to embrace
her to give them both comfort.

"Would you like something? Shall I make coffee?"

"I couldn't drink another thing. I feel as though I've run
the Marathon. Everything is a bit topsy-turvy."

"Perhaps you should go to bed," Mary suggested, her face
pressed on his chest so he could not see it.

Afterwards she lay in the dark, her eyes wide-open, a hand
on her filled, bare breasts, her body stiff, and fought the disappointment and the edge of fear. It was the strangeness, the excitement; it would be better next time. She put
her hand out to where Harry had partly turned away, felt his
cheek. Shaking, she brought back her hand and touching the
fingers to her tongue, tasted the salt. She took him and held
him, her lips on his ear.

"It will be all right, darling. I understand. Really and truly
I do. It'll be all right. It won't change anything. Believe me, it
will be all right."

Alone again, and more alone for being husband and wife,
with a bed to share and a flat for Mary to play at housekeep-

ing in, they grew in understanding. Mary's eyes were seldom shadowed in that time. Harry let his idleness soak him, the fierce tensions of body and will washed out in an almost mindless intoxication. He watched like a painter for intimate glimpses as Mary dressed and undressed. For the scooped, speckled shell of armpit as she stretched overhead, the hardening profile of tipped breasts, the thighs that were sometimes covered with gooseflesh in the chill of morning, the absorption with which she polished her long, fair curtain of hair. Even the lace stuff of Mary's underclothing held discoveries to be made, like the perfume bottles and the jars set out with brushes, pins and jewelry on the glass-topped dressing table. Harry blanked his mind to the softly swelling belly that was the cause of all that had happened. It was a confusion to him. He put it aside. That would be resolved when he was back again with Persons.

Mary's happiness, because of the growing mother in her that grew with the growing child, was lost on Harry. The weeks passed. Alec McBride came to dinner. Gabby Charlton often telephoned and tried to space her visits.

In the last week Harry returned to his work. It was like the middle of night to Mary when the alarm woke them early enough to get him in time to the dairy. She would return to bed, fretful and lonely, to wake again at the normal hour to the suddenly desolate flat. Before the week ended, Harry was broken out of his forgetful peace, jogging again with the swinging milk basket, timing himself to the clock that ticked away in his mind. The milk round had been more than a job; it was a planned addition to his training, a part of the purpose between him and Bill Persons. "Yer dad was that keen yer should have a trade, Harry." He had chosen his trade when he resigned his apprenticeship and sought to explain to his mother. His trade was to go where other men had not ventured, to run over the top of the world. Each day as he ran through the waiting streets, the need to be committed pressed inside him. He knew why he had failed at the Crystal Palace. That was over now; it could not happen again. Bill would listen to Alex McBride; he was just having one of his tempers. The Swedish tour was not far away. He would have to get back to the track, get back to work, be ready for Bill when the time came.

They moved into Gabby Charlton's house and it was still all unreal to Harry. He let it happen to him because there were no handholds he could grip. He let it happen to him because it was an abeyance, a painless gray tumbling fall that the man in the tweed hat alone would stop.

Harry set himself the grinding schedule on which he had prepared for the International. The old difficulty of tensing neck muscles returned. He invoked Bill Persons: "Drive with your arms. Keep your head aligned straight on the spine. Don't stamp holes in the track. You stretch and you float, lad. You stretch and you float." He kept Bill at his shoulder as he ran, pale eyes encouraging him. But there was no word from the farm, no answer to his notes. The telephone did not answer when he called to hear the other man's voice.

Six weeks before the date of the Swedish tour, Harry Hayes began to feel panic. The secretary brought him his mail as he left the Club on a Friday. Harry had continued to forward his mail, unopened, to Bill Persons. But this day the Swedish stamp and the crest of the Athletic Association caught his attention. On a nervous impulse he opened the envelope. The letter said that advice about the tour's cancelation had been received from Mr. W. Persons. The Association greatly regretted the need and hoped that Mr. Hayes would regard the invitation as open for the following summer. Harry could hardly walk to the gate. He was trembling as though he had a fever.

Alec McBride had waited again in his accustomed corner, gloomily drawing patterns in a wet patch on the bar. He looked at Harry.

"You'd better have a stiff drink."

"No. I'm training."

"It will do you more good than harm," McBride said, and ordered two large whiskies.

When he had read the letter he handed it back and sighed.

"He can't mean it, Alec. Surely he can't mean it. We were working for the Olympics. That's what everything has been about. He can't mean it. Bill wants it as much as I do—more, perhaps. Alec, you've got to talk to him. He will listen to you."

McBride sighed again and drew with his finger on the bar. "I did go to see him. I didn't want to tell you."

"You did? What did he say? What happened?"

"Harry, he just went off his head. I couldn't talk to him. You know what Bill's like."

Harry slumped on the stool. "Why? That's what I don't understand. Why? He had a right to be upset, but I've written and explained all that. He can't just walk away from all we've worked for, everything he believes in. What did he want me to do? Leave Mary to have the baby on her own?"

McBride said softly, "He's a strange man, Harry. A strange and terrible man in some ways. Did he ever talk to you about the war?"

"Not much. Why?"

"It doesn't matter. I can't speak for Bill, but from what I know of him, I think he feels betrayed. Not personally, perhaps, but for the idea you had between you. I think he might feel that you've betrayed the idea and that would mean more to him than anything he might feel personally. You know what I mean?"

White-faced, his voice firm, Harry said, "I betrayed nothing. For a little while I was ordinary and human. Is that unforgivable?"

"No," McBride said. "I wouldn't think so. He probably misses you as much as you miss him. He loves you, you know. But there's something else you should take into account. You and Bill were reaching for the moon. A thing like that—there's no room for anything else. Perhaps you can be a father and do it. I don't think you can do it and be a husband."

Because he knew what McBride meant, had known it without being told, Harry was bitter.

"You mean that sex thing?"

"Not just the sex thing, the whole involvement. I've been round the great ones for twenty years, trying to understand them. They're not like us." McBride stopped and looked comic. "I mean they're not like ordinary people. You know that. You're one of them."

Harry shifted uncomfortably.

"Yes you are . . . I don't make mistakes about these things. I've known all the great ones since Nurmi. I've seen them marry and fail. Do you want me to name names?"

Harry shook his head, staring before him.

"Some of these cyclists, they're so afraid of a wet dream they wear a cotton reel to bed, tied round them on a string, to keep them from sleeping on their backs. That is probably superstition. The point is, they believe it matters. It takes everything, Harry. You are not going to have everything to give it."

"Yes, I am."

McBride lifted his eyes to the passionate voice, studied the dark, determined profile. "And Mary? It's not in a woman's nature to understand these things. She's only a bit of a girl. What kind of life will she have widowed to a living husband? It's another world, Harry. When you go in, you go in alone."

"I wasn't alone with Bill."

"No," McBride said, "but Bill has been there. Bill went in during the war. It's been his country ever since."

They sat silently for a long time.

Harry stood up. "I've had enough of this. I'm going to go to the farm and have it out. One way or another, Alec—with Bill or without him—I'm going to run them down at Santa Anna."

He had left his drink untouched. McBride reached for it. He drank it thoughtfully and ordered another. He had got it said and was glad for it. Harry had known; he had known all the time.

"They're not like us."

"What's that, Mr. McBride?" the barman asked.

"I was just saying it's a fucked-up world," McBride answered and pushed his glass over the bar.

Harry walked to the farm from the station. There was sunshine, as there had been on that first day. The stubbled fields smelled hot. A hare got up and ran. He had missed it all more than he had known. He had no apprehension. He would let Bill rant himself out. His own strength and his own need would be all the argument he needed.

There was no car there. The tank with the opening cut for the aircraft door had grass growing long against its sides. The old cottage sparkled in its white paint but the windows were dead and drawn. A tarpaulin near the tank covered something bulky. Harry lifted an edge pegged down with bricks. Under it was the pump from the submarine—the lung for the mountain, as Bill had called it. He hammered on the heavy oak door compulsively and listened to the echoes. The borders of the kitchen garden, which was always so neat, were full of weeds. In rising agitation Harry prowled the house until he could bear it no longer. He began to run, up from the house to the tractor shed on the hill, past the brier hedges and over the flints, back to the village on the circuit where he had first followed Persons. He ran in slippery-heeled shoes, pulling off his tie. . . .

As the summer wore on and Mary thickened, Harry ran twice with the Club. He ran against the Cyrstal Palace mark that Bill had set. It had been there. On the Club track, before the International, alone with Bill in the last moments of twilight, he had gone up and touched it, known he could go through, had backed off in peace and let it be. He had to have it now, not only for himself. Wherever he was, Bill would hear about it. But although he pushed through the four-minute wall, it was harder than it had ever been. The distress which Bill's snapping eyes and smile immediately eased away remained with him after he had left the track. All this will and all his effort only pushed the mark farther away.

The wonder he had taken in Mary's hot secrets, the glimpse in which he had delighted, gave him no pleasure now. As he waited in the bed for the darkness and Mary made her slow toilet, he held a book before his eyes to block out her straining belly. Mary tried to understand, her own moods suspended on Harry's. But he moved away from her under the covers. In the dark she could sense his sleeplessness, although the tall, remote body lay quiet.

Harry Hayes lost his title to a young Oxford runner at the championships that year. That clinched it for Gabby. It ended the talk of greatness which McBride had tried to push down her throat. She was free in her conscience now. In pride and excitement Mary had sat with her mother to watch the championships on television. It had been Harry's wish that she not join Len Sparks and Liz in the party that went up from the Club. Gabby had approved. She had said that the awful crush was not suitable for a girl in Mary's condition. After the race, dumbly pale, Mary had made no comment. Gabby had turned off the set and hurriedly suggested tea. Mary had gone to her room.

She could not see his face; his dark head was bent to the driver when the slam of the taxi's door drew Gabby's attention to the window. She heard him in the hall and on the stairs, heard the click of the bedroom latch. She frowned when she heard their muffled voices. The walls of the house were thick; it was unusual for sounds to carry. The voices went on and stopped, waited and went on again. Gabby hurried to the stairs to listen. Mary was weeping, a high uncontrolled sobbing, as desolate as a keening. She heard Harry's voice loud as she dashed up the stairs and rattled on the locked door. The crying rose more helplessly.

Gabby rattled harder, struck the paneling with her fist. "Open this door. Open this door!"

Mary was telling her to go away, in sobs that swallowed the words. Gabby beat harder.

The door jerked open. Harry hit Gabby with his shoulder

as he pushed past, spinning her hard against the wall. Mary was standing, shaking, her face in a corner, like a small child being punished.

They sat on the bed while Gabby tried to rock the stiff, stricken body of her daughter, pulling at the hands which would not be pulled from their spread over her streaming face.

"What did he say? What did he do? Darling, tell me what happened."

"It's me. It's me. He hates me."

"What nonsense. Come now, control yourself."

Hysterically, Mary pressed her hand on the swelling at her waist. "This is what he hates. My baby. He says this is why he can't run. He says this is why he's one of the nothing-men now. He said I've taken it all from him and have it in here, that all his strength is here in my disgusting belly."

"My God. He said that?"

"What can I do? He hates me. It's my fault. I don't want this baby. I've got to get rid of it. You've got to help me get rid of it."

"Oh, my God, my God."

Sick and lost and horrified, suddenly lined and gray, Gabby Charlton sat rocking her hysterically sobbing daughter.

In his despair, the cracked stuff of his life littered on his mind like the smoking remains of an explosion, Harry Hayes wanted only to be free of that house. He ran, his feet treading nothing, toward hopes that narrowed and receded, screeching into foggy limbo. He was well beyond Gillsham when he came to himself, on a hill of houses that overlooked the motley spread of South London. His legs wobbled. There was a red bus shelter on a corner where couples talked softly and waited. He sat on the hard seat against the wall, breathing lightly to calm himself. The bus came, the shelter emptied. Other travelers waited or alighted. Other buses stopped, lit up now, the conductors swinging on the platforms. It was dark when he rose and walked again, topped Royal Park and went down the hill toward the industrial suburb. It had no meaning, but because his feet knew the way, he was back in the long depressing street. The yellow tub in which his mother had watered flowers still stood in its place in the basement courtyard. Harry went on, to the crowded shops and the bustling main road into London. Cards on glass-fronted notice boards, printed and smudged with ink, advertised bedsitters, bed and breakfast, rooms with use of kitchen, models available for private photography, secondhand prams, massage, lonely-hearts clubs. He could not go back. He had to have a place to lie down. Somewhere to be alone in, where he could lie down and sleep forever.

For a night and a day Harry Hayes slept, dreamed and woke in the poky room suspiciously let to him. On the second day he bought a clean shirt and a razor and shaved the dark, stubbly beard. That afternoon he called the dairy, apologized for his absence and resigned. He was certain now, and clear-headed, had mapped a new life for himself and Mary on the stained ceiling of the rented room.

There were six bright little apartments in the new development set back from plots that struggled to be green. Town houses, the agent had called the jerry-built dwellings that were accelerating toward their slum destiny before the smell of new plaster and paint dried on the prefabricated walls. Harry signed the lease and paid the deposit with money he had drawn from his savings. It left him with enough to get settled and the little place was partly furnished. It would see him over until he took one of the job offers Bill had tossed into the farmhouse fire. For the first time in months, some of Harry's peace returned. He felt the power of command again, as he did when the world shuddered and bent before his will on the track.

Nervously and sternly, because he was ashamed, he waited in the telephone box with his thumb pressed on the button. He heard her voice and dropped the pennies.

"Mary? No, I'm all right. No, I've just been doing things. There's nothing to worry about. I've got a surprise for you. I want you to come to this address. . . ."

In the next few days Mary moved in, over Gabby's protests. She drove herself over in the little red car with her hand baggage, and linen and towels reluctantly provided by Gabby. Awkwardly, they settled to arranging the new place around them. Harry wrote letters and waited anxiously for the postman. Alone again, with difficulty because of unspoken things, still hardly touching in the new bed beside the upstairs window, they tried to grow back together. Mary's aching uncertainty, her mute need, troubled the severity Harry could not put away. He wanted to comfort her, forget everything, wash the hurt from her eyes. Compassion would rise up, disorganized, like broken lumps in his throat, but when he tried to speak, something older and truer stopped the words on his lips.

He was still Harry Hayes. Even in defeat, he had a name and a reputation. An ethical drug house that had approached him in the past was glad to appoint him to the Promotion Department. It was a relief to him to have a job settled. The pay was more than he had ever thought to earn because he had not thought before about jobs. The male pride in which he returned home was lit by the warmth of his interview. He bought a bottle of the German wine that Persons favored.

"I've got it. Start on Monday. Twelve fifty a year."

Because he could not help it, because her face was so vivid, he curled her into his arms.

Softened by the wine, uncaring now, he lay in bed and watched her undress. There would be another summer. He would train at night. It would be hard, but it had always been hard. Mary's face on the pillow was turned toward his, the fine blond hair striping her cheek. He touched his hand to her belly, held it there, the fingers spread. Her eyes widened at him. A streetlamp shot gleams on the bed. He leaned and kissed her, feeling the long, curved underlip tremble. She did not move. When he lay back, her widened eyes still searched him.

"Harry. The baby. Did you mean what you said? Will it be all right about the baby?"

"Yes, it will be all right. Everything is all right now."

"I've got to know. I can't wait. It's getting big inside me."

"I want it. It will be all right."

Her face did not change but she closed her eyes; tears squeezed under the lids. She began to shake. He propped himself up, the need to comfort her welling over now.

"No. Don't say anything. Don't say anything you might regret."

He had not been able to give her comfort before, and now he needed to, for his own sake. She held him away until her tremor stilled, opened her eyes in her own time. He humped against her, pulling at the nightdress, pushing at her with his hand. Mary gasped, her head jerked back as though he had knifed her. Frantically, she turned and pulled him into her arms.

By the end of that summer, names Harry Hayes had never heard had shredded with their spikes the records which a year before the world had thought unbeatable. In America, Australia, France and Africa, a new breed was running into history. The thing which had been his, his and Bill's, had fragmented and distributed itself into the possession of others.

Through the cold, wet days, in the dark after work, on the drenched cinders of the Royal Park Club, Harry Hayes ran race after race against the terrifying times of the new record breakers.

Unexpectedly, as her pregnancy advanced, Mary was nauseated. As her breasts and belly and hips swelled, the oval of her face hollowed and lengthened. Black-eyed and sweating, she retched in the bathroom.

Gabby was with her every day. Now that Harry had a proper job, she put herself out to be gay with him. But the ruin of her princess was as much as Gabby could bear.

Dr. Pitt said, "It's just morning sickness, Gabby. The baby is doing splendidly. I must say it's a bit unusual at this late stage. Are you sure Mary isn't worrying about something? Have a talk with her. She should be putting on a bit more weight."

Gabby called Alec McBride and went up to London to join him for dinner.

"Really! I'm so furious I could spit. He's out on that darned track every night instead of being at home with Mary where he should be. The child is sick with loneliness. All that man thinks about is what other runners are doing. He's got this Gold Medal thing in his head. He doesn't give a fig about Mary or the baby. For heaven's sake, see what you can do. Try to bring him to his senses."

40

THE WINTER advanced. Toward Christmas the first snow had fallen and melted, fallen again to harden on the unplanted earth behind the kitchen. Harry Hayes rode the commuters' train, made his round of the chemists, pressing on them the display material and glucose samples he carried in the company sales case. To begin he had been impressed by the confident young men who worked with him in Promotion. They had treated him with interest because of his name, made efforts to include him in their business gossip, the triumph of order books and their absorption in market shares. He was lost and often pained by their derisory accounts of sexual adventures with the secretaries and typists and could not manage their clever, brittle talk in the pub where they ate lunchtime sandwiches. They raised their eyebrows and lowered their voices when Harry entered the office, indicating his order book with patronizing smiles.

There had been excitement in having trains to catch, in being joined for the first time to the daily crush and drama of the work force that rolled in and out of the great metropolis. But that was dulled by his growing shame and embarrassment for the ease of manner he did not have with the chemists badgered by salesmen. Solitary and agonized, he would stand outside the shops, bumped by the pavement traffic, and force himself to enter, force himself to smile. In the crowded, cough-filled carriage where wet umbrellas ran pools on the floor, lurching and banging between stations in an unloving pressure of bodies and smoking breaths, Harry Hayes began to feel the last of his heart run out.

In the "town house" Mary continued to be nauseated, her eyes black-patched by shadows. She seemed to cling to him with her eyes, needing only his smile for her to cheer and smile back. He was falling again, faster now, and without warning the nerves in his legs would tremble. There was a sweet taint of illness on Mary's clothing and stains on her nightdress sometimes in the morning where her breasts had dripped overnight.

While despair grew in him and would not be put down, Harry went out night after night and ran in the fog and the rain. He had no targets now; he ran for preservation, for the peace he could get no other way. He ran each night until he was spent, tearing holes in the dark, a ghostly figure in a faded track suit, running back into his hard, clean, free world. No time clock ticked in his brain; he neither thought nor counted the distance. He ran a great circle through the muffled nights, far out beyond Gillsham.

The training route Len Sparks had surveyed as the Club's Marathon captain left the back gate near the cycling track and followed the quiet roads on the hill crests to a common where South London thinned into the country. It was twenty-six miles out and back. Harry had run a mile against the clock, trying again to find the passion that had once driven him through mark after mark. In earlier months the locker rooms had been as cold and echoing and empty as the beat of his frightened heart. But now, for weeks while he had run through the night, the track and fields had been busy with preparations for the coming season. He had changed out of spikes into gym boots when the Marathon team came through from the locker rooms. Len Sparks was with them.

He had put on weight in the winter. The younger men poked their captain and joked about their expectations of carrying him back. The nerves and frustration that crawled in Harry's stomach had not been stilled by the mile. The need to run in company, like the good times on the farm circuit, in companionship with Bill, to share again and not be alone, lifted him to his feet.

"I'll come with you, if you don't mind."

"Good Lord," Sparks said. "We are being honored, men."

"It takes a bit longer than four minutes, Harry," they told him, laughing as they walked to the gates.

Because he was Harry Hayes and because of their pride in being Marathon men, they ran with him, smiling, waiting for him to tire. The Club champion paced away, to tease the four-minute-mile man. Harry Hayes closed with him, his blood beginning to hammer. An ironic cheer went up behind them. Len Sparks had dropped out.

They reached the common and turned for home, two men running with Harry. The Club champion was straining now, his face beginning to set, and put on speed, drawing farther away. Harry was running fast and loose, moving in his nighttime rhythm. Up ahead the other man turned, looked back again over his shoulder. Harry reached out with his arms to draw on invisible ropes. Rage locked in his chest. His body tilted slightly into a miler's posture. The man he was with fell back as though he had been pulled from behind. Hayes ran on and on through a succession of one-mile tapes.

Len Sparks was pinning a notice on the board when Harry walked in, his eyes blurred, and slumped down on a bench.

"A bit different from the mile, eh?" Sparks smiled. "Where did you drop out?"

"I didn't."

"Didn't what? Didn't drop out?"

Harry shook his head.

Sparks stopped, his thumb on the drawing pin. "You did the course? You went all the way?"

"Yes."

"Where are the others, then? Where's George Stock?"

"I left him behind about five miles back."

Sparks walked outside and looked over the field to the gates. He came back and stood over Harry, the pinned paper still in his hand.

"Good Lord," he said. "They're not even in sight. Stock is not even in sight."

Three days later, at Len Sparks's excited urging, Harry

Hayes rose early and walked in the dark to where Sparks waited in his car at the back gates of the Club. Sparks wanted him to run the course against the clock while the streets were empty of traffic. The Cambridge Blue wore an overcoat over pajamas and slippers. He advised Hayes how to pace himself, had drawn landmarks on paper.

"Give it all you've got. I'll be here waiting after breakfast."

Harry Hayes had no idea how to time himself, or run the Marathon. He went off in the dark on instinct, in the loneliness he had run in at night to escape the satiety of the life which shamed him. A leadenness unlike anything he had known was on him at the fifteen miles, but the fear and frustration which had broken his rhythm when he tried to explode in the mile was of a different order from the stress he welcomed now. He ran the long road stirring with pedestrians to where Len Sparks waited in his suit and bowler, a watch in his hand, his wife in the car to put him off at the station.

Sparks caught him, opened a door, let the gasping man down across the car's back seat. Sparks had stopped the clock, turning it in his palm for affirmation as he paced the pavement, winking at Liz who shook her head and smiled at her husband's excitement.

Harry sat up.

"How do you feel?"

"My legs are aching like hell."

Sparks got in behind the wheel. "I'll drive you home."

"Have you time? You might miss your train."

"To hell with the train," Sparks said. "I'm driving Britain's next Marathon champion."

Harry Hayes had found something he was able to do alone. He had lost something and found something. "If they moved the tape back fifteen yards the great miler would die before he hit it." Bill had been right. He had needed Bill for that. It was too cruel, too fierce, to do alone. It had to be there when the bell rang the terrible last-quarter warning. It had to be reached for and got and exploded through while seconds ticked off in his head. There would be nobody at his shoulder, nobody to go around in the long, man-breaking grind of the Marathon. The race would be run where Harry was at home, in the lonely, willful country of the mind.

Harry Hayes ran and won his first Marathon at an interclub meeting. In the early months of summer, prepared by Hagerty, the Royal Park coach, and attended by Len Sparks,

Hayes won the Marathon against top competition at a publicized Oxbridge event.

World Sports magazine ran a feature: BRITAIN'S EX-MILE CHAMP MAKES SENSATIONAL SWITCH TO SET NEAR-RECORD MARATHON TIME.

The *Sunday Express* headed its sports page: THE COMEBACK OF BRITAIN'S IRON MAN.

Harry Hayes had returned to where he had to be, in a hard, clean, free world he had made for himself. The house on the terrace livened in the sunshine. The bare, tumbled earth, which had run and bogged outside the kitchen through the winter, had greened with grass and colored with unexpected bulbs in the last of spring and the first of summer. Mary stopped being sick, got back some of her light and color. Gabby Charlton talked about her athlete son-in-law and dropped gay hints about Santa Anna.

The new milers set new times. Keino went to Britain from the Empire Games in Jamaica to top his two Gold Medals with the second-fastest mile ever run. Harry watched with a pang. It should have been his. It could have been his and Bill's. He willed the thought away and went savagely back into the country where a man must endure. He could do this without Bill. He could do it without any other human being. But ahead there was still Santa Anna. He would have to have the mountain Bill Persons had pulled down from the sky. Coldly, in a rage of will, Harry Hayes set himself to break the British Marathon record. When he had that, he would find Persons. The days to beg would be over.

Because they had worked it out, settled a relationship easier for Mary to bear because of the late stages of her pregnancy, the carefully worded letter had crashed in her mind with a force that stopped all thinking. Her reaction was a giddying mindlessness in which she was as dislocated as a mesmerized person. She had been incoherent when she telephoned McBride.

The Jermyn Street address had a grand sound but after twelve years the place was still frankly an attic. Its conversion from storerooms to flat had mostly been managed by Alec and witnessed his incompetence with tools. Women friends had furthered the decoration, doing bright, witty things meant to demonstrate affection. It gave the rooms an impression of patchwork and transcience which some visitors found unsettling.

McBride changed into a cardigan. He was rueful about this embroilment in the lives of Gabby Charlton and her daugher. He enjoyed Gabby's company, the calculated flirtatiousness which was her means of dealing with men. It sparked their evenings with a hint of danger. He wondered what could be up. Hayes had the Marathon championship. There would be nothing to stop him now.

The first sight of Mary frightened McBride. She was dressed in a housecoat, should not have been out on the streets. Her eyes looked hot and dry; she moved her heavy body jerkily.

"Mary, how did you get here?" McBride noticed with another shock that she wore bedroom slippers.

"In a taxi."

McBride poured drinks, his hand faintly unsteady. "Here, sit in the big chair. Water or soda?"

"What?"

"Would you prefer water or soda?"

"Oh." Mary frowned as though the decision was difficult. "I don't know. It doesn't matter. Alec. Where is it that Bill Persons lives?"

McBride started. "Persons? He lives in the country, but he has been away for some time."

"No," she said in a high, wondering voice, "he's not away. He is there, wherever it is. I thought you might show me the way. I used to know the name of the village, but for some reason it has gone right out of my head."

"You shouldn't be worrying about Persons, Mary. You shouldn't be worrying about anything. What has happened? Have you been having trouble with Gabby?"

"Gabby? No. I've had no trouble with Gabby. We had a tea party this afternoon. You see, he's left me, Alec."

McBride's drink jumped in his hand. "Harry?"

"Oh, yes. He's gone back to Persons. He says he will be living at the farm from now on. He wrote a letter. It was on the table when I got home. Persons has got something he needs, Harry says. Isn't it funny? I used to think I had something he needed. Of course, I will have to go and get him. I thought you would show me where Persons lives."

My God, McBride thought, she's in shock.

"It's probably a mistake, Mary. Look, let me take you home. You shouldn't be out dressed this way."

"Mistake? No, it's no mistake. He's taken his clothes, you see. He says he is going to run a Marathon no man will ever equal. He says he's going to set it and get old and watch them break their hearts trying."

McBride stood up. It was pushed out of him, he could not

313

stop it. "My God. Persons and Hayes. A Marathon nobody will ever beat. Persons and Hayes, two men like that—they could do it."

He had forgotten Mary. But McBride's face and McBride's words reached and found her at her dangerous distance. She saw him and heard him over and over as the furry edges fell away from her mind. Her face changed, her eyes cleared, the echoes dropped into silence. Very slowly, painfully, she twisted in the chair, laid her cheek against the leather. She began to shake and heave. She was finished, closed out, solitary forever. A low, moaning sound broke from her.

"What makes them run? Somebody, please. What makes them run? Help me, somebody. What makes them run?"

Sick at himself, McBride drew Mary Hayes to her feet.

A month before he set the new Marathon time, Harry Hayes learned from the village postmaster that Persons had returned to the farm. In that race, where a long, cruel rise topped a hill, in a clump of encouraging spectators, a tweed hat had flickered on his blurring vision with a meaning his mind had not grasped. A stocky figure stepped out. Harry's blood had iced as the transparent pale gaze reached out and held him. He had tried to make a smile of the grimace that struck his lips off his teeth. As he came close, Persons had nodded once and gestured with his elbows. Harry Hayes had tucked in his arms and gone away, running strongly toward the finish.

The sales case he had come to hate as the symbol of humiliation was left forever in a trash bin at the railway station. At the village Harry Hayes walked steadily on the track to the farm. His heart beat strongly. There was no room for uncertainty, but he was crowded by an excitement that changed the will inside him.

He watched Persons for minutes before he spoke, where he scythed the tangled weeds that had sprung up on the borders of the kitchen garden. The old Vauxhall stood in place. Affection lifted in Harry as he watched the strong, blunt face, but something had changed; he had to put down a sudden taste of bitterness.

"Bill?"

Persons was half turned, the scythe on its downward stroke. He stopped it, lowered the curved, gleaming blade and leaned on it like a stick. He seemed reluctant to move, then faced Harry, wind feathering his thinning hair. He said nothing, his eyes wide.

"I want to come back, Bill."

Persons straightened and turned his head away for a moment. "Why? You've managed on your own."

"No. I couldn't manage. I lost the other thing, Bill. It's too late now to get it back."

"Yes," Persons said, "it's too late. You had it and gave it away."

"I didn't give it away. I let it be taken from me."

"Perhaps."

They stood apart, watching each other awkwardly.

"You were wrong about me, Bill. Everything I put in the letters I wrote you was true."

"Perhaps," Persons said again. "It doesn't matter."

"The thing we were after. I can do it another way. I'm going to run a Marathon nobody will ever beat. It comes naturally to me, Bill, like a bird singing. Remember what you used to tell me?"

"I remember."

"I need the mountain, Bill."

"Yes. You'd need the mountain."

"Santa Anna isn't far away. I need the mountain now."

"How about the girl?"

"I'd have to leave her."

"Can you do that?"

"Yes. There's no other way, I tried the life of the nothingmen. It hurts harder and deeper than anything you do on the track."

"If I say no, you will go ahead and try to do it anyhow?"

"You know I will."

"Yes. I know that."

"Shall I go back to the village and get my things?"

Persons leaned again on the scythe, his head bent. When he spoke the first glint of heat snapped in his eyes.

"You're man enough to know what you want. Go back and get your bloody things."

Harry Hayes walked away, past the rusting tank and the pump with its moldering tarpaulin cover. He had to use restraint not to break out of a walk. Bill Persons leaned and watched him out of sight. Then he dropped the scythe, hurried across the garden and whipped off the cover of the pump.

41

ALEC McBRIDE, nervous about it, left Mary in the flat while he went for a taxi. It was raining when he slipped into Jermyn Street: a fierce and sudden squall that filled the gutters. He cursed helplessly as he darted from the shelter of the doorway; then he glimpsed the lit sign of a taxi that was turning into the narrow one-way street. A parking space opened on the far side of the road. The taxi driver was irritable about being asked to wait.

Mary was sitting frozen in the big leather chair when McBride ran puffing up the stairs. He owned no umbrella and wrapped her in his raincoat, being careful on the narrow, twisting staircase. Helping her across the pavement, McBride did not see that Mary stepped into the rushing gutter and remained there stupidly while he sought for a break in the traffic.

Wiping at his face and sopping hair with a handkerchief, McBride gave Gabby Charlton's address. Mary's voice rose so urgently that the driver stared with suspicion for a moment.

"No, Alec. I want to go to my own house. I must go to my own home, Alec."

She leaned back when he comforted her, closed her eyes. Alec McBride sat miserably while the taxi turned left and set off for Westminster Bridge.

He thought Mary was weeping when she began to tremble, but she opened dry eyes, her teeth chattering. She said, "I'm so cold."

He reached to pull his raincoat tight about her, saw the pooled water that spread from the soaked felt slippers and the blue on the pale bones of her ankles.

"You're soaked," McBride said. "There, get those slippers off. Put your feet up on the seat."

Mary was shaking uncontrollably when the taxi took the hill toward Royal Park.

"I'm taking you to your mother's," McBride said. "I've had enough of this nonsense." She did not answer.

Mary Charlton was ill for three weeks, more seriously than the old doctor dared let Gabby know. Her blood and kidneys were infected. She was delirious with fever for a time.

Nobody told Harry Hayes. Gabby Charlton forbade it. Alec McBride argued it with her but he knew he would have to give up. Gabby would have killed Harry had he entered that house. Toward the end of those weeks, when the nurse could be trusted alone with Mary, Gabby packed and emptied the bright little house on the terrace. In the incinerator that stood near the garage she put every trace of Harry she could find and stood over it while it burned.

Harry Hayes had returned to his hard, clean, free world, and between waking and sleeping every minute he lived and every breath he drew was accounted for and scheduled by Persons. The mountain had been prepared and installed; Persons had brought workmen from London so as not to raise village curiosity. The big tank was secured now, an ominous steel room within another room, the wall filled and closed behind it.

There was an excitement about this adventure which dispelled the last reserves of which each man was aware in the other. When they worked on the tank, laughter tickled them because it was their conspiracy and secret, the mountain Persons had pulled down from the sky. Every published mention of the unequal chances at Santa Anna deepened their satisfaction.

Persons had fitted a small observation window into the mountain. The barometer was angled there so it could be read from outside the tank. On the gauge the difference between a register of 168 mm. mercury and 559 would be the difference between the pressure at sea level and at 8,000 feet.

On the day Persons tested the mountain he was vivid with excitement. He had run the pump and they stood in the small room, already feeling the suction. The aircraft escape door was ready to be bolted into its seals.

Harry laughed. "Well, what are you waiting for?"

Persons snapped his eyes. "We've forgotten the most important thing of all."

He rushed out, rushed back with a bottle of beer and smashed it against the tank regardless of the bursting glass and the froth that splattered his shirt.

"I christen you Santa Anna. God bless this mountain and all who climb her and may the devil take the hindmost."

He slammed and bolted the door, his breath whistling.

The pump whirred outside, coming to them faintly. They waited at the porthole, screwing their eyes to read the gauge through the heavy plastic. At last the needle flickered, steadied, slowly began to count backward. Persons strode to the door, his ear against the seal, scooped the beer off the tank and used it to test the hinges. The gauge dropped steadily.

It had been a tank, easy and familiar, booming and banging when they worked on it. Now it had become a machine, charged and ominous. Waiting for Persons, Harry Hayes felt that it was his lungs that were being emptied of air.

"It is all right?"

Persons did not answer the first time, moving fast and quietly between the porthole and the exit hatch snug in its heavy rubber seals.

"Bill, is it all right?"

He smiled then. "It's all right. What do you say now, lad? I've built you your own bloody mountain."

Bill Persons depressurized the chamber to 9,500 feet. For three days he kept it there, checking every few hours, his alarm set to wake him at night. He had gone over the schedule with Harry.

"We know from Dr. Pugh's work that acclimatization can begin in twenty-four hours and that rapid improvement is experienced over the next twenty-eight days with, say, eighty percent of complete adjustment to be expected in six weeks. We will start you off with twenty-four on the trot, a break of twelve hours, bed down every night for six weeks, with work during the day on the bicycle ergometer against increasing resistance. When we get you acclimatized all you should need is a few hours in there, twice a week."

Harry had swallowed, swallowing on his dryness, face white and stiff. Persons continued to make notes he did not need, greatly concentrated.

"What do you say, a live test tomorrow?"

It was within reach and it had never been closer. He had forged it in Harry Hayes's body. He had emptied himself out of his own useless carcass and been reborn in the boy. At Santa Anna it would be his will that would pitch into the scabbed face of death. It would be death that would croak and fall back, flapping its fetid crepe, wind crying in its empty eye sockets. Death lived on the fears that men let eat them in unnoticed mouthfuls. Death feared defiance as men feared death, and when one man claimed territory in the kingdom of death, he claimed and won it for all men, for all time.

It was within reach and it had never been closer; he would run over the top of the world. The mountain was ready. He would take the boy's body up and up until he ran downhill at Santa Anna.

Bill Persons lay in bed and did not hear the storm that whistled and bent the trees and hammered against the windows and doors. It had not been the same and could not be the same and he had made himself fierce to forget it. The girl had no meaning; he could imagine her, imagine how she had heated and whined over Harry. But something he had not provided for twisted in his mind. He could not forget Harry's baby.

He had left Mary, and Gabby Charlton would see to her welfare and cherish the opportunity. Mary would be cosseted in the big, rich house; there would be no more nausea at stove or sink. He had left because he had to, and after the despair a hope and belief grew that Mary would understand his reason and need. But there had been no word from her while the month became months—no note, no message. She had not understood or had not wanted to try. They were cut from each other's lives. In the waking hours which Person's kept crowded there was only time to work or think of the mountain, cold and blank with a dark life that could be felt when the pump whirred and he was drawn to lay his hand on the metal. But Mary was often there to disturb his dreams, she and her baby that he could not yet believe in. He thought of the coming baby as Mary's baby. She and Bill Persons thought of it as his.

It was like the worst moments before the mile. Balls of cotton wool bloomed in his belly, his hands sweated, his breath caught on the hammering of his heart.

"Here we go," Persons said. The door slammed and suddenly Harry's own last words boomed and echoed in the tank. He stepped across to sit on the stretcher. It slid under his weight, prancing with a screech of its metal legs against that other metal. The pump started and it was louder than a whir, as sharp as tapping hammers in the tank. Persons' face loomed in the porthole, horribly distorted, like the reflections in a trick mirror. Harry stretched out to wait.

His body had chilled with perspiration before he sat up to shake the dizziness out of his head. On the heavy seams of the tank the rusted rivets began to shine, then run with condensation. He became aware of a rank smell and puzzled before he identified it as traces of oil let in from the pump. The humanoid face that stared in the porthole rearranged its features as it moved. The mouth worked, asking something. Harry blinked, shook his head, held up his thumb to the porthole, dropped his head and closed his eyes.

He stood it as long as he could, while the pain increased in his ears. He only had to give thumbs down for Persons to stop the pump. His ears were bursting now, choking his heart with fear. He stood and lurched to the porthole, trying to shout for relief. The crooked face behind the thick plastic stretched its awful crooked eyes, while the slashed mouth framed impossible words. The pressure in his head burst then. A gobbet of blood gushed from his nose to drown the contorted, watching face and make a running red eye of the porthole.

Harry Hayes was in a bad way when Persons got him down off the mountain, trickling air into the tank from the inlet valve, rushing between it and the bloodied porthole. Persons was stiff with his own fright. When the blood burst he had barely stopped himself with his hand on the locking bolt of the hatch. He wasn't sure what would have happened had he wrenched open the door but he had an idea and it sickened him.

It was a week before they tried again. Harry had to have the mountain. It was he who named the day, once again climbed into that fearful reverberating chamber. Persons had taken him up too fast in the first test. They had satisfied themselves about that.

Cutting the pump and restarting it, his Halloween face outside the porthole registering neither anxiety nor relief, Persons slowly pushed Harry Hayes up the mountain. At 8,000 feet he stopped the pump and kept him there for twenty hours. Harry slept some of it, read some of it, ate sandwiches and drank from a thermos. For the twenty hours Bill Persons hardly moved from the porthole.

Mary's baby was born prematurely and there were complications with the birth because of the infection and the fever she had suffered. There was strength as well as grace in the rich curves of Mary's body. She did what she was told in the sudden labor as though the pain had raised her out of the indifference that had clogged her movements and speech. The baby was a boy, long and fine in the limb like its father, with a shock of dark hair. When she saw it and the sister put the baby to her heaped and heavy breast, Mary Hayes had smiled such a wide, certain smile, her eyes wide and glistening with tears, that Gabby Charlton had needed to turn away and look in her bag for a handkerchief.

"Well, miss," the old doctor asked, "how do we feel?"

"Just wonderful." Mary smiled. "Just wonderful. Oh, he's so beautiful."

For five days Harry Hayes stuck it out in the tank when the time came to exercise on the bicycle. Each time the cold perspiration clamped him. His head was seared with pain. He felt dizzy and had to stop while the bile came up and poisoned his mouth. Bill Persons faded visibly with worry. Night after night he searched in his books for comfort or an answer. He was ready to give up, but it had gone past that for them both. This was a battleground and Harry was inflexible in his will. Shaken, weak, on the sixth day he climbed again into the echoing tank and lay on the stretcher while Persons took him up the mountain. The bicycle on its stumpy, spread legs waited like a rack to torture him. But this time there was no cold perspiration, only a little headache and nausea. There was strength in his legs at last. Condensation ran on the rivet heads. He took deep lungfuls of the oily tank air. The face that seemed as fixed in the porthole as the plastic that distorted its shape saw Harry turn weakly to smile and lift one hand in a thumbs-up salute.

Alec McBride waited for Persons on the stool in his corner of the bar and looked down his crumpled nose at the large whisky and the pile of half-smoked cigarettes in the ashtray. He lit another and wondered moodily why he was doing it. He had cut his cigarettes back to a few after meals. He had got there early. He needed a few drinks' start.

Persons was beside him before he had noticed his entrance, his tweed hat cocked at its defiant angle. He looked tired but the eyes were as dangerous as ever. McBride had never lost his awe of Persons. He was pleased by the warm greeting, the strong handshake, Persons' arm on his shoulder.

"Well, Mac, you look fit."

"I suppose I'm as fit as I've got a right to be, Bill. You don't have to be in top form to work a typewriter. You look in pretty good shape yourself."

Persons laid his tweed hat on the bar. He had got much grayer since McBride last saw him.

"I don't know. I sometimes feel very old these days."

McBride said, "Not you, Bill. What will you have?"

They tried to talk generally but it was a sparring outside both men's natures.

It was big, blunt McBride who asked the first question: "How is Harry?"

"In great shape." Persons was enthusiastic. "He's got what he wants. Number-one Marathon selection for the Olympics."

"What else could they do? Hayes and Persons are an unbeatable combination."

Persons shook the ice in his glass. "How's the girl?"

"She had the baby."

Persons jerked his head, eyes glaring. "I thought it wasn't due."

"It was premature. She got sick. That brought it on."

"Is it all right?"

"They're both all right."

"Is it a weak baby?"

"No. It's as strong as a bull."

Persons nodded. "Good, good." He shook the ice again, was swallowing the whisky when he stopped. "As strong as a bull? It's a boy, then?"

"The dead spit of its dad."

"Go on." Persons was smiling. He stopped himself. "Glad to hear it."

"It's a great little boy. It's got a great little mother."

Persons gave McBride a slow, cold stare. He put his hat on, cocked the brim. "I've got to be getting back to the farm," he said.

"What's the hurry, Bill? I thought we'd have dinner."

"I've got to get back," Persons said.

After Persons had gone McBride stayed at the bar, wondering, drinking too many whiskies and smoking too many cigarettes. He decided again that everything was fucked up in a fucked-up world.

When the first baby pictures arrived from the photographer Mary wrote Harry a letter. She took days about it, waiting until Gabby was out or writing it in bed at night. She could not forget that he had not come during the illness but now she readily found a dozen good excuses for that. It was a piteous letter because she had struggled so hard to make no demands. To hardly hint at reproach. It was full of the baby, how he looked, what he did, how he didn't show a trace of Mary's family. It was full of questions about Harry and how proud she was, how proud the baby would be, that he was to represent Britain at the Olympics.

Mary wondered about names and asked Harry if perhaps he would like the baby named for Bill Persons. The letter was signed "With all our love."

Bill Persons opened the letter, as he had done with that first little note from Mary, across the same table, before the same fireplace, so many events ago. There was a great deal of mail for Harry now. Some came direct to the farmhouse; the bulk continued to arrive from the Royal Park Club. Photographs of the child slipped first from the big envelope posted by the nurse as a secret from Gabby. Bill Persons raised his eyes. There was no boy reading in the old leather chair. A

322

hard man, father to the child, slept in the sweating mountain.

It was a very long time before Persons finished with the photographs and finished with the thoughts that began and ended with the beginning and end of his life. He took out the folded pages and sat another long time over them. He couldn't open the pages or touch them easily, but there was something he had to know. There was brandy in the sideboard. Persons fetched it, tossed the tea he had been drinking to hiss and smoke on the logs and poured the cup full of spirits. Once he walked to the mountain and stared in at the sleeping figure wound in sweaters and blankets.

The brandy in the bottle had lowered and so had the untended fire into which Persons stared. He had unfolded the letter to read the last few lines, the thing he needed to know. It was there: "With all our love."

But there was something else too in the last few lines, where it could not escape his reluctant eye: Would Harry like the baby named for Bill Persons? The baby looked back from the photographs, awake in the crib, small, urgent and quick. In one he was cuddled to his mother's cheek, his head dark against the fall of blond hair, the girl's face Persons had never imagined.

Bill Persons made his decision that night and it took all night and all the brandy. He would give Harry the letter and photographs when the Marathon had been run at Santa Anna. Harry already had so much, and Persons knew it; he could feel it by the emptiness in himself. There was another thing Harry had to have, and Persons knew that too. Until he got it there must not be anything else because that was the price of it. When Bill Persons brought Harry Hayes down the mountain next morning, the young man went to bed and slept fourteen hours.

THE EVE

42

IN THE YEAR since Bombay Sam Clark and Rex Prentice had noticeably altered in appearance. Clark's criticism of his partner's ballooning waistline had eventually taken effect. Prentice had a home gym, copied from Clark's, installed with a steam bath in his basement. He worked out there using Clark's old schedule and had trimmed off sixteen pounds. The pressure of commanding the Games project kept Clark on a shuttle to Santa Anna. He rarely had an opportunity to use his gym and, when he tried, was often too tired for a workout. Clark was wearing his suits a size larger and was having trouble with the collars of his shirts.

The open-end budget the partners had been offered for the sensational Bombay presentation had grown beyond anything ever expected. Prentice and Clark had a contract to service public relations, press, radio and television, ticket and program printing, and the visitors' facilities for the Olympic Games. The Madison Avenue office had doubled its staff; the partners had exercised an option on floor space.

General Pisarro had personally called Clark to an audience and there had been hints about a forthcoming decoration.

The Santa Anna team lived and worked under the threat of the calendar. The passing of each week in that year was as painful to Clark as the pulling of a toenail with pliers. When a month passed, Clark felt it like a reduction in height. His eyes were baggy, his digestion had gone, and the scalp under his crew cut had been rubbed raw with worry.

He told Prentice, "If I live through this Crissake thing I'm going to lie on my back in the sun for six months. I'll level with you—we wouldn't have a prayer without Luba. The way she goes to work on these secondhand Spaniards is a beautiful thing to watch. Where I get the *mañana* bit, that Luba has them so horny they go back to work doing pole vaults."

Prentice was going through the index to the master plan, a

bound book six inches thick. "Have we got it taped this time or is it like always, a dozen new things cropping up?"

Clark scrubbed his head. "I don't know. Right now I'm too pooped to know. There's going to be a hundred thousand visitors in and out of that mountain in not much more than fifteen days. Maybe a quarter of a million. There's going to be seven, eight thousand competitors, ninety-four nationalities. There's going to be more languages being talked at once than anyone has heard since that tower."

"Babel," Prentice said.

"You see that memo from Pip about smile coupons?"

Prentice looked in his in-tray. "I'm behind on memos."

"Every visitor gets six smile coupons. They hand them out everywhere they get the big smile. The hairdressers, waiters, whatever, collect them. A hundred cash prizes."

"If you get a big smile while your wallet's being lifted, you should remember to pass out the coupon?"

"If you get a big smile while you're picking up a dose, you should remember?" Clark asked wearily. He rubbed his head. "Pip's got another. The way the trams and buses are down there, the conductors won't fight through the crowds. Visitors get a free public travel pass. They wouldn't be able to pay anyhow."

"I like that," Prentice said.

The bloodless triumph of General Maximilian Pisarro set a precedent in Latin America. The retirement of the Republic's President, for urgent reasons of health, was announced at a press conference, called for 9 A.M. on the eve of a national fiesta. Some of the foreign correspondents did not bother to attend; they expected only a further report on the progress of the Olympic preparations. Bueno was spared nothing. Crumpled, obedient, broken by betrayal, he sat dazed while Pisarro announced that at the wish of the President and Cabinet he would assume caretaker control of Santa Anna's Government from one minute after midnight next morning. Bueno had been officially informed that the Americans had transferred their support to Pisarro. It was forcefully put to him that disturbances of any kind would be ruinous to the political stability the world required of any country that was host to the Olympic Games. Bueno surrendered to this appeal to his nationalism. An attempt of his to communicate directly with George Cole at the Santa Anna Bureau in Washington was allowed by General Pisarro and forwarded through the Santa Anna Embassy. Bueno was informed by coded cable that George Cole was absent on sick leave, had forwarded his resignation to the Secretary of State and was presently incommunicado. The cable was authorized by Robert E. Schultz, Acting Chief of the Bureau.

At one minute past midnight, all influence dangerous to Pisarro had been quarantined. The public reaction to the carefully planted rumors was blunted by the observances and entertainments of the fiesta on the following day. When the announcement was made in the headlines of the national press, it was reported that when Bueno had rested he would honor Santa Anna's Olympic Games Organizing Committee by accepting its presidency.

In the next month General Pisarro moved to honor his clandestine promise. On every building site from the great deepwater harbor at San Bernardino to the stadiums, hotels, Villages and transport systems in the capital, a squad of soldiers stood over the crews. Beside every contractor there was an officer; on every specification, an Army engineer.

In the second month Pisarro opened the jails, thereby adding free labor to the work force. A Castroite demonstration was crushed with quick, bloody violence. The imposing of a severe penalty for pilfering from the construction sites was enacted into law.

When these rude shocks had abated, the Santa Annans began to stir with civic pride. As the travel editors of the world's press arrived to report on the food, customs and services of the next Olympic city, they did so to a changed climate. Latin pride fed and grew on this swell of favorable notice.

Sam Clark began to brighten. "Something has happened down there," he told Prentice. "All of a sudden the joint has started to jump."

Six months after the eclipse of Bueno, three months after Pisarro's formal assumption of the Presidency, Robert E. Schultz was confirmed as Chief of the Santa Anna Bureau.

"What do you think of your bogeyman now?" Lance Dobson asked warily about Pisarro, dining with Schultz at his invitation.

"We were wrong. You were right."

"Some men have to have power. They will get it any way they can. It's like a sickness. They can't breathe properly without it. The way Pisarro behaves from here on is partly up to us. He can be devil or angel—whichever is the price of keeping the power."

Schultz needed to believe in Pisarro; his guilt demanded it

of him. "When has a power man had enough? What if he looks outside Santa Anna?"

"That's the name of our problem," Dobson said. "Down there and everywhere else."

Prentice was derisive. "Barbecues, baseball, boating. If it's going to be that way, how the hell do we get anyone to go?"

Pip Harris said, "The organizing committee is insistent. It impresses the officials and chaperones. In any case, they have to get out of the hay occasionally."

"They didn't at Tokyo," Clark said moodily, tapping his research on the subject. "Before those Games were through, you had to go clear to Nagasaki to buy a condom."

Prentice said, "Guards—they've got all these guards on the Women's Village."

"Guards." Clark tapped the notes. "The guards came away from the Tokyo Games weighing an average of eighty pounds. What do you expect, Crissake? You've got eight, nine thousand of the fittest young men and women in the world. They've been working their arses off for years, staying out of the hay. They're so stitched up with nerves they burst into tears if a door bangs. Then it's over, maybe in the first few days. Those hormones start clicking like castanets. You've got about three thousand lays going at a time. I got one here." Clark tapped his research. "Went through the American contingent single-handed without knowing the language. I got an Empire Games here some years back, they had a riverbank you could walk a mile on without touching the ground."

Pip Harris smiled and stroked his beard. "Look at Luba," he said.

Clark had all Luba's attention. She colored at the inquiring faces. Luba tossed her short, black helmet of hair at Pip Harris. She had not let it grow. Luba was not susceptible to modes and looked more arresting than ever simply by being different.

"Don't be horrible, you," Luba said. "I think it's nice like that. All those poor young people starved for love."

Clark said, "It's a gluttony problem we have. Not starvation. There's stuff in these notes setting records that makes what they do on the track look silly."

Prentice said, "So we give them barbecues, baseball, boating. Does that wrap it up?"

"It will do for openers," Clark said. "What we really need

is a flying squad to apply the whitewash if something spooky comes up."

Clark had taken to heart General Pisarro's hint about the decoration. He didn't want any blots on the copybook. He had a clear impression of the decoration. It would be some kind of enameled cross with jewels on it and would be worn on a crimson sash.

Pip Harris doodled. "A kind of under-the-carpet committee."

"That's it." Clark was pleased. "An under-the-carpet committee."

"A lawyer, a flack, a local politician and a few strong-arm men," Harris said.

"And a doctor." Clark tapped his research. "Believe me, we need a doctor."

Scott Reynolds opened the letter as he crossed the quadrangle to the guinea-pig unit, reading it as he went. Scott was taking Dr. Liz to a drive-in movie to celebrate her new car.

The *Daily Globe* letterhead told him the note was from Laurie Rounder. As Scott expected, Rounder wanted to congratulate him on his Olympic selection and looked forward to renewing their acquaintance in Santa Anna. There were other scraps of news.

Scott Reynolds stopped dead. "I'll be goddamned."

He shook his head in astonishment and raced up the steps.

Dr. Liz was crossing the corridor. She turned eagerly when she saw him. "Goodness, what is the time? I'm just going to tidy up."

"Never mind that." Scott waved the letter. "Listen to this."

"What is it?"

"It's a letter from Laurie Rounder, that English sportswriter on the *Daily Globe*. You remember Sunny? Sunny Pintubi?"

"Oh, Scotty. Not another Sunny story."

"This beats all. Rounder says Sunny has made the Australian team."

"Oh, Scott, how wonderful for him."

"Wait," Scott laughed oddly. "He's going to run the Marathon. How about that? Doesn't that cap everything?"

"No!" Dr. Liz said. "Surely not."

"Surely is. How is that for a full circuit, Liz? He's going to be running against me in the Marathon." Scott couldn't get over it. "Any of the boys still here?"

"Yes. Dr. Mack is checking out the new diet sheets."

"This they won't believe," Scott said. "You go on and powder your nose."

At the drive-in they sat close in the little English car that was conspicuous and loomed over by the big American models.

"Now I know how a dwarf feels." Scott tried to adjust his eyes to the screen. His thigh touched hers as he fidgeted. Her frank shiver awoke tenderness again. Scott brushed his lips on her forehead and settled himself.

It had been like this since the first casual contact. She was helplessly eager, helplessly inexperienced. It had been new to Scott. He had not thought a mature woman, one exposed to the realities of medicine, could possibly be so innocent. The faintly angular body was empty of all pretense or deceit. It was as open as the slanted gray eyes that lit for him with such pleasure, worrying him with their candor. Scott had promoted Liz, as Harvey Tonkin used to call it, because there was something about her his eye recognized, and because the routine at the guinea-pig unit had become a bore and he needed distraction.

When he made the first casual and expert advance, Dr. Liz had not even observed the formal ritual of protest. She had come clumsily into his arms, her breath shaking, her angular body shaking, her slanted eyes crystal-clear. It was too easy. Something had happened to Scott. There was nothing to take because all was given. He had recoiled from the responsibility. It angered and worried him. Her confusion had made it worse.

Scott had gone to the record player. "Where do you switch this thing on?"

She showed him. Then she had said, "Would you like coffee now?"

"I'm off coffee this month. You know that."

"You can have a dispensation. Doctor's orders."

Scott had left early. At the door of her neat apartment they touched lightly again.

Liz had looked up. "I haven't offended you, have I, Scott?"

"How would you have offended me?" he had asked testily.

"I don't know. There's a lot I don't know."

Scott said, "You're a virgin, aren't you, Liz?"

"Yes."

"Haven't you ever had a beau?"

"Not really."

"Why not, for God's sake?"

She was shaking again. "Oh, I don't know. Too many studies, perhaps."

"Someone, sometime, must have made a pass."

"Oh, yes . . ."

"Well?"

"I've just never met anyone I liked enough to, you know, feel that way."

Scott said in sudden exasperation, "You seem to feel that way to me."

"Yes," Dr. Liz said. Scott kissed her quickly and left. He had been uneasy all the way home. This was one you wouldn't just walk away from.

Scott kept himself formal with Liz but he came back to her in his mind. When she went home for two weeks, Scott felt her absence as a nagging loss that impaired his concentration, left him dissatisfied and moody. He was so glad to see her back at the unit, he asked her to dinner that night.

Scott thought he was keeping his distance, handling Dr. Liz carefully. She understood and tried to make it easy for him. He wasn't keeping his distance. It was a different, more surreptitious involvement. But she still trembled like this when they touched.

"Scotty. You aren't even looking at the screen."

He started. "Oh, wasn't I?"

"You're thinking about something."

"Yes, as a matter of fact I was. I don't know, I've got me a strange feeling. As though something is fated."

"Watch the film," Liz said. "You're the wrong type to be mystical."

Sam Clark had interviewed the short list of applicants personally. The facilities planned for the comfort and convenience of the world press were the most elaborate in Olympic history. It was close to Clark's heart, like the promised decoration that had become as important as money to him. Clark had a lot of pride in his record as a working journalist.

"The world is going to decide what kind of games we are running on the copy these guys file. So I'm going to give them everything. A building of their own. Closed-circuit TV, tables, typewriters, bulletin boards, a restaurant, a bar, a bus service, a telephone exchange, a telecommunications room for cables and radio photographs. What we need is a hotshot communications man to get the show on the road. You know what it's like down there. You can bust a gut making a local phone call."

Now Clark looked in on Prentice, rubbing his hands.

"You know what I got? A retired communications man out of the Pentagon. A full Brigadier General, Crissake. He handled the lines on one of those atomic tests. A guy like that, we could wind up with a satellite. I'm sending him right on down."

Clark looked in on Pip Harris, told him about the Brigadier General, and then told Luba Ivanova.

Luba had her own staff now. She worked them hard and was unforgiving of mistakes. She had dismissed on the spot a confident young man who, overcome in his judgment by the musk that exuded from Luba, attempted an intimacy one evening.

"You got the proofs of those maps and games plans?" Clark asked.

"Production is checking the color register, no?"

"Don't ask me, Crissake. Has anyone checked out Mathew C. Kaverly's accommodations? There's a list of do's and don't's as long as your arm in from IOC headquarters, Lausanne. This needle shower and this king-size bed. This nonfat yoghurt and this private dining room. You know what the athletes call the old man? F.U.C. Kaverly."

"Truly?" Luba said, giggling.

Clark said, "I thought that might get to you. Back to the salt mines."

When he had gone, Luba frowned at her papers. Perhaps she should have put Mathew C. Kaverly in Sardar's suite. Then she decided not to worry. These other ones would want to be in the new hotels with their tacky smell of new plaster and paint. Sardar would like the lofty old rooms with their Spanish courtyards and terraces. They would remind him of his place in the lake. Luba dreamed about that a little. Sardar must still be unmarried; there was no maharani on the manifest.

The Australian Amateur Athletic Association, ridden with factions and egos like its counterparts in Europe and the Americas, reached a rare unanimity over Sunny Pintubi. After his three Marathon wins under Percy Cerutty, the executive board of the Association was only left to follow public opinion. Sunny Pintubi was a national celebrity, the greatest copy maker since young Herb Elliott ran himself and Cerutty to fame. The press had given Sunny Olympic selection long before the czars of amateur sport confirmed it. Sunny was a revelation to Cerutty: the perfectly constructed running machine, visual proof of his theories and convictions. It was all there. The lean aboriginal leg, almost unmuscled on the calf. The powerful chest and biceps, the long low loping stride, fueled by lungs like bellows.

The will to work the perfect machine belonged to the timeless dream of the desert. The days of a life are uncounted in the search for food on that stricken landscape, and competition is unknown between men.

The bloody ego of old Europe also survived in Sunny Pintubi. It was there in his shame and his need for pride. Cerutty taught Sunny to run the Marathon in the only way he could win: to run for the horizon from the start, to leave the others at the gun while they plotted and conserved, to run to the end of that awful 26 miles 385 yards with one steady, unrelenting beat of power.

Sunny ran like that, needing nobody, nothing. In that first race Sunny had gone away and they waited for the crack-up, or the change of pace the shrieking muscles must demand, the rhythms that rest and rouse the will while the driven body runs 26 miles 385 yards. The next man home in that first Marathon could not believe that he had not won. He had concentrated on the strides ahead; he had not run, head up, for the horizon. He could not believe that he had not won, because he could not believe that Sunny Pintubi had run the distance and finished.

They understood when Sunny ran and won again to a hysterical crowd at the 4-A championships. The Marathon men were aware of him now, and struggled to hold him when he ran the third time. But they had not been trained to run like that. They were wrong for it in their minds, and wrong for it in their bodies. Out of tune and out of pace, they struggled while Sunny ran on one beat, head up, arms low and easy, footfall low and easy, toward the spinifex fire on the horizon which Cerutty had burned into his brain.

After that race, in front of the camera of the National Television Channels Outside Broadcasting Unit, Sunny had answered the questions gravely.

He also added something of his own: "There are thousands like me back in the bush."

Charlie Gilmour got the news from Gus Drake, who had got it privately from the 4A's official. Even Gus Drake's voice was strained. He had called Harcourt first, but there was no one at home.

"You wouldn't read about it," Gus kept saying. "Seventeen and a half thousand quid."

Gilmour did not really know what he was doing. He blinked his sandy lids against the urgent need of tears. He changed out of his overalls into the suit he kept in the office cupboard, and left the factory without a word.

In the beer garden at the Narrabeen pub, as the afternoon shadowed and chilled, the cellarman spoke to a barmaid.

"He's got something on his mind, that bloke. He's been staring at the table for hours."

The barmaid said, "He's got something on his stomach. He's been putting the drink away as if it's going out of fashion."

An hour later, Charlie Gilmour rose from the table and the metal chair fell over with a crash. Charlie pitched his head back, like a dingo baying the moon, opened his mouth, supported himself with his hands on the tabletop and delivered a cry that stiffened the other drinkers in their chairs.

"You bloody little beauty . . . you little blah-huddy beautyyyy!"

He was still baying while the cellarman and the licensee bundled him out of the garden.

Big Jim Harcourt eventually passed out at the bar of the R.S.L. Club after buying drinks all night for everybody, and was driven home by two fellow members who had so benefited from the windfall that the trunk of Harcourt's car was stoved in, reversing out of the parking lot, and the front fender was crumpled on the gatepost.

The world had its own troubles and they had got no better or worse. That is, if you were not an Indian dying of famine, or a soldier in Vietnam, or a rice farmer being crucified by both sides, or riding an express toward a buckled fishplate, or born to the wrong tribe in Africa, or in the road of the cyclone or where pestilence breeds, or feeling suddenly sick in Hiroshima, or at home having a highball when the body cells begin to go mad. The world had its own troubles and for the most part felt them ease a little as ninety-four nations across the globe converged upon Santa Anna.

On the tracks and the fields, in the wet lanes of another element, in the square rings and banked circuits, the crucibles of trial waited to prove one man, one woman, the superior of his or her kind on earth.

Ninety-four nations put out flags and readied the young for the arenas, to prove the national superiority of their national ways of life, their superior aspirations, religions, bloodlines, opportunities and histories.

In Santa Anna the bandmasters rehearsed their musicians in ninety-four national anthems.

The expensive prostitutes, gamblers, con men and pick-pockets calculated the cost of travel from where they were against an estimate of their prospects. The tradesmen, merchants and souvenir makers waited over their stocks. The currency racketeers set up their contacts among waiters, taxi drivers, bootblacks and beggars.

The shabby spies memorized code names, checked out drops, watched and waited for other shabby spies from ninety-four countries.

Sam Clark smoked three packs a day and took pills in order to sleep.

The athletes in ninety-four countries lived to their own loud heartbeats.

The meteorological forecast for Santa Anna's Olympic weather would have gathered dust in the command post had all dust not been filtered from the air. For nearly two months the old man had done little but watch the programmed fountain and listen to the bird music. The reports on the Lausanne printer were acknowledged but not always read.

It was hard for the old man to believe, and because of this his menace had been ineffectual. He had been ineffectual before the vote, stunned by the opposition which had only hardened and gathered a hostile force as he bullied and persuaded and maneuvered. He could hardly believe it then, and in the recess had sat alone in his suite instead of dealing and politicking, instead of using the crushing power he had been forced to temper on the floor. He had let the recess go unused while he sat alone in his suite, and in the afternoon vote they had risen up and destroyed him.

It had been his creation, one Germany, a great achievement of the Olympic spirit. It had been the pointer to one Korea, the seed of the hope that would one day end that greater partition, the walling of China from the world. There had been no East or West Germany in the great parades when the youth of the world met freely under the meaning of the Olympic flame. It had been one people, a German people. One flag, a German flag. They had taken it from him. They had taken a people and ripped them apart. They had taken the flag of unity and torn it into two political rags.

Conrad Carson had counted the vote, moving as softly as an undertaker among the delegates, the shabby undertaker's black of his suit grayed on the shoulders by the dandruff that fell out of the short hair fringing his bald head. He had announced the vote to the executive table, his eyes lowered.

Hans Stein had glanced once at Kaverly and licked his lips. "Are you sure?" he asked Carson.

Carson had looked directly at Kaverly and the triumph of the moment had blazed in his pale face while the old man stared back at him steadily.

"Yes, Chancellor, I am sure."

The sun had set on the desert. The cold was already sharp. The old man sat at the fountain, the bird music singing around him. In the house Miss Kaverly worried. She was reluctant to go out and tell her brother to come in, but she could not risk the cold much longer. She had had to bring him in several times. He sometimes did not notice the passing of the day. The curtains in the house closed electronically on the setting of the sun. The Olympic flag had electronically run down its pole. Every day since her brother had returned so strange from the conference, he had flown the Olympic flag at half mast. Miss Kaverly got the old man's jacket and nervously left the house.

In Lausanne Hans Stein worried a cigarette out of its crushed pack. He tried to make his voice convincing.

"I don't think you should take this too seriously, Conrad. The vote was a great shock to Mr. Kaverly. After Santa Anna it will probably be forgotten."

Conrad Carson's pale face was red with blood and malice. "He's given me three months. I'm forty-eight. Where will I get a suitable position?"

"I wouldn't take it too seriously. Leave it to me."

"He does what he likes. With you, with me, with everyone. I have had to bear his arrogance, and his insults. He's demented. Now this. Why? How dare he? For what reason?"

"He has had a lot to contend with. There has been nothing but trouble ever since Bombay. Then there was the uproar about the television contract. You know how idealistic he is. You were indiscreet. You laughed in his face when you tabled that vote."

Carson shook on his venom. "I'll make him pay. You'll see, I'll make him pay."

PART THREE

THE EVENT

Santa Anna

43

IT HAD BEEN a slum, a reeking shantytown behind the old bullfight arena. Even the earth had been unclean, soaked with drainage and poisoned by waste, its odors raked by the sun. The mixed-bloods who lived there had resisted the reclamation, built roadblocks and barricades, stoned the surveyors until they ran. Army tanks had crushed the defenses, Army trucks had transported the protesting population to an old camp outside the capital, Army engineers had dynamited the crumbling tenements and bulldozed the flapping huts. The unclean earth was turned and cleared of its wreckage to sweeten.

When the administrators of the first teams arrived some days before the athletes, trainers, doctors, masseurs, managers and officials, Santa Anna's shantytown had been metamorphosed from a grub into a butterfly. Dual highways with overpasses divided the new enormous Olympic Village into halves. The buildings gleamed white and cream in lines of pine trees uprooted high in the mountains and transplanted in full growth. Lawns of sod flourished in the courtyards of the athletes' U-shaped housing blocks, each flat roof studded with flat, round buns that sucked the fresh air and passed it through the air conditioning housed there. Long lines of taller administration blocks backed the athletes' quarters. At the far end of the settlement to which it gently sloped, the great stadium glinted its rearing white amphitheater over the bright green of the field and the darker note of the cindered track.

In the fifteen hundred apartments, eight thousand rooms were ready for the athletes from ninety-four countries. Spaced over the great complex, five restaurants, capable of serving every national dish, would feed two thousand diners at a sitting. In the hospital two hundred beds had been dressed with linen, the pharmacy stocked, two surgeries prepared. A

Bible lay on the church pulpit. The cinemas, sauna baths, gymnasiums and information offices had rehearsed their staffs and tested their equipment. The bus and railway stations echoed emptily on final preparations. The five training fields and training tracks awaited the christening of spikes. Jeeps buzzed between the stadiums, the swimming pools, the new hotels on the heights, the equestrian sites, the canoeing lake in Retiro Park, the Marathon course, and the new road that ran unimpeded to the yacht basin at San Bernardino.

In the Village the ninety-four flagpoles standing beside the dual highway looked meaningless and vacant. All Santa Anna bit its nails and fretted as it waited for the first team to arrive, the first national flag to fly and bring the Village to life. In the remade city on the heights, in all the transformed countryside, at the great passenger terminal on the deepwater harbor and in the smallest shop and bar, the labor and bustle of four years of building had changed to an aching void.

The release began imperceptibly, a spattering of visitors as easily missed as the first drops before a rainstorm. In the new hotels the smell of paint, timber and mortar faded as the guests arrived. The suites, rooms, restaurants and corridors warmed with body sweat, the smell of clothing, soap, toothpaste, tobacco, alcohol, leather. The first visitors, who had arrived like raindrops, spattered into a shower. The first national flag broke out in the Village. The first cruise ships and rescheduled liners berthed at San Bernardino. In one day three flags were hoisted with ceremony in the Village. The first athletes in track suits and gym shoes were seen and excitedly pointed out. From the heights at night they saw the Village gradually light up. The shower became a storm. From ninety-four countries the athletes, officials and spectators streamed into Santa Anna.

The phenomenon which gives the world pause every four years had renewed its cheat and its promise.

Alec McBride and his longtime photographer, Addie, flew in early. McBride planned a series on the British team's reaction to Santa Anna's altitude during acclimatization. In the crush at the airport McBride heard his name called over the public address system. A liaison officer accredited to the British press corps received McBride and Addie and presented each with a dossier. The dossier contained a letter of welcome from the chairman of the Press and Television Committee, a program and a badge, a hotel room number, a list of committee members with their day and night telephone numbers, a plan of press seats in each stadium, complimentary passes for transport and places of entertainment, and a map detailing the facilities at the press center. On the ride into town messages in many languages welcomed them on bright new billboards.

McBride checked through his dossier. "If this is any indication, somebody has pulled the finger out."

Addie was examining the private bars and restaurants of the press center's impressive layout. "It looks great," he said. "This is going to be one Olympics where I can get away from the seething gladiators."

Sam Clark had made his first impression on the press.

The city of Santa Anna nested into the mountain in the shape of a broken bowl. On the heights the bowl was secure, cupped. Beyond the Avenida de España and the Presidential Palace the bowl broke over cliffs and the distant view to San Bernardino. Because there was no wide spread of city to absorb the jam of humanity, Santa Anna hummed like a hive through all the hours of daylight and most of those of night. From the old Hotel Esmeralda, backed into the mountain, the courtyards and terraces witnessed an unremitting flux. There was no peace anywhere on the landscape. Vehicles ran and swerved, headlights reaching everywhere at night. The cobbled guts of the old city behind Retiro Park were packed with tourists, the bars and restaurants spilling noise like something solid. The brave bulls and the cowardly bulls and bulls that scarcely merited the name went to a hurried slaughter in continuous *corridas* while visitors either sickened and averted their eyes or exulted and tossed hired cushions into the ring.

And in Olympic Village, that other city within the city, behind the guarded gate and checkpoint where every credential was scrutinized, the gladiators strained and trained and sweated, counting their heartbeats, measuring their breaths, dazzled by their hopes and fears, agonizing over trivial pains, pouring out confidences to sudden intimates.

Rumors as pervasive as smoke blew and ebbed. The Russian champion had pulled a muscle and was out. The Australian freestyle ace had slipped at the training pool and dislocated a shoulder. Two Scandinavian girls had been caught climbing the wall on a rope thrown over by a black African.

And more specifically: "I heard about it from a girl who was at the European Games at Budapest. You won't believe it. You know what they do? They've got to feel you. They stretch you out naked on this table and then the doctor puts his fingers right in you! Isn't it awful? They feel to see if you've got any testicles. You know, little ones inside of you. Can you believe it, testicles? They open it up and feel. That's why those Russians wouldn't take the medical at Budapest. They've got them. Little testicles inside them. It makes me sick."

"Well, I think it's a good thing. They've been getting away with it for years. You know that huge discus thrower? I was in the shower with it. I couldn't look at it, it was so revolting. And then I saw it looking at me. I nearly died. I couldn't get out of the shower fast enough."

As they fought for form, tried to eat, fretted and despaired about acclimatization and lay sweating and aching in the dark at night, contesting the event in their minds, hearing the giant clash in the stadium, seeing the dizzying mass of a hundred thousand spectators that thumped their hearts like a drug, the tension inside the Village stockade rose like an infection to the heights.

The humming hive loudened in the broken bowl on the mountain. The various nationalities met in their own bars, nightclubs and restaurants. National anthems and remembered war songs rang in the streets in the early mornings. There were boasts and fights in the old city. The Santa Anna police moved in after midnight, patient and discreet with the foreigners, sudden and violent with their own kind. The vomit in the gutters was swilled away at daybreak.

From headquarters at the press center, Pip Harris had already sent his under-the-carpet committee on its first actions. The Prentice and Clark team of experts, as thoroughly drilled as soldiers and as tense as soldiers skirmishing before a battle, reported on regular schedules by walkie-talkie to a listening post set up by Clark's retired general. Clark was in uproar. On the exhaustive checklists with which his personal assistant followed him everywhere, a major detail had been forgotten. The seating plans in the stadium had not been divided into national blocs. Clark had screamed at the midnight meeting: "What are you guys trying to do to me? Put the French between the Hungarians and the Russians. Get the English and American blocs between the Germans and Israelis. We've got an Olympics coming off here, Crissake, not the Third World War."

On the Qantas flight out of Sydney, removed by the length of the aircraft from their wives, Big Jim Harcourt and Charlie Gilmour ordered more champagne. Gus Drake had been unable to persuade himself to fly. He had booked a sea passage and later canceled it after a *Reader's Digest* article on famous shipwrecks that began with the story of the *Titanic*.

Harcourt's content was nagged by a single flaw. Charlie Gilmour had turned over his share of the win in England to Father O'Malley's mission. Harcourt had been disgusted. It irritated him like a grass seed in the sock. Harcourt felt that Gilmour had given him the knock.

When Scott Reynolds and another guinea pig won Olympic selection, Dr. Ernest Murrow was granted permission by the American Olympics Committee to continue tests during acclimatization. Dr. Liz and a physicist accompanied Murrow to Santa Anna.

This unexpected continuity, the warmth of Scott's daily contact with Liz, eased the tyranny of introspection in which the onrushing reality steeped his teammates. On occasional leaves from the disciplines of preparation, Scott and Liz wandered the heights and slopes of the city, rode old carriages behind caparisoned horses, bathed with the tourists at Retiro Park in the great artificial lake lipped by beach sand.

Out of the dressing shed, waiting for her among the tables served from the palm-thatched bars, Scott remembered he had not shown Liz the cable. He turned, on the thought, to seek her. She was marked by her height, even in a crowd at this distance. The dark brown body in the bikini called for attention among the luridly pink European skins. Because the responses of her body had been so overt, both a welcoming and a shrinking, Scott had rejected his curiosity. His surprise fixed him now. Liz moved toward him through the crush, seeing nobody else, poised slightly on her toes, moving as he would never have imagined she could. Exposed, the angularity of frame lightened the heavy breasts and hips which Liz kept strapped in clothes, and found its own symmetry in freedom. Her dark hair was gone under a white cap covered with plastic curls. It made her head look small and sleek, multiplied the impact of the generous body. When she touched his arm, Scott felt her fingertips tremble. Her lips were uncertain.

Scott said, "Liz, where ever did you get that tan?"

She continued to look directly into his eyes. "When I knew I was coming, I bought a sun lamp. The bikini, too. I've never owned one before."

Scott smiled his pleasure and surprise.

"Do I please you?" she asked. "I don't look ridiculous, do I?"

"Ridiculous? You look wonderful. You are the sexiest-looking thing on this lake."

The taxi stopped at the roadblock. The guards looked over from the gate as Scott stepped out.

Liz said, "It was a wonderful outing, now you must hurry or we will both be in trouble."

Scott kissed her and shut the door. The taxi began to back for the turn.

"Just a minute." Scott ran back and hung on the door. "I've been meaning to tell you all afternoon, Liz. You remember Harvey Tonkin, my buddy in Bombay?"

"The one you stayed with?"

"I had a cable from him this morning. He's in Washington, on his way down here. He and Bob Schultz are flying in together. Win, lose or draw, it's going to be quite a party."

"Tell me tomorrow," Liz said. "Look at the time. You're supposed to be in the gym."

The apartment Scott shared had two divan beds, built-in wardrobes, a writing desk, table, bookcase. Double doors opened on a balcony. The bathroom was well equipped and spacious. It looked like any modern motel.

The opening of the balcony doors woke Scott, flooded the room with moonlight. He had been deeply asleep and turned irritably to check the wristwatch on the bedside table. It was a little after one. For the past three nights his roommate had risen almost punctually at this time, to plunge his face under a noisy tap, rattle the balcony doors, pace there sighing, flexing his right hand and arm. Scott's roommate threw the javelin and tension had hit him hard. For a week he had complained of shoulder twinges. A row of lucky charms—black cats, Maori Tikis, a St. Christopher, a rabbit's foot—was laid out on the shelf beside his bed. Every day, before training, he rubbed one of them on his javelin to check for the strongest medicine. Most of the athletes cherished some superstition and need for the comfort of a little magic.

He had told Scott, "Goddammit, man, I don't dig you. Comes lights-out, you fall into the sack and snore up a storm. You got no nerves? Don't you know how it will be when they send us out there? I can get sick to my stomach just to think about it. In all this Village there is not a natural-sleeping man goes into the sack and snores it up like you do."

"You've got to live right, Barney. What did the doc say about these twinges?"

"What did they say? I had the full treatment. They did everything except give me an X ray. You know what they said about these twinges? In the head, Barney, they told me. Where you got twinges is in the head."

Scott lay back and settled. He did hit the sack and snore and that was true. He had sweated and worked years for this, and one way or another it would change his life forever. It would change his life and he cared about that, but in the same way it hardly reached him. He knew that Liz helped to cast this calm. He had never been able to get close to the coaches the way most of the others did. He realized this now because he got that feeling from Liz. It was total involvement and total security, total trust and faith. It had been Liz who first noticed his blood count, Liz who had taken his ergometer tests for a check-out all down the line. Nature had given him an ace in the hole and that cast a different calm. He had believed it because Liz believed it and had set up the tests to prove it. He began to know it that first week in Santa Anna, watching other athletes struggle, seeing their nausea and headaches and the dropped performances and the panics more damaging than either. He began to know it then because nothing had touched him; he had gone out and driven himself to prove it.

After his first hard run, Ernest Murrow had spread his plump chin and looked at Scott over his glasses. Scott had zipped up the track suit.

"Well, Doc, how do I check out?"

"All I have to say to you, G. P. Reynolds, is as follows."

Murrow had given Scott an exaggerated wink.

Scott began to drowse. Seeing Sunny again had been a strange disappointment. There was a contact between them but Scott had been embarrassed by the change. Sunny was bigger, stronger, altogether different. He acted differently, spoke differently, a distance had opened between him and the world. Scott Reynolds narrowed his eyes at the dark. Never for an instant had he thought of Sunny this way. Now he knew what had nagged him, the change, what he had recognized, not realized in the change: Sunny Pintubi reminded Scott of a Negro.

The man on the balcony continued to pace, stretching and flexing his right arm. Light shone in an administration building, capping the athletes' blocks beyond the elevated highway. Scott Reynolds began to snore. The man on the balcony threw a javelin.

"God damn him," he told the moon.

Sam Clark had been standing drinks at the press-center bar. He checked his watch. He was to lunch with Bueno at his residence and afterwards attend a meeting of review with the Games Organizing Committee. Clark wasn't looking forward to the luncheon. Bueno was hard going. There was something wrong, he was fading away to nothing, often fell mute in the middle of sentences.

Before leaving, Clark called on Pip Harris. "What've we got on last night's scandal sheet?"

Pip Harris reversed a clipboard and pushed it over the table. "Nothing elaborate. The usual quota of parents missing teen-age daughters."

"It's the atmosphere," Clark said "It's like a city in wartime. There won't be a decent mattress left in town when this thing's over. I was in the old quarter last night. All this foot-stamping, guitars, castanets—it almost got me. Where's Luba?"

"She's having lunch with that Russian kid."

"Again?" Clark said. "That Luba's kept her nose clean up to now. What's coming off here?"

"I would say that nothing is coming off, if you see what I mean. Luba's enjoying using her Russian again. Did you know that Sergei was born in the same village Luba's father came from? She's got a lot to talk about."

"The hell you say? I didn't know that. You tell Luba to see me. I don't want any of our lot in a tangle with these commissars. What does the kid do?"

"He's a swimmer. The 200-meter butterfly."

"If he gets too close to Luba," Clark said, "he's going to be a butterfly with a busted wing."

In a small restaurant in the old city, Luba Ivanova leaned intently forward over the table. The young man wore blue trousers and a white open-necked shirt, the sleeves rolled high on developed biceps. His brown hair was short in a swimmer's crop. His features Slavic, handsome, strong in cheekbones and jaw. He laughed a lot, restless on the chair, energy crackling on him.

Luba said, "But, Sergei, you should not have done that, broken up your parents' flat."

"I didn't break it, that was the others. There were some wild ones. They had drunk a lot of vodka. Yuri Alexandrov —he is my comrade—had brought the jazz records back from Poland. Yuri is a student in the School of Mines, but he makes money in the black market. Yuri wants to enjoy life while he can. When he finishes his studies in the School of

346

Mines, he will probably be appointed to the new territories."

"What did your parents say when they returned from the Black Sea?"

"My father flogged me. He was a member of the Party and very upright and severe. The caretaker told him about the jazz records and the vodka bottles. Nobody had been able to sleep. My father was going to have me charged in the People's Court, but my mother persuaded him out of it. It is very difficult when your father is a Party member. You have to set a moral example."

"Is that why you neglected your studies, because your father flogged you?"

"Yes. I was seventeen then and stronger than my father. It was hard, because I made myself submit. Then my father is a teacher in the Pedagogical Institute. That is also difficult. It was a matter of pride to him always that I should get higher marks than others. I was sick of it. I longed to be free. To deal in the black market, drink vodka and play jazz records like Yuri. It wasn't possible."

The Russian filled Luba's wineglass and poised the bottle above his own.

Luba snatched the glass. "No. You promised." She poured water from a carafe. "Just a little now, in there."

Sergei roared with laughter, drawing attention. "I am a Russian. Have you forgotten how Russians can drink? My grandfather is eighty-four. On his birthday he drank vodka toasts for four hours and had two bottles of wine with his meal."

"Your grandfather was not swimming in the Olympics," Luba said severely.

Sergei scowled and shook the glass of wine and water. "Swimming. I am sick of it. My headmaster said, 'You have talent as a swimmer if nothing else. It is your duty to develop this talent for the good of your country. Take this note to your father.' My father said, 'Thank God there is something you can do.' He is always saying 'thank God' or 'in God's good time.' It is ridiculous in a materialist. My father knows influential people. In three months, I was in the army as a private, swimmer. 'This is your last hope,' my father said, 'you could become a Master of Sport.'"

"What is that?"

"A Master of Sport? It is a diploma, and respected. One instructs, lectures, coaches. A Master of Sport has privileges. It is all in the Plan. There are three thousand Masters of Sport made every year. In the army, instead of drilling, I swam. Instead of route marches, I watched slow-motion films of Australian and American champions. When the others were learning to drive tanks and trucks, I was learning swimming technique. It was awful. I hate swimming."

Sergei broke off a crust and dropped it in his glass.

"That is how I am. Waterlogged. Soaked to death with swimming."

Luba said, "Sergei, I think you are a boy for making difficulties."

He looked pleased; then he scowled.

"Yes. I am very difficult. I am what my father calls a good-for-nothing *hooligan*, depraved by Western influence and my good-for-nothing friends."

"Hardly a *hooligan*." Luba laughed. "Not with those muscles and that haircut."

Sergei touched his head. "It has to be like this. When I am a Master of Sport, I will let my hair grow to my shoulders. Now, enough of this. Tell me more about New York, about the young people."

Luba shook her head. "No more today. I must get back to work and you must get back to the Village."

"When you spoke to me at the reception, why was that?"

"I had not met any Russians since I was a little girl in Saigon. I wanted to talk."

"Yes, but there were many of us. Why did you choose me?"

"I looked for the nicest face," Luba said.

Sergei stood up, leaned over the table and kissed her. "I feel strong. When you say that, it makes me feel strong. Do you know, I hardly understood you at first. You use old-fashioned words, and your accent is funny."

Luba opened her purse to pay the bill. "That is why I looked for the nicest face. Somebody *sympático*."

"Somebody what?"

Luba told him in Russian.

At the door Sergei clasped his forehead and hurried back for the parcel under his chair.

"What is it you carry in that?"

"My training suit. First, I put on a shirt and trousers. Then the suit. When I get out, off comes the suit and I am a citizen, an American perhaps, who can tell?"

"Sergei, you must not take such risks."

"It is because I am so difficult." Sergei laughed. "My roommate feels as I do, but he is tractable. He says, 'I won't tell, *tovarich*, it's your neck.' Before the events, you will

348

come and dance, won't you? I know how to get out at night."

"No. You must behave. You will get us both into trouble."

"I will come anyhow. I will come to your hotel and find you. I will drink vodka and shout in the hotel, 'Tell Lubushka that Sergei, the difficult Russian, is here.'"

In the taxi, Sergei undid the parcel and pulled the training suit over his shirt and trousers.

He grinned at Luba. "Tell the driver to stop in the trees."

The training suit had been wrapped in a copy of *Pravda*. When he was well away from the taxi, Sergei opened the paper and strolled toward the Village, intent on the pages, using them like a screen.

Luba was impatient. She flounced her hips.

"He is just a sweet boy. You're getting nerves, no? Why shouldn't I talk with him? I am half a Russian."

Clark said, "Yeah, which half is what I want to know. These Ivans are dynamite, Luba. They've got more watchdogs on their team than athletes. You've got to keep your nose clean."

"Communists, Communists, you Americans are sick about Communists. In Saigon it was the same. He's a Communist. Bang! It is very silly and not nice."

"Yeah, and he's a running dog of imperialistic fascist revisionism. Bang!" Clark said.

Luba wrinkled her nose. "What does that mean?"

"Who the hell knows? You just let that Ivan get decadent with one of the locals. We got enough worries, Crissake."

"Pfftt," Luba said.

One clear, blue day followed another. In the mornings and evenings, the air hung cold and fresh. Cars, buses, motor scooters tooted down the mountain on the curving road over the plains to San Bernardino and panted up in the evening, the engine hoods hot to touch. The fiesta on the heights had changed its mood. The visitors had done their sightseeing. Now they needed the drama: the release that came as ninety-four nations clashed in the arenas. It began with the announcement that swept everywhere with the force of wind before a storm.

The Olympic torch had left Athens.

Addie had picked up a tip for McBride, drinking around the bars. They sat in the stands and watched the Dutch swimmers.

"That's Kroon, the champion," Addie said. "The thickset boy. That's Van Ebsen, with the watch and towel. This is it, he's calling them on to the blocks."

Kroon and his backup flung their arms and speared into the water.

"Two hundred meters," Addie said. "That's four lengths."

McBride lit a cigarette. Van Ebsen, the coach, paced the poolside. Kroon led from the first turn, drew away a little farther at the second turn. The butterfly stroke churned waves to slap and splash against the walls. Addie touched Alec McBride on the arm. "Here it comes." Kroon had made the last turn. He had covered a third of the length. Suddenly, as though something irresistible had propelled him, Kroon shot forward, in a dazzling, thrashing finish. At the pool's far end he hung heaving. Van Ebsen knelt to him, his voice soft. After minutes, the coach helped his swimmer from the water. The other boy stood with them, dripping. Van Ebsen put the towel around Kroon's shoulders. They passed down the pool's far side into the dressing rooms behind the starting blocks.

Addie pointed into the water that still lapped. "Can you see it?"

Where the Dutch swimmer had spurted into his soaring finish, a drain cock rippled its outline through the water.

In the bar at the press center, McBride said, "I know the swimmers were experimenting with hypnotism some years ago, but that was more the do-it-yourself kind, the power of positive thinking. This Aussie official was drunk, you say?"

"Stoned out of his mind. Kroon has a mate in the Australian team. Kroon told him. He told this official."

"Van Ebsen does the hypnotizing?"

"He does it in the dressing rooms."

"Well, it seems to work. Kroon took off like a rocket."

"Wouldn't you? If you were hypnotized to look for a drain cock that turned into a shark in the home stretch? They're bent, these gladiators. They make me sick."

"They're not like us," McBride said. "Don't order for me, Addie. I've got to go to the airport."

The reception lounges were packed. Hotel guides and car-hire representatives pushed among the passengers. The loudspeakers shouted each other down in a medley of languages. Porters trundled their trolleys, called warnings. McBride felt the welcome chill as the perspiration on his chest dried in the air conditioning. He continued to search. The welcome went out of his face.

350

"Oh, no," McBride said.

Gabby Charlton, in a vinyl hat shaped like a space helmet and a linen suit trimmed in vinyl, was pushing toward him. Behind her, Mary was seating the baby in a collapsible pusher.

Gabby waved.

"There he is, darling," she told Mary. "Alec. Over here, Alec."

While McBride bent to kiss them, Gabby fluttered on.

"Don't look so black. It wasn't my idea. Mary fretted about leaving the baby. Of course, she couldn't possibly handle him on her own, so what could I do? I had to come." She bent to straighten the baby's bonnet. "There now, see, Uncle Alec is here to meet us. Doesn't he look marvelous, Alec?"

"He looks fine," McBride said flatly. "Gabby, you promised to stay out of this."

"Oh, don't be a bear." Gabby was nervous. "Somebody has to look after one small boy."

"You could have looked after him at home."

"I told you. Mary didn't want to leave him. My goodness, men are exasperating. You might say hello to Mary instead of standing there like a storm."

Mary smiled. "When you two are quite finished."

He looked at her properly and some of the darkness left his face. She wore a sleeveless sheath dress in the same vinyl as Gabby's, with shining black vinyl shoes. The blond curtain of hair sparkled with lights. The strong, round knees were bared by the short skirt.

McBride said, meaning it, "You look gorgeous, mother. Better than ever."

Arranging transport and luggage, Mary was able to ask, "Have you seen Harry?"

"Yes. Quite a few times."

"How does he look?"

"He is trained to a razor's edge, Mary. He's not easy to talk to." He had a question of his own. "What does Gabby think she is going to do for accommodations? This town has been booked solid for months."

"Gabby has a suite next to my rooms. It was booked at the same time, I discover."

"Oh, no," McBride said.

"Don't worry, Alec. It is true that I didn't want to leave the baby. If Harry doesn't care to see me when this is all over, it won't be as bad, having the baby with me."

"One of these days, I am going to lay Gabby across my knees."

"It's a bit late for that."

"It's never too late," McBride said.

44

HARVEY TONKIN'S happiness beamed on his face like lights. "That Scotty. He looks just great. Doesn't he look like a million dollars, Buddy? When I saw him there in the lobby, the old Stars and Stripes on his chest, well, I dunno. This thing has got me. When you look around, the whole joint jumping, and think we fixed it, it's a funny feeling. Back there in Bombay I couldn't have found Santa Anna on a map with both hands. For the first time since I joined the Department I feel like Harvey the operator. T'hell with it. Let's kill another bottle."

Schultz had put on weight. He sat in the big cane chair with his legs stretched. He still brushed his hair forward.

"Not for me. I've got a dinner appointment."

Harvey had been walking up and down in his pleasure. He stopped with the champagne uncorked, a little more wrinkled, his eyes a little more pouched, but unaged, more than ever like a depraved little boy.

"I thought you were joining Liz and me for dinner. What's this appointment? Can't you take a raincheck?"

Schultz shook his head.

"Official?"

"Yes."

"That's what happens when you get into the big time. It's not about to happen to me. I'll probably retire as the world's oldest vice-consul." He looked critically at Schultz and popped the cork. "I always said you'd make it, didn't I, buddy? That deputation to meet us. I was looking around for the Secretary of State." He filled his glass thoughtfully. "You think Scotty has anything going with this lady doctor?"

"You can't be a golden boy all your life," Schultz said sourly.

"You can goddam well try. When they trap me they'll have to use a net."

The telephone rang. Harvey took it. "It's the Embassy car."

Schultz lost his boredom.

Harvey handed over his hat. "How about lunch tomorrow?"

"I've got a full day, Harve."

"A drink before dinner then?"

"I don't know how I'll be fixed. Why don't I call you?"

"Yeah. Do that."

Harvey watched the door after it had closed behind Schultz. He walked to the balcony and looked down past the great stadium to the Village, the packed streets, the broken bowl starry with lights, the stirring beehive buzzing.

"T'hell with it."

He drank the champagne, grinning with satisfaction, opened his fingers and let the glass smash on the tiles.

"*Olé!*" Harvey said.

The taxi driver sat impatiently, listening to his meter tick.

"Well," Scott asked, "did you like him?"

"Which one?" Liz said.

"Both of them, I suppose. Harvey in particular."

"He's a darling. Just as you described him. His friend is more reserved."

"Maybe that's what happens when you become important. It was great seeing Harve again. He will show you a good time tonight, Liz. When Harvey goes, he really goes."

"I wish you hadn't suggested it."

"Why not? Harvey's my best buddy."

"That's exactly it. You've had such wild times together. He might find me a drag, Scott. He is very sophisticated, really."

"Nonsense," Scott said decisively. "How would he find you a drag? He likes you, I could see that."

"I do hope so."

"You wait and see. Dress up in that red outfit. Knock his eyes out."

"I'll try."

They came close.

"Well, this is it until the balloon goes up."

"I know. I don't know what to say."

"It's all been said. I'll just stew in my own juice, get the charge up. Liz, I don't have to tell you, do I, what having you here has meant?"

She leaned against him. "Oh, Scotty."

He lifted her chin. Her clear slanting eyes ran with tears. "Come, now. What's this about?"

"I'm sorry. It's everything. It's as if none of it was really true before. Oh, Scotty, it's such a terrible race."

Scott swallowed. "Who's got the ace in the hole? Who's got

his own lady doctor to prove it? I'm a freak, remember. I've got a head start on the world."

She wiped her eyes and nodded.

"True?" Scott smiled.

"True."

They were silent, leaning together.

"Liz, when this is over . . . I mean, any way it comes out . . . Liz, when this is over, I want you and me to go away together. A few days somewhere, down on the coast away from everyone, in a village on the beach."

Liz sniffed and blinked her eyes dry. "Scotty, that will be wonderful. Shall I find a place, book the rooms?"

"Yes," Scott said. "You find a place. And, Liz, just book the one room."

He had kissed her forehead, got in and slammed the door on the already moving car before Liz could speak. When he looked back, a long way down the road, she had not moved, still stood fixed to the spot.

In the packed, noisy club Harvey led Liz off the dance floor and sprawled into his chair, panting.

"One thing about being a short-ass, Liz, your partners have to hold you up."

Liz was flushed, laughing. "Hold you up? I couldn't even catch you. Where did you learn to dance like that?"

"In In'ia. On hot coals."

At the next table a big man put on the matador's hat again. "Hey, *toro!*" he shouted.

The woman next to him snatched at the hat. She was close to tears with exasperation. The big man lurched to his feet, fumbled out of his jacket, and using it like a cape, taking mincing little steps, circled the woman's chair, flapping the jacket at her.

"Hey, *toro!*" he shouted again. "You old bag."

"Charlie, can't you do anything? Everyone is looking at us. Betty, this is awful."

The sandy-haired man blinked heavy eyes. "Sit down, you great galah."

The big man flapped his jacket and backed away. Near the door he fumbled into the jacket, lifted the matador's cap and bowed.

"You can all get stuffed," he announced, clapped on the matador's cap and disappeared through the doorway.

At the table, the woman covered her flaming face with her

hands. The sandy man blinked at the empty doorway. He lifted his head and widened his mouth.

"Hey, *tor-ro!*"

It was too much. The two women scrambled for their hats and bags and hurried out of the club.

"Aussies," Harvey told Liz.

It was he who was president here, not that man in the palace. It was his kingdom. They were his subjects, the flower of the youth of the world. This was his fulfillment and hope, the triumph that reared its own monuments and riveted the world. The old man forgot his wounds. Day and night he gave audiences. The great and powerful passed through his suite. At glittering dinners they hushed when he rose. The crowding press followed him everywhere. His was the power, his was the pomp. In all the world not a jackal bayed.

There he is. There he goes. That's him. That's Mathew C. Kaverly. There was no weight of years on him now. There was no more forbidding chill in his marrow. He went to bed, when he did, as a duty, impatient for the rise of the sun. He had no need of sleep, since sleep came quickly when he stretched at ease on the outsized bed. The servant who brought his hot chocolate last thing at night heard the words the old man sang as he undressed.

"It happened in Monterey, a long time ago . . ."

The old man put the cup back on its saucer and turned off the lights.

". . . it broke somebody's heart and sad to say that it was mine. It happened in . . ."

He smiled at the dark room. The Olympic flame had left Athens.

Sergei Mikhailovitch left the telephone booth and went back to the amusement hall. He sat on a bench at the Ping-Pong tables.

"Here, Sergei. Take a bat."

Sergei brushed the hand away. The Ping-Pong bat bounced on the rubber flooring.

"I am going to bed."

"Come, Sergei, it's early. What's up?"

"Leave me alone. I'm going to bed."

Three times he had telephoned, rehearsing his English. Three times he had got the same message. Miss Ivanova was not available. She had left with the Maharaja of Sardar. Sergei picked up a stone and hurled it violently against a trash bin.

It had been Sam Clark's idea. The flame was flown in from Athens to the secondary airport at San Bernardino. On the flag-hung road from the coast, one athlete from each of the competing nations was stationed to relay the sacred flame to the looming bronze bowl that topped the great stadium. With the sun flashing on its polished sides, the bowl itself was like a flame of metal.

Clark had said, "It's a simple matter of timing. If we bring it in from Santa Anna airport, we've got nothing. But we run that flame all the Crissake way up the mountain. We time it to come off the plains after sundown. Every few hundred yards on that mountain, we have a runner. Can't you see that, at night? Everyone who can move on a crutch will be at the cliffs, watching that flame climb up the sky. Everything's going for us. It's a new moon. We put an honor guard on the flame overnight at the Presidential Palace. Next morning we kindle the torch."

The new moon hung like a sliver of fingernail. Cars were parked everywhere on the cliffs and jammed at vantage places on the curved mountain road. Before the sun teetered on the humped skyline, glazing the clouds, and fell to submerge the mountains into sudden darkness, they had watched the highway that stretched across the plain to the coast, dotted with cars and clumped fields, searched through binoculars for the glint of fire. In the warm darkness even the earth and trees seemed to take short, harsh breaths. Not a car on the mountain showed a light. In the waiting dark, smokers were conscious of the red that burned on their cigarettes, and shielded the light in their hands. On the heights they heard the dull roar from watchers lower down as the flame appeared, smoking and guttering, wheeling light and shadows on the sweating faces of the athletes who labored upward, one aching arm high, to pass on the flame and stand with heaving bellies as it danced upward again in the dark.

In the Presidential Palace General Pisarro moved smoothly among his guests. Bueno smiled and accepted the congratulations as president of the Games Organizing Committee. His hand shook when he lifted his glass. Bob Schultz looked across the room to a group around the old man; he was curious now, no longer concerned about being recognized and remembered. Behind the fortressed walls and over their own loud humming, the VIP's in the palace heard the great, shaking roar as the flame topped the mountain at last. They readied themselves for the small ceremony that would preface the vigil of that night.

Sam Clark took an exhausted nightcap in Rex Prentice's suite.

"It's hard to believe it's over, Crissake. I feel as though I'd lost a leg or something. Have you ever known a night like tonight? It was like that ball they had before that battle."

"Waterloo," Prentice said.

"Yeah, Waterloo. It's hard to believe it's over."

"It's not over," Prentice reminded him.

When the sun rose, the sky was clear and the air cold and brittle. The great stadium sharpened into color. Trees crowded the concourse. A hill, which had been leveled on the crown and planted with grass, snuggled one side of the building, drawing it into the landscape. The slopes of tiered seats shone pale blue, like the sky at that hour, checkered by divisions of white-painted concrete. In each tier the square entrance tunnels were framed solid by white-painted concrete. The cupped field was shaved as flat and smooth as the green baize on a billiard table. On the field's margins the white-laned tracks drew lines on the darker cinders. Opposite the tunnels from which the athletes would enter the arena from the dressing rooms, the official stand backed a small rostrum. Here, a single ladder of steps climbed abruptly from the ground to the tall bronze bowl that topped the topmost tier and waited to fill with fire.

The great stadium warmed and sparkled its colors. Nothing stirred in the sunrise.

By ten that morning a hundred thousand spectators had blotted the blue walls of the amphitheater from sight. The beehive hum of the city had fused in one undulating roar. Dust rose in tall clouds about the concourse, as though the pounding feet and buses and cars had squeezed it by their weight from the concrete. Hawkers, ticket touts and uniformed attendants scrambled and pushed for attention. Officials in badged blazers sweated and worried in the din. Ice-cream and soft-drink cartons, candy wrappers and peanut bags, blew and littered, shed from the crowded humanity like something organic, falling like leaves from a tree.

In the hot sun they scuffled on the concrete cliffs, made newspaper hats against the glare. The nine saluting cannons on the center of the field pointed their muzzles to the sky. The bandsmen took off their heavy caps, wiped their foreheads, blew into their instruments as though to clear the polished brass throats. Soldiers sat crouched at a long line of boxes, peering into their wire-meshed tops, holding tight to pull-strings. Behind the bronze bowl that dominated everything, the young lieutenant of engineers peered out nervously. He had rehearsed himself a dozen times.

"What if it doesn't work?" he had asked.

"Shoot yourself," his colonel had told him.

There were two cocks to turn. One, gasoline pre-ignition to heat the jet. The other, to start the flow of oil. It was important to keep out of sight, to get the timing right.

The runner was out of the tunnel and on his circuit of the stadium before most of the spectators saw him. The nine-gun salute jolted them to attention. They opened their throats and a wordless wave of sound rose and carried to the heights. Smoke hung on from muzzles of the cannons. Smoke lifted from the torch, streamed behind like a pennant. They rose in the official stand when the old man got up, one arm out in the salute of an emperor.

Slowly, painfully, past tier after tier on the ladder of steps that reached to the sky, the bearer of the torch jogged the climb to the towering bronze bowl. The stadium hushed as he climbed. From the tiers opposite, the torchbearer's toiling white figure was small on the black concrete ladder. On either side of the steps the myriad faces darkened as the flame passed and heads turned to crane upwards. He was there at last, walking the steps, to turn on the platformed pinnacle. Solitary, erect, he stood in salute, one arm stiffened at his side, the other stretched overhead, the Olympic flame and the pennant of smoke bent toward the stadium by the breeze. Then he reached to full height and plunged the torch into the bowl.

It was very still. Black smoke eddied, darkened, thickened, blew back over the stadium. And then the flame burst out in a gush, blazed high and steadied. The mob voice roared into storm. The soldiers at the boxes pulled on their strings, the wire-meshed lids flipped open. With a whir of freed wings a thousand white doves beat upwards in a cloud. The brass bands at either end of the field crashed into the Olympic anthem. Through the entrance tunnel, flags waving, the uniformed teams and officials from ninety-four of the Earth's nations began the grand march past. In the official box the old man stood staring out blindly, his humped shoulders trembling. From time to time he lifted his arm in an emperor's salute.

45

ACROSS THE broken bowl of Santa Anna, at the arenas, pools, cycling tracks, rings, mats, gymnasiums, football fields, fencing halls, on the Retiro Park lake and on the green and cinders of the great stadium, the athletes clashed and clashed day after day in the rolling roars of the crowd.

Day after day, the one who was champion of all his or her kind on earth mounted the victor's dais in a fanfare of trumpets while unbelief spun away on a god's power and triumph. In the stands the victor's countrymen rose to their feet, waving flags, bawling their national anthem over the braying brass of the bands, their hot eyes glittering with emotion, blood hot with patriotism, hearts fierce with arrogance. On the dais the victors bent while the ribboned medals of gold were slipped over their heads. The victors straightened, threw their arms high, high overhead, and every voice that thundered the sky was raised for their single acclamation.

Alec McBride tapped out "ends" on his typewriter and pulled the copy sheet from the roller. Ordinarily, he would not have troubled to file the story. The finals of the 200-meter butterfly would be decided between Kroon of Holland and Mikhailovitch of Russia. Each had won his heat decisively. McBride had written: "If Kroon surges home to steal Russia's only remaining chance for a wet Gold Medal, watch for a par in this column that will *hypnotize* you."

McBride was hot and dirty and tired. He decided to give himself a drink before changing to take Mary Hayes to dinner. He had talked with Harry and Persons in the Village. They were both keyed to a pitch that made conversation a trial. It was natural. There had been collapses in the heats, attributed to the altitude. It had been on McBride's mind as a worry and he had been careful to avoid the subject.

"Have you heard anything about those grassed trout in the hospital?" Persons had sounded arrogant, mocking. "The Manchester boy is in rather poor shape. They're going to need all their ambulances for the Marathon."

It had shocked McBride. His eyes had gone immediately to Harry. Harry's face was drawn, but his eyes smiled back, unconcerned.

"Let's hope not," McBride said.

"You know what their trouble is?" Persons was still smiling, still hard and mocking. "They came up when they should have been going down."

McBride said, "You don't have much team spirit."

Persons snorted. "For what? For a lot of half-prepared men and women so beggared by poverty and the stupidity of their officials that they'd be hard pressed to compete on equal terms with the first Bantu free state? Don't talk to me about team spirit. Every other Government that matters has made some attempt to support their athletes, to support national prestige. Have you heard an American team captain lecturing his athletes? 'This is for America. We've got to beat the Russians. Go out there and kill yourself if you must, but bring back that gold. The country's behind you, the President's behind you. Be a hero for America. Go out there and bust a gut.' The British came to Santa Anna gasping for oxygen and will leave gasping with shame. Afterwards we will comfort ourselves that it's the game that matters, not the winning, while the whole world dismisses us with scorn. My team spirit is for Harry and me. We will beat the bastards our own way."

McBride checked his watch. He padded on wet feet out of the bathroom, wearing a robe, to pour another drink while the air conditioning dried the damp from his skin. His back was to the door when the knock came. McBride swilled the few unmelted slivers of ice around the bucket.

"Come in."

The door opened tentatively, the face appeared in the jamb. McBride held up the bucket.

"Ice," he said. "I asked for ice half an hour ago."

McBride put the bucket down and stared at the man so incongruously dressed in a shabby black suit.

"Mr. McBride?"

"That's right."

"Permit me to introduce myself. Conrad Carson, assistant to the IOC Chancellor."

"Come in, Carson. What can I do for you?"

"I apologize for not calling from the lobby. I did not want to draw attention to my visit."

McBride was trying to identify the accent, the slightly stilted speech. "Oh?" he said.

"No. I've come, I have decided to come, on a rather delicate matter."

"Are you sure you've got the right McBride?"

"Yes. I know your newspaper. I get the airmail edition in Lausanne."

McBride turned his back and poured whisky and soda into a second glass. The man needed a drink. He was quaking with nerves.

"I'm afraid I'm out of ice," McBride said. "Please sit down."

Carson took the drink, sitting awkwardly forward in the big chair. The polished skin of his bald crown gleamed in the light. Dandruff flecked his shoulders. His tongue licked at his lips.

"It is very difficult to know where to start."

"Start at the beginning," McBride said cheerfully.

"The beginning?" It seemed to confuse Conrad Carson.

"Then start at the end." McBride was impatient, thinking about the time.

It seemed to trigger Carson. His head came up. "He dismissed me. After fifteen years he dismissed me. I am not young. I have no prospects."

"Who dismissed you?" McBride looked at his visitor carefully.

"He did. Mathew C. Kaverly. The president. He dismissed me."

McBride sniffed through his crumpled nose and put his glass on the table. He had been hit by the stale fumes of drink on the other man.

"Sorry to hear it. Now you must excuse me. I have a dinner engagement."

"I know the whole story. I know how Santa Anna got the Games. It was political. The Bombay conference was manipulated by agents. Kaverly blackmailed the French into voting for Santa Anna. He sold the Games to Pay Television to buy off a revolt from the federations. That's why the Games are here in this altitude. That's why those men are in the hospital. He does what he likes, you know. It couldn't have happened in Mr. Brundage's time."

McBride opened a packet of cigarettes, trying to process his thoughts. "You say that political agents manipulated the Bombay conference. What kind of political agents?"

"Secret Service agents."

"Oh," McBride said, keeping his eyes down to light the cigarette. "What sort of Secret Service agents?"

"American agents."

McBride looked up then. "You're sure of this?"

"Yes, yes. There was other trouble. The Russians wanted the Games for Prague."

McBride looked sadly into his drink, then tossed it off. He twirled the empty glass, watching the light wink on the rim.

"And you want to sell me the story."

Carson licked his lips. "The truth should come out."

"Yes," McBride said.

Carsons's voice was tremulous. "It should be worth a great deal of money."

"Yes," McBride said. "I imagine it would take care of your lack of prospects, Carson."

Conrad Carson got to his feet. "Can I take it we have an arrangement?"

McBride shook his head. "No," he said. "*We* don't have an arrangement. Not you and I, Carson. I write about the clean people. I'll contact the paper. If they want your story they will send a specialist out."

Carson said, "I want to make an arrangement. I thought I could make an arrangement with you."

"I'll contact the paper. You'll get your answer this time to-morrow."

"You will be here?"

"I will be here. And, Carson, telephone, don't call. You stink up the rooms."

Because he had come to it at last, got it said and done, the fear and relief, the greed and the tasted revenge had exhausted Conrad Carson beyond shame or insult. He nodded at McBride and closed the door behind him.

Alec McBride stood, his head on one side, fists in the pocket of his gown, and shuffled a bare foot on the carpet. Then he sat at the table, laid out cigarettes and matches and reached for the whisky bottle.

In the entertainment hut the young swimmer eagerly opened his mail, laughing with pleasure as he read.

Kroon asked, "Good news?"

"It's my kid brother, he's six. Mum asked him what he wanted for his birthday and he said a track suit with 'Australia' on it, like Snowie's."

The boy opened another envelope, glanced at the letter and unfolded the newspaper clipping. He screwed up his handsome, brown face. "Jeez, fancy having that take a go at you."

"What is it?"

"A Noah's Ark. They reckon it's the one tore a girl in half just before we came away."

362

Kroon said, "A Noah's Ark? What is this?"

"A shark, Kroonie. Take a look. A bloody great tiger shark."

The hunters had beached the killer on an inlet between rocks and squatted behind it for the picture. A length of timber propped open the enormous mouth. The serried rows of tangled teeth hooked out of the exposed jawbones. The tiny eye in the snouted head was fixed malevolently. The shark measured twenty-two feet.

"Middle Harbour is lousy with them. I had a mate used to fish there who lost his fox terrier off the rocks. A Noah came clean out and grabbed him. This girl who was torn in half was only in three feet of water. She and her boyfriend were chipping oysters."

The Australian returned to his letter. "Jeez, my sister's got a new boyfriend. That makes about twenty this year. Listen to this, Kroonie."

He looked up. The Dutch swimmer was gray. Sweat beaded on his upper lip. His throat worked to swallow. His eyes were bulged glassily at the clipping.

"Kroonie, what is it, mate? Do you feel crook?"

The Dutchman made an effort, shoved the clipping off the table with his arm and dropped his head.

"Kroonie, what's the trouble? Will I get a doctor, Kroonie?"

"No, no. In a minute I will be better." The Dutchman's voice was muffled on his arm.

"Would you like a glass of water?"

"Please, yes."

He smiled weakly when he took the carton, gulped the ice water and sat up. Color rose on his face.

"Now I'm better."

"Jeez, you gave me a scare, mate. Just take it easy. I got like that before the finals in Jamaica. It's nothing to worry about. You'll eat that Russian tomorrow night, Kroonie. I've watched him. He's sloppy on the turns."

Kroon said, "Yes."

"Do you feel well enough for a walk? I could do with a bit of fresh air."

"Yes," Kroon said. "Thank you."

Luba lay in the tub, sucking crème de menthe over ice, clapping her rosy knees to foam the bubble crystals. She was thinking seriously about Sardar and frowning. Her free hand absently fanned a hard, dark nipple. Luba could not understand herself and frowned for that, too. She had been very good for a long time. Absorbed in the work and responsibility. When she went to confession in New York her regular priest was surprised by the triviality of Luba's sins and had more than once inquired about her health. She had often thought of Sardar and the magic night in the lake palace where she had been the Princess Luba. But the memory was recalled for its beauty and glitter, to be fondled like a bracelet of diamonds, admired for its perfection, with no involvement of heart or nostalgia.

She had forgotten his voice, the deep, very English tones. He had sounded like a stranger when she telephoned. Luba had gone almost casually to the lobby, she had worked hard that day with Clark, duties still buzzed in her mind. She had walked straight past Sardar. He had been partly screened by the winter garden.

"Princess Luba."

In that instant Luba had felt a flame on the lobes of her ears. She did not turn at once and Sardar had called again. He was smiling, holding a Panama hat. Gray streaked back from his forehead. He was a massive man, a little stouter now.

In a rush, the moonlight that had beamed across Sardar's bedroom from the lake, the white, shafted light in which she had stepped so deliberately to let the sari fall, came back to Luba. She saw herself there and the strange, hurt expression on his face as he had watched her. She felt weak, tiny and shy.

It had been much like that ever since. They had been almost formal with each other. Luba wasn't used to being shy; it irritated and confused her. She clapped her knees in the tub, foaming the bubbles, thinking about it, frowning, sucking noisily at the iced crème de menthe. They had only once laughed properly and had fun. That was when Sardar had given Harvey and the lady doctor lunch in a private room.

She sat naked before the mirror, the powder in the cropped pubic hair making a tiny white apron. The dense, short black hair was curled forward in two horns on her cheeks. The knocking was loud and familiar, a bustling rat-tat-a-tat. Luba picked up her watch. It was 8:30. She did not expect Sardar for an hour. She made a quick, inquisitive inspection in the glass and hurried to the bed for her robe.

She had locked the door. The handle was being rattled when Luba turned the key. Immediately the door pushed open.

"I have come," Sergei Mikhailovitch said in English.

He wore his white shirt and blue trousers, and carried the usual parcel under his arm. He turned the key in the door while Luba gaped at him, then unwrapped the parcel and extracted a bottle of vodka from the track suit.

"A toast to my success tomorrow," Sergei said. "Where have you been? Who is the Maharaja of Sardar?"

He opened the bottle, filled a glass and drank it.

She could do nothing with him. She was a prisoner in the room. Neither entreaty nor vituperation would move him. When Luba had run for the door he beat her to it and pocketed the key.

"You said you would come dancing. You promised me. I have come. We will dance, if necessary, here in your room. You have not been true to your word."

When Reception called at 9:30, Sergei glared at the telephone. "You are not here. Do not answer."

"I must," Luba said tearfully. "Sergei, please go. There will be so much trouble. How will you swim tomorrow? Sergei, don't be a fool."

"I am not being a fool. I am being difficult. You were difficult. Now it is my turn."

The telephone continued to ring. Luba was lost. There was nothing she could do that would not cause trouble.

"You are not here, remember," Sergei said, his face reddened by the vodka.

She lifted the telephone while he watched fiercely.

Luba said, "Miss Ivanova is working late. Please to say she is sorry."

"Put it down," Sergei said. "Where is the music in this room?"

Once, he had gone into the bathroom. Luba took the bottle and ran to the balcony to empty it into a plant. He found her there and snatched the bottle away.

"No, Sergei. You must not drink. You are horrible like this. Please, it is not too late. You must get back before they miss you. If you get drunk how will you swim?"

Sergei smiled, put his arms at his sides and fluttered his hands.

"I am a fish. They turned me into a fish. When a fish can't walk a fish can swim, I believe."

"Oh, my God," Luba said, and poured herself a vodka so that Sergei would not drink it. She fought him off when he wanted to dance.

Sergei turned up the radio and danced by himself while

Luba gagged on the vodka. She knocked over several glasses before he noticed.

Later, in a sweet, aching voice, Sergei Mikhailovitch sang old Russian songs.

"This my grandfather taught me. Come, sing with me. We are Russians. Your father was born in my grandfather's village. Your father deserted the revolution. If he goes back to his village my grandfather, the general, will no doubt cut off his head."

Luba began to sing, tears spreading the mascara which widened her eyes in the fashion Sardar admired. She was quite drunk and wondered why she held out her glass. Then she remembered that Sergei must not drink. Anything else was hard to remember.

In the bars and clubs, in the Village where those who would contend tomorrow lay awake and listened to their hearts, in ten thousand bedrooms on the heights, life played out its movable dramas. In the old city a great group of Polish spectators marched like soldiers, a standard-bearer carrying the flag on his belt while they bundled everything and everyone before them. Their marching songs resounded on the leaning buildings. Their feet beat in step on the gutted, cobbled lanes. That afternoon in the 400-meter run, a Pole had bent on the dais for the Gold Medal. Another Pole had bent for the Silver. The Russian had stared straight ahead and bent stiffly for the Bronze.

And outside San Bernardino, in the hot, sticky night of the coast, the Italian cyclists sang and toasted their hero in wine and cognac. The beach house had been rented for the purpose. In the big room and on the thatched patio, they sprawled in the cane chairs, fondling and nuzzling their girls, walked crookedly to splash in the dark, tepid water.

At first when the girl screamed in the bedroom, they hardly paused to gesticulate and smile. There had been other girls screaming. It was Lucibello's night. He had raced 109 miles on the roads that day to win the Gold Medal for Italy. When she screamed again, and then again and again, the men stopped, pushed the girls off their knees. Doors banged and then she was among them. A tumbled, naked girl, crying hysterically in French and English.

Sam Clark was drinking at the bar in the Esmeralda, permitting himself a little relaxation. Harvey Tonkin was buying champagne for everyone, escorting a tall dark air hostess. He wore her Spanish comb in his hair and climbed off his stool from time to time to make the girl stand alongside him. She was six to eight inches taller than Harvey.

"Look at that. I got a whole lotta woman here, you can believe it. This a whole lotta Spanish woman. Back on your stool, Señorita Grande."

Clark took the call on the bar telephone, pressing one ear with his finger. "He what? Who did? Lucibello? You sure of this? Yeah, yeah. Crissake. Where? Oh, for Crissake. What kind of Scandinavian girl? Check the name in the team lists. Pull down the shutters on everything. Yeah, yeah. I'm on my way."

Clark dropped the telephone and sat frozen for a moment, staring stupidly.

Harvey said, "Make some room in that glass, Sam, old buddy."

Clark did not answer. Then he swung on the stool and rushed from the bar.

"How about that?" Harvey asked with surprise. He shrugged. "T'hell with it."

At the press center a few late-working journalists were using the communications room and strung thinly along the bar. In their own office, Pip Harris was replacing the telephone as Sam Clark rushed in.

"Have you got anything new? When did it happen?"

"About ten, as far as I can make out."

"When did you get it?"

"About eleven."

Clark looked at his watch. "Crissake, that was two hours ago."

"I've been trying to raise you. We've been telephoning all over town. I thought you must be on a job with Luba, somewhere. Her hotel said she's working."

"Not with me she isn't. You heard from the hospital?"

"As you walked in."

"Well, come on give it to me."

"Dead on arrival."

Clark sat on a chair. "How can he be dead on arrival? He won a Gold Medal today."

"It won't help him now," Pip Harris said. "All the gold medals there are won't help him now."

Clark rubbed his face. "You got the under-the-carpet committee on this?"

"Straight away. It was our doc who called."

"But what happened?" Clark asked, his voice rising. "I can't see any sense to this thing."

"The doc says he had been drugged for the race. Digitalis, cortisone, Lepazol, Benzedrine—it could have been anything. They use them all. Doc says it was probably Benzedrine. It can be carried in the glove, taken any time in a race of 109 miles. You can't be watching all the time. Then there was the exhaustion, the strain of the altitude. Then there was the alcohol. Then there was the sex."

Clark stared at the floor. "Crissake, he didn't give himself a chance."

"That's about it," Pip Harris said.

"How are we going to get this under the carpet? Have you checked out the girl yet?"

"We're safe there. She isn't an athlete."

"You said the San Bernardino police reported her to be a competitor when they took depositions."

"She was wearing a track suit."

"So, that makes her an athlete."

"No. She's a team hostess."

"What's a Crissake team hostess?"

"The Scandinavians are practical."

"You mean?" Clark's voice was rising again.

"That's what I mean."

"I'm going to get some coffee," Clark said. "You want coffee?"

"Get a pot."

When Clark came back he asked again, "How are we going to get all this under the carpet?"

Pip Harris studied his chief. "You know what, Sam? I think his own officials will have to whitewash this."

Clark looked up hopefully.

"They've already made a claim on the body. Look at it this way. Lucibello won a Gold Medal today." The Englishman stroked his sleek beard.

"So?"

"It's not Lucibello's medal now, it's Italy's. It has gone up there on the scoreboard. If they do a postmortem, if there's drug in the body, that Gold Medal could go to the French ace Lucibello beat. You know how mad about cycling they are on the Continent. Can you see Italy handing France a Gold Medal?"

Clark scrubbed his crew cut and sipped the coffee. "You know, I've never seen a Gold Medal. You imagine busting your gut, using years of your life, maybe dead on arrival like Lucibello, for a chickenshit lump of gold-plated lead hung on a rag?"

368

Pip Harris said, "I don't believe I've thought about it."

"Neither have I," Clark told him. "And I'm not about to start now. It's going to be a long night."

Luba Ivanova swallowed the cold saliva that rose in her mouth. Almost immediately her stomach knotted and heaved, the room glazed. With one hand reaching she crossed to the bathroom, slammed the door. Sergei barely noticed her go. He was dancing, the tails of his white shirt fluttering. He heard Luba's retching, coughing ruin over the loud beat of the music, let his arms drop and pinched his eyes at the room as though it surprised him to be there. She came out blindly, swallowing, the baby mouth shining with spittle, and pushed at him weakly, unable to talk, when he put his arms about her for comfort. Luba found the bed and fell there, moaning softly into the pillow. In a minute her breath came loud and coarse, bubbling in her throat. Mascara streaked the pillow. The robe opened on the strong, naked legs. The tan she had got at the Retiro Park lake looked like tall, dark stockings. Sergei Mikhailovitch tried to think. He shook her shoulder to wake her. Luba moaned and turned, sprawling her legs. He tried to think, to clear his head, aware of some disaster, but he could not identify it or think what to do. He could not lift his eyes from Luba. In the yellow reflections of the sitting room's light, Sergei Mikhailovitch lay on the bed and tried to take Luba in his arms.

In another wing of the hotel, on the floor above, in a suite that looked down the Avenida de España, Sam Clark brushed his teeth and observed the pouches under his eyes. The sky had been lightening with dawn when he got back from meeting the Italians. It had been a madhouse. Clark was not sure what had been decided. It had not yet got to the press; everything was clamped down tight. Pip Harris had been right. The Italians had forbidden a postmortem.

Clark was still tired, jumping with nerves, as his team waited around the table at 9:30 next morning in the press center headquarters.

"Where in hell is Luba?" Clark asked irritably.

Prentice, too, was late. It soured Clark. It seemed to him that his partner could carry a bit more weight on this operation. They waited silently, looking at their watches.

"Take your time," Sam Clark said, before Rex Prentice had closed the door.

"We've got trouble," Prentice announced.

Clark blew out his breath in disgust. "Rex thinks we've got trouble," he told Pip Harris.

"One of the Russians has defected."

Sam Clark's mouth dropped wide-open.

When Luba opened her eyes, she puzzled at the black streaks on the pillow. The noise she had heard in her dreaming, the sawing sound, continued. She shut her eyes again, listening. Images of recollection blurred in her head. Her mouth was parched and painful. She licked her lips with a dry tongue. She moved and felt a weight pressing her. Luba's eyes struck open as though widened on pain. She lay frozen, while memory cleared and washed her. Luba started up. Sergei Mikhailovitch lay beside her, snoring loudly and peacefully, his cheek pillowed on his palm.

Behind the closed door of the bathroom where she had led him, Luba shook on Sardar's shoulder.

"And I didn't want you to know he was here and I just said I had to work late. You believe me, no?"

He tipped her chin and nodded. "You clean that dirty face and get dressed. I will talk with the boy."

"No," Luba sniffed. "He has little English. I will have to make translations. Sardar, what will they do to him?"

Sardar sat on the bath and inspected his Panama hat.

"I don't know." He looked up. "Go on, wash your face. Is your head aching?"

"*Boom, boom,*" Luba said, miserably, running water into the bowl. She clenched her fist and struck herself quite hard on the forehead. "Like this, *boom, boom.*"

"The first thing is to get him away from here."

"Back into the Village, no?"

"I imagine it's too late for that. I think it would be best to take him to my rooms, then we shall see. We will telephone Clark. It's his business to make up stories."

Luba said, "He will kill me stone-dead, that Clark."

There was a noise from the bedroom. "My God." Luba stared over the towel at Sardar. "Sergei is awake."

Shortly before midday, while the rumors of a Russian defection were already blowing on the heights, the Maharaja of Sardar and Luba Ivanova left the Hotel Olympics with a young man in blue trousers, white shirt, Panama hat and sunglasses. He carried a parcel wrapped in a newspaper.

Sam Clark stood on a table at the back of the press center

bar. The room was packed with reporters. He had just read a short statement issued by the American Embassy, denying a Russian charge that a defector had been given asylum. "That's it," Clark shouted. "That's all we've got. The American Ambassador has offered, as a gesture of Olympic goodwill, to open the Embassy and its outbuildings for search by a representative body from the Games Organizing Committee."

To the shouted questions he answered, "We don't know. Apart from filing the complaint, the Russian authorities have not identified the missing competitor."

In his own rooms, crowded now by Prentice and Clark staff, Clark was given a message requiring him to report personally to General Pisarro.

"One thing," he told Pip Harris, "this will take the heat off Lucibello."

"One nail drives out another," Harris said.

A staffer, who had just entered, panted up. "I've got it, Mr. Clark. The defector."

"Quiet," Clark shouted at his staff. "Let's have it," he said.

"It's a twenty-year-old swimmer. Sergei Mikhailovitch. He's due in the butterfly finals this evening."

For the second time that morning, Clark's jaw dropped wide-open. As the crowded room buzzed on the news, Sam Clark and Pip Harris shot glances at each other. Perfectly synchronized, each said, "Luba!"

Sam Clark swallowed. "Crissake!" he added.

The shadows were lengthening. The sun burned over the humped mountain, soon to balance there and slide from sight, leaving the clouds shot with red before darkness. Clark sat on Sardar's balcony and watched it, poured himself another whisky for strength.

"I wouldn't give a good goddam if they sent him to Siberia for life. That Luba. They can have Luba too. In the salt mines they can have them both for life."

"Come, old boy," Sardar said. "It's a storm in a teacup, really. Luba's not to blame. She made herself ill trying to keep the boy sober."

"The Russians don't think it's a storm in a teacup."

"Are we agreed, then? If he swims it will make all the difference to the boy's future."

"I've got six hundred hard-nosed newspapermen here. You think they're going to believe a story like that, this kid panics and runs away because he can't face the strain? They'll laugh me out of business."

"It has happened before, Clark. It's on record."

"Last-minute panic?"

"It's not infrequent. A few Games ago an American athlete couldn't come out of the dressing room."

Clark looked interested. "That would help. I could use it for background." He thought about it. "It's a hell of a lot to swallow. Where's he supposed to have been, Crissake?"

"Wandering about, getting his nerve up."

"It's a helluva lot to swallow."

"There is, of course, an alternative."

"What's that?" Clark asked.

"He spent the night with an American-White Russian executive on the staff of Prentice and Clark."

Clark gagged like a music-hall comedian. When he had taken another drink to clear his throat he gave Sardar a frank inspection.

"Any time you step out of the maharaja business I've got a slot for you with Prentice and Clark."

Sardar boomed his laugh and clapped Clark on the shoulder. "We won't be hard on Luba, will we?"

Clark considered it. "If Luba were a boy it would be easier around here."

"That, for Luba, would be difficult," Sardar said.

"In spades." Clark agreed.

The sun went down.

The Aquatic Stadium was open to the sky, the heavy, yellow cork lines which divided the lanes shining on the floodlit pool. Because of the excitement of the Russian swimmer's defection, the four thousand seats in the tiered stands were crowded, the press box full, the walls behind the top tiers lined with standing journalists. Mathew C. Kaverly sat grimly in the official box. Behind the numbered blocks, cables tangled to the photoelectric eyes. The smell of chlorine and dampness was everywhere. The press had already dubbed the event "The Final of the Empty Lane."

The big car stood parked close to the building, the Olympic flag flying on its fender. Sardar hurried across the moonlight and opened the door.

"Now, quick. They're going to the blocks."

Sergei swallowed and tried to smile. He put out his hand. "Much thanks," he said in English. "Very much thanks."

Luba Ivanova kissed him. "Don't worry. Sardar will fix things. When you are a Master of Sport I will come and see you."

"I will take you to my village," Sergei said. "I will be no more a difficult Russian."

Behind the blocks the young men got out of their track suits, nerves twitching on chests and biceps, knelt to splash their faces from the pool or slip into the water, gasping deep breaths, pushing back the short hair from their foreheads. The officials backed away. The referee took his chair. The whistle blew to order the swimmers up on to the blocks. In four languages the loudspeaker identified the competitors.

Block 4 gapped in the lineup for the Final of the Empty Lane. The spectators sucked in their breaths.

Sergei Mikhailovitch ran from the tunnel and stepped up on Block 4.

It was not understood. The starter gaped and lowered his pistol. The referee shouted, began to climb down from his chair. Then, as Russian officials pushed and clambered, the press rose in its box and the stadium broke into uproar. In the rush the swimmers flopped into the water, jostled and surprised off their blocks. In the dressing room entrance, Sardar and Luba Ivanova strained to see through the crowd. Mathew C. Kaverly roared and shouldered his way like an old and massive bull.

In the return of order, the shouting Russian officials announced that Sergei Mikhailovitch could not compete until his absence had been explained.

The old man roared at them.

"Here," he said, "Mikhailovitch is an athlete first. Anything else comes afterwards."

Confused and protesting, the Russians were backed away by other officials and other attendants. The loudspeaker appealed for silence. The referee announced a ten-minute break to allow the finalists to settle. They swung their arms, stepped on and off the blocks, shook their muscles to loosen and relax. The stadium waited in a charged quiet while concentration on the coming effort possessed the athletes again. Sergei Mikhailovitch stood stiff and unmoving on his block, eyes fixed on the pool's far end.

The start came as a relief, and the stands poured out their excitement. Kroon and the American were fastest off the blocks. The Japanese, the Englishman and Sergei struck the water together. Kroon led from the first turn, as the yellow cork lines dipped in the swell and waves banged on the pool sides. In the second fifty meters, Kroon drew farther away, while Sergei and the little Japanese fought each other, heaving the water before them. At the third turn, Sergei Mikhailovitch lost a head to the Japanese. Kroon surged on, in the advantage of less disturbed water. They came to their feet in the stands as Kroon turned for home and the Japanese and the Russian touched together. With his lead unshaken the Dutchman swam into the certainty of an Olympic Gold Medal.

They heard the bubbled scream before lagging senses could identify or explain it. Kroon tossed up an arm, rolled in the water, banged against the yellow cork line.

Twice he shouted, went under, surfaced, then hung deathly still across the lane. On his inside the Japanese faltered. In Lane No. 4 Sergei Mikhailovitch, heaped the unbroken water.

In the first tier of seats closest to the pool, in the shock of the Dutchman's collapse, a white-faced woman asked, "My God. What happened? I thought I heard him shout shark."

"Cramp," her husband said, as officials lifted Kroon from the water. "He had it won, the poor kid. He's all knotted up with cramp."

The clamor in the stadium rose and fell on the drama. Their eyes burned hot and hands and voices shook with the memorable excitement. When Sergei Mikhailovitch weakly mounted the victor's dais, and the Russian anthem crashed out, the roar was heard on the heights.

The specialist flown out by the editor of the Sunday edition leaned forward and clicked off the tape recorder. He stood and stretched, pushing the small of his back with one hand. McBride was leaning forward, his elbows on his knees, drawing in a large ashtray with the butt of a dead cigarette, his brown eyes distant and mournful. After a time he sighed and sat back.

"Why do they do it?" he asked the specialist.

"Nine times out of ten, it's the money. Sometimes there's a sense of public duty, but mostly that's a cover for the money motive. It can be a need for attention, the human desire to expose secrets. In this case there is a revenge motive, but mostly it's the money. Everyone has a price for his story, Mac, everyone. I've had them all. Priests, politicians, peers, film stars, burglars, murderers."

"Nice work," McBride said.

"It's a living."

The specialist walked to the balcony and filled a pipe. McBride ran the tape back, finding what he wanted, sat and listened to Carson's agitated voice, then he cut the tape.

"He's identified himself as the stool pigeon in all this. He hasn't left himself a rag of cover. Why would he do that?"

"That's the technique, Mac. That's what they pay me for. Most of them wind up putting their names to things they wouldn't have believed possible. This is a big one. It adds a quarter million to our circulation."

"Have you talked money?"

"Not yet. We're still dickering. I was eight hours getting that lot. There's more juice to be squeezed yet."

"What is it worth?"

"Could be worth fifty thousand pounds."

"He'll earn it, poor bastard," McBride said. "Are you going to type up any of this?"

"Just the good guts. They'll want to see it at home, before they make a price."

McBride said, "You know, they could blow the Olympic movement wide-open? It could give the Communist bloc the excuse they need to start a breakaway?"

"That's not my line of country," the specialist said.

"Look, Des, I want you to do something. I want you to give me a carbon of your notes, to show Mathew C. Kaverly. These accusations could be wild. We can't wreck the last real International for a quarter million circulation."

The specialist looked hard at McBride, cupped a match to his pipe. "We're on different sides of the fence here, Mac."

McBride said, urgently, "It's just a chance that these accusations are wild. Why would the CIA want Santa Anna? This isn't a story about one of your peers or politicians. It's the whole Olympic movement. We've got to think of what it means, what it means to the athletes. They're not like us."

The specialist was a long time answering. "You get off a service cable, get it cleared and I'll hand you a carbon."

McBride got up. "I'll telephone. I'll book a call now."

"No," the specialist said, "I've coded them at home. By now they know what we've got. If you get the green light to give Kaverly a copy, I want to see it on a cable."

When he had gone, McBride stood on the balcony looking down over the buildings and the flags to the flame burning high against the sky, topping the dark walls of the stadium.

46

IN THE CLASHES of conflict, as the eliminating events crushed the hopes and devotions of years, or bore up the finalists in dread and excitement, the mood on the mountain became dangerously charged. Across the world, as the white-faced winners stepped up for their medals, striving to realize the moment in the quaking roars of acclamation they would hear in their ears for a lifetime, the mass media of the competing countries were busy tallying the scores. Expatriates of every kind and color reminded themselves of their origins as the headlines announced a win over the world by countries they had turned their backs on. Europeans negotiating in black Africa went soft-voiced into conference rooms after Ghana and Ethiopia stood for the golden glory. As the two great powers fought for the medals, the agitated officials and coaches worked on their agitated finalists.

In the Olympic Village those for whom it was over lay face down on their beds or savagely prepared to kick over the traces. In the stands, hotels and nightclubs the national groups hardened their eyes and fraternized with discretion. Following a disputed decision between East Germany and Great Britain, a skull and crossbones flew next morning on the standard of the Union Jack.

Sam Clark's under-the-carpet committee worked a twenty-four-hour alert.

"I can pick the trouble," Clark said. "It's getting so I can pick it. If it's India and Pakistan in the hockey final, we're going to need steel helmets on general issue."

Pip Harris said, "You can bet on India. They've owned the hockey Olympics for going on thirty years."

"I'm serious," Clark said. "If it comes out India and Pakistan I want a riot squad down there."

Clark was right. Pakistan won the hockey. It required tear gas and riot police to get the players off the field.

The athletes for whom it was over organized a road race, picking teams as children do, danced and swam together, stormed the old city at night like troops on leave. For most of them it was once in a lifetime. Each wanted a once-in-a-lifetime memory. Scott's roommate had been eliminated early in the javelin throw and convinced himself that the doctors had been wrong about his arm.

"All these pains I was getting. You remember what they told me? In the head, Barney. In the head's where you've got these pains. They robbed me, you know that?"

Barney was so depressed he was beyond cheering. At night he walked the balcony for hours, swinging the offending arm, throwing imaginary javelins. It was hard on Scott, who fretted with his own tightening nerves.

Early one morning, Barney prodded him awake. Scott had

een dreaming the Marathon, a bad dream, and came up ard on his elbows, sweating. It was the Marathon and the eld was going past while Scott labored in nightmare to catch hem on the bicycle ergometer he rode for the guinea-pig ests.

"Steady, boy." Barney was dressed, sitting on the edge of he bed, smiling. "You know what I just got me? A job in the fficial box. Right there in the stadium, in Kaverly's official ox, whamarooroo."

Barney had set his Olympic record, got himself something o remember.

The patriotism that seethed in the stands as the brass bands lared out the anthems was eased by the generosity of the thletes. A tiny Filipino in the 10,000-meter run, outclassed nd exhausted, deliberately chose the outside lane, running xtra distance, to permit the leaders to lap him on the inside nd not deny them the chance of a record.

In the 100-meter freestyle swim an Australian was given he decision over an American when the automatic timing locks failed to agree. In the frantic controversy that fol- owed, the judges stubbornly adhered to their arbitrary ruling, trongly supported by the Russian officials. On the winner's ais, streaming tears, the Australian tried to pull the Ameri- an up alongside him.

The athletes competed against the mark, the time or the istance, against what the human body could and could not lo. The coaches sweated out their reputations, the signing-on ees in coming contracts. The officials and organizers counted p their medals, bullied, cajoled and despaired.

It was as bad now as ever it would be, for any of them, no matter what happened after this. They closed their eyes on ear, tossed and sweated on fear, unlidded their eyes on fear vhen the sky lightened. The Marathon men waited for the lay, every face and voice hushed around them.

McBride sat in his hotel room typing from notes. He had alked that morning with the Marathon contestant from New Zealand.

"Sometimes I feel like being sick. Occasionally, I am. It's lot so good when someone is watching you vomit your heart ut. Running the Marathon is like taking part in some big roduction, a tragedy. It's worse than being an actor. An ctor gets stage fright just before he goes on. A Marathon nan can spend a week of hell before a big one. It's just you gainst the distance. You've got to finish even if you come in on your hands and knees. This is vital. If you finish, no matter what your time is, then you've beaten every man who dropped out. You're building up all this nervous energy and that's what makes you so short with people. You get to hate the crowd. There's definitely a sadistic streak in the crowd. They want to see you stretched on the rack. Anyway, you go onstage and you do your part as best you can and then you're in the middle of your death throes, and the bloody crowd is getting a great kick out of it. There's been all this talk about the altitude and that's there too, only nobody ever mentions it. There's been those other chaps in the hospital and you keep thinking about the distance. Then you worry about the weather, keep checking the temperature. It's been getting hotter every day for a week."

McBride typed on, remembering the man's face, the way his hands twitched on the table, the difficulty he had with the cup of weak tea. He remembered Mary Hayes in his Jermyn Street flat, stricken in the old chair, her cheek crumpled in anguish on the leather.

"What makes them run?"

McBride lifted his own big hands, spread the fingers, watched the shaking. He thought, If I feel like this, how must *they* feel?

The meanness in men is often dissembled by their appearance. In López it was overt. His ratty little face was dark and pockmarked; gold tips winked on his nicotine-blackened front teeth. He was shabby and furtive in spirit and shabby and furtive to look at.

The small leather business left him by his father had quickly failed López's grandiose plans of expansion. He was penniless at thirty, although he had had the foresight to marry earlier into a family with a little influence. His brother-in-law was a captain in the Army.

The Captain had contrived a job for López in the supply department of an American oil company, out of regard for his sister and exhaustion from López's borrowing and wheedlings. At the first audit Lopez was dismissed, without charges through the intercession of the Captain, more interested in saving his own face than his brother-in-law's skin. López briefly became a Castroite after that, but the prospect of a revolution that would bear him up in triumph and revenge was too remote to justify the risks and tedium of conspiracy. López was a man with his future behind him when the decision to back Pisarro was made in Washington. This altered his life and that of many others.

Of the ninety-four countries whose headlines counted the medals, while flood, famine, fire, coups and wars were moved to inside pages, Santa Anna made a unique golden count. In four years the plunder the conquistadors had dreamed of had reappeared in glittering heaps. The businessmen who crowded Olympic delegations, with national pride and idealism noisy in every utterance, had bloated in Santa Anna as they bloat elsewhere every four years. The contractors and subcontractors, the suppliers of a hundred materials and items, fell on this once-in-a-lifetime bonanza for which many of the athletes had beggared themselves.

When the Army under Pisarro had seized direction of the Games, López got an appointment to the Santa Anna Organizing Committee, managed by his desperate brother-in-law. The Olympic Village had not been sited then. Bueno had been unable to decide to dispossess the slum dwellers behind the old bullring until alternative accommodations were provided. Pisarro did not share this concern. In the first weeks of his power the order to level the settlement was given.

López, clerking on the Organizing Committee, had been one of the first two civilians in Santa Anna to get the news.

There were others shrewder than López who had sought the information. There would be fast access roads to the Village, gas, water, electricity, telephones. There would be playing fields, parks, sauna baths, restaurants and a hospital. The land around the Village would be the prime development area of the city. It had happened before, would continue to happen, outside some city every four years. It had happened at the Rome Olympics, had been questioned in Italian papers. In Rome the land around the stadiums had been bought up by the Vatican.

When the teams and tourists had arrived in Santa Anna and swarmed the city, López was already familiar in the expensive bars of the old Esmeralda and the new hotels on the heights. He sometimes dined and drank there with citizens of obvious importance. He smoked imported white tobacco by then instead of the local black and his teeth were the better for it.

It was a once-in-a-lifetime phenomenon that everyone shared, badge seller or bootblack. In the Village the athletes received living expenses. Nothing corrupted their amateur status.

As the Games continued, the fevers had heightened. East

and West fought for the medals. It wasn't over for López yet. His cup was to be filled to the brim.

In the beginning it had been the better man, the better woman. As final after final was decided on the heights, news of the sailing came up from San Bernardino, the equestrian teams on the plains below sweated their mounts to the last point scores. Now it was nation against nation, pride against pride. No longer was it Jazy running a heat, it was a Frenchman running the final. When the Marseillaise was played, the cheers were for the new glory of France. When Sweden won a Gold and a Silver in the same event, the Swedes wept and embraced in the stands.

Hour by hour, on the booming speakers, announcers kept the score. The boxing, fencing, gymnastics, skating, wrestling, canoeing, weight lifting: combats many spectators had never connected with the gladiatorial Olympic calendar.

On the looming tiers of the great stadium, in the crush of a hundred thousand bodies, the medal score of East against West was excitedly penciled on programs, the backs of cigarette packets.

The stress of the altitude had handicapped performance. It rankled in the press and the spectators who looked for records to be broken. Prostration among the athletes had become worryingly prevalent. As the heats passed to finals, rumors of sickness in the Village escaped the security screen. Competitors who had not unduly suffered in their events had later collapsed with dizziness, headache, cold perspiration and symptoms of tachycardia. Alec McBride noted in a dispatch that many athletes had suddenly become "very old" in behavior. The press became critical and uneasy. Sam Clark instructed Pip Harris to work up a background sheet.

"We need six hundred copies of that mimeographed by five o'clock," Clark said, looking at his watch.

"Not to worry." Harris was checking the piles of reference being prepared for him by assistants.

"You got anything from the coaches?"

"Not much. These coaches can't get away from themselves. Here's what I got from the Hungarian: "The coach must strip the athlete of everything, all inhibitions, all complexes, all religion and politics. The athlete must be psychologically freed. He must be shocked into realization of what he really is. If in the process of breaking down before building up, the athlete cannot take it, it is just as well to know because that athlete will never be great.' "

"What's that got to do with someone falling arse over tea-kettle?"

"Don't ask me," Harris said. "The German League of Sports reported that their committee of scientists and doctors established last year that physically fit athletes should suffer no permanent ill effects at this height."

"The ill effects shouldn't be permanent?"

"That's it."

"Great," Clark said. "That's just great." He sat down and lit a cigarette, looking moodily about. "You hear about that little Australian piece the chaperone wanted to send home?"

"Luba told me."

"She got off the hook."

"How come?"

"The way I hear it, they gave her a hard time. Wanted her to name names, bring charges. The kid's only sixteen years old."

Harris said, "The way I hear it, that would be quite a roll call."

"She stopped them dead."

"She did?" Harris was worrying over his papers.

"The first name she gave the chaperone was one of their own officials."

"That's the way the Games gets them," Harris said.

Clark got up and prepared to leave. "Six hundred copies by five."

"I've got it." Harris did not look up.

On the afternoon of the 400-meter relay the stadium began to fill an hour early. Nationalism was at a peak. In the bars and restaurants and hotel rooms the spectators had gossiped in special excitement. That morning, in the gymnastics, the East had turned the tables on the West. On the unofficial scoreboard America was only one Gold Medal ahead. From the Ambassador to the least important official, the American contingent was pinch-faced with hope and anxiety. This would not be man against man, the mark, the time or the distance. This would be team against team, nation against nation, on the scoreboard of East against West.

In the Village the Russian and American relay runners were sick with the exhortations of their coaches and officials. On that afternoon, in those circumstances, it would be war, not sport, in the stadium.

The young Russians and Americans beat on a common hope, a common fear, that made nonsense of the differences between their flags. Each had labored with the best in him to give his best on the day. Now they rested, hearing the exhortations, each in the same nightmare of dropping the baton.

In the blazing sun lapping waves of sound beat on the stadium walls. Perhaps there would be an upset; perhaps the British or French team would win. Across the heights at smaller stadiums, at pools, rings, mats, cycling tracks and fields, others for whom this was the greatest day knitted their foreheads in disappointment at the few straggled spectators who would be their witnesses.

The pistol cracked. The men with the batons leaped away. On the first leg, the spectators had already come to their feet, national blocs shouting their support in the garble of a dozen tongues. The batons slapped from hand to hand. Back and forwards on the cinders the runners grimaced with the pain the spirit feels when it tries to leap from the body. The polished batons glistened with sweat. Six inches ahead of the Russian the American last-leg man hurled himself to the finish.

As the time flashed to the announcement system, its boom was smothered in the shouts of the mob.

At the field's other end, a man stood and shook in a different excitement. Power rose in him. He ran forward, toward the athletes, waving his official red flag.

His name was López. He had been fired by an American oil company, humiliated for years by the hated *Yanquis*. Now his moment for revenge had come at last!

Grinning, his gold teeth glinting in the sun, he marked a foul. As the shouts of the mob changed to cries of anger and dismay, the long lines of riot police quickly filed across the stadium and lined up in front of the stands, their rifles held at the ready.

López shook his head and moved toward the other officials: by waving his flag he had disqualified the Americans for passing the baton short of the mark. . . .

The *Time* correspondent had dubbed it the medical Olympics. The amateurs of the world, upon whose bodies and devotion the spectacle was reared, submitted to the teams of scientists and medical specialists for whom they were movable laboratories. There was profit in them other than money. The East-West rivalry for medals had another projection in space. Human stress bubbling in brain and nerves, the oddity of one physiology against another, had become data to plot, as critical as the programming of orbits and the magic of metals that would plant one flag or other on the moon.

As the days progressed toward the Marathon, Scott Reynolds considered wryly that he was earning his guinea-pig money. Each morning on waking they took his pulse. Dr. Murrow, smoking his pipe, tested Scott's blood pressure after breakfast. Every second day Scott handed in a urine sample. Every four days Dr. Murrow would say, grinning fatly, "Vampire time, G.P. Reynolds." Before and after exercise the blood samples were tested for hemoglobin and hematocrit. Scott worked on the bicycle ergometer which had come to pursue him in dreams. The small blood vessels in his ears were examined with a spectrograph to measure by their color the oxygen used in the circulation. Blood acid was calculated. Every day with increased irritation as the Marathon ticked closer, Scott doggedly filled in the questionnaire. How did you sleep last night? What did you eat today? How do you feel? Have you had any gastric upset? Any irregular or unusual bowel movements?

For two nations, the earthbound athletes at Santa Ann foreshadowed the new astronauts.

The medical examination of women at the European Games had focused an attention that spilled over at Santa Anna. The Eastern bloc, which had suffered most by the new ruling, raised a question about the use of steroids to suppress the menstrual flow. Many of these preparations were banned as stimulators of performance. In the ludicrous wrangle that followed, steroids were disallowed to female athletes unless they had been regularly used for twenty-eight days. The matter was posted for international discussion before the next Olympics.

Clark said, "These officials are scraping the bottom of the barrel."

Harris said, "I think that is rather indelicately put, Sam."

While the athletes contended, the national officials fought a bureaucratic Olympics of their own. No quarter was given in this shadowy contest of maneuver and minor advantage. The fencing world had been shocked by a Chilean who had tumbled the European masters in the heroic épée event. As the Chilean progressed through the preliminary strips, quarter and semifinals, the European officials concerned with this classic buried their differences on the common alarm. By consensus a new examination was ordered of the Chilean's equipment. One of his six épées proved to exceed regulation by one fifth of an inch. This was the weapon, the Europeans claimed, used to defeat their champions. The Chilean was ordered to refight his contests. While the despairing young man gallantly fought to requalify and his maddened teammates clamored for a ruling that would permit him to fence for the Gold Medal subject to later ruling, the directors decided that the original timetable would stand. Time closed the Chilean off the scoreboard and the amateur épée championship of the world.

On the balcony of his suite Mathew C. Kaverly looked down over it all. They were going to give him the Nobel Peace Prize. When he learned it he had needed to be alone. He had held up the torch as faithfully as a human being could do. The tears of joy and humility ran down his cheeks.

The sun rose in a special anger as though it knew the day and had prepared for it. By noon men carried their jackets in the streets and women wore their lightest frocks. They had heard with shock about Lucibello. He had been unable to unwind after the excitement and stress, had taken too many sleeping pills. The Italians flew their flag at half mast. Lucibello and his Gold Medal had been jetted home to a hero's reception in Rome.

On the 26 miles 385 yards of the Marathon, official cars checked the preparations, the refreshment stations, the press boxes, the standby points for ambulances. A helicopter whirred and hovered, rehearsing its communications and the route. The TV cameramen sited themselves in a tangle of confusion and cables.

It was almost quiet in Santa Anna. While the sun burned. While everything and everyone waited on five o'clock.

The 26 miles 385 yards had been measured out and back from the great stadium. The route ran through Retiro Park, along the Avenida de la Independencia, past the Presidential Palace on the cliffs to the long, cruel grind on the airport freeway. From midafternoon, while motorcycle police patrolled, screaming their sirens, peasants and laborers from the tin mines beyond the mountains and up from the coast at San Bernardino packed this long, straight stretch, flashing their finery, sprawling, shouting, eating and drinking. At the return to the Avenida, painted arrows would point the survivors into the Calle Isabel la Católica, a cruel run over the cobblestones of the old city. Long before five o'clock, the bars with windows on the streets were crowded. Old women and children sat on the balconies overhead, or prepared by putting out chairs and taking in their washing. The sun burned; perspiration started quickly on their chests and in their armpits.

In the dressing rooms at the great stadium, coaches, officials, doctors and masseurs milled and worked on the Marathon men. On the cliffs of tiered seats above them, one hundred thousand spectators jammed and chewed on their excitement and impatience.

Bill Persons pushed Harry Hayes into a lavatory and slid the catch on the door.

"Sit down," he said.

He squatted to take Harry's feet in his hands, running his fingers in the tops of the heavily cushioned training shoes, testing for wrinkles in the socks. He checked the laces and knots, pinching at the tight leather.

"You're absolutely comfortable?"

"I'm all right." Harry Hayes could not bear the mad excitement that sweated and blazed in the face so close to his.

Persons croaked when he spoke. "This is it."

"Yes."

"Everything we've talked about, everything we've worked for. This is it. Now and forever."

"This is it."

"I've given you everything, haven't I? I squeezed my heart's blood out for you. I built you a mountain. Nobody will walk up that tunnel the way I've fixed it for you to walk."

Harry Hayes closed his eyes, swallowing on sharp, dry stones in his throat. The voice croaked and almost broke.

"Larazo ran himself to death at Stockholm, trying to win the Marathon for Portugal. I told you, remember? Dorandro Pietri displaced his heart half an inch, but he recovered. Remember how I told you? Jim Peters finished in a coma, but he finished. He got up off his hands and knees to win. You remember? You remember what I told you? Richards did not know he was leading in 1948, he was crying with hallucinations."

Harry Hayes opened his eyes, faint with fear. "Why are you . . . what do you mean . . . what are you telling me, Bill?"

"The two-hour Marathon. The thing that can't be done. The mark they talk about in whispers." The croaking voice broke, tried to speak and silenced. The fingers pinched helplessly at the boots.

"No," Harry cried, "I can't do it! Nobody can do it! For the love of God leave me alone!"

Persons' voice was wild now. "Yes, you can. You can. I know it. You can, Harry lad, you can. When they can't remember the others they'll remember us. They'll tell their kids about it in a hundred years. A two-hour Marathon. A new meaning to what we are. You will go out and roll back the dark."

In the cramped cubicle, pressing against the walls with his hands, Harry Hayes thrashed his head, his face bloodless. "No, I can't. Nobody can. It's close to four and a half minutes every mile."

"You can, you can. We're almost there now. A mountain —I built you a mountain. Everybody dies . . . everybody . . ."

Persons trailed his voice, the blazing eyes stunned. Then with absurd clarity his tones were cool and even, and he stood and spoke over Harry's head.

"You see, you can do it. Death is the adversary. You can do it if you are ready to run yourself to death."

Harry Hayes pushed past him. The door banged.

The dressing rooms had emptied. The sixty-two Marathon men had walked the tunnel with their handlers. Persons was still standing in the lavatory under the leaking cistern when the stadium shook for the start. Persons heard nothing. Spittle worked on his lips. He willed himself not to flinch, although all his body shook with protest. He had beaten them before, he would beat them again, all of them, all their kind everywhere. This was all they could do, it was all they knew, it was the trivial boundary of their power. The Kempei Tai guards twisted his arms again, forced the baton across his ankles. Persons shut his eyes and waited, a tiny smile on his lips. There was no limit. He knew it.

The long pain of waiting was over. In the pack of numbered singlets, in socks and out of socks, bare-headed and capped, barenecked and in knotted sweat cloths, the sixty-two Marathon men, brown, white, black, yellow, jumbled and ran the two circuits of the stadium into a crucible of the spirit where the lies and deceits and pretensions men live by cannot abide or signify. As they streamed into the tunnel and the roar died behind them, each man sought for his separate thrall. As they cleared the tunnel and saw the sky, Sunny Pintubi's chin lifted, seeking the horizon, the smoke of the far spinifex fire. As he moved away Scott Reynolds reached his hand and scrabbled at Sunny's singlet.

"No, Sunny. Take it easy."

At Retiro Park Sunny Pintubi ran head up before the pack, the favorite, Akbah of Ethiopia, making stride for stride at his shoulder. Harry Hayes fought for rhythm, his face pained, trying to pin his bolted imagination and will to the awful mark Persons had set him.

At the Presidential Palace an official wiped a handkerchief over his forehead and put the walkie-talkie to his ear.

"They're out of the Park." He looked at the sun burning hot and low. "They might pick up a breeze farther out."

"If there's no breeze here on the cliffs, there's not much chance of one farther out."

"You never know," the official said hopefully.

In the great stadium the announcement system crackled.

"While we wait for the starters in the men's 400-meter relay, here is some early news of the Marathon. The first competitor has just passed the 5-kilometer mark. It was Hayes of Great Britain and his time was 14 minutes 15 seconds."

The system bleeped and silenced, cut in again.

"There seems to be some mistake in the time. I'll announce the correction when I receive it. Next came Akbah of Ethiopia; Reynolds, United States; Pintubi, Australia; Anthony, Canada; and Kenji, Japan."

Under the trees on the concourse that circled the stadium, Bill Persons had stopped in his pacing. The changing smile wiped the lines from his face. He slapped his tweed hat against his legs. There was no mistake in the time, this was it, he was out there and going after it. Going after a two-hour Marathon. Persons began to pace again, seeing Harry, projecting his will to aid him, quivering with excitement. Persons laughed aloud. He felt alive enough to burst. For a while, he had felt funny. He couldn't remember the start.

Already as they hit the long rise on the Avenida the Marathon men could taste fear; the height and the heat had begun to bite. The pacemakers had not faltered. The distance between them and the pack had widened. Akbah was demonstrating the advantage of living and training at height. On the rise he and Hayes had altered stride, like a gear change, deepening their drives to deliver on the climb the pace they had measured on the flat. The helicopter whacked over the Avenida. The standing crowd packed deep on either side.

In the stadium the electric scoreboard flickered into lights:

MARATHON 10 kms
HAYES—G.B.—28 minutes 29.3 seconds
AKBAH—ETH.—30 minutes 14 seconds
REYNOLDS—USA—30 minutes 22.4 seconds

The announcer cut in over the scoreboard:

"We have just received word that Hayes of Great Britain covered the second 5 kilometers of the Marathon course in 14 minutes 14.3 seconds. His time for the first five miles was 22 minutes 50.1 seconds."

A cheer went up from the British section of the stands, joined by a mumble of surprise around the stadium.

On the green, athletes and officials shook their heads. Hayes and Akbah would bury each other.

They were out on the treadmill of the freeway, reaching for the halfway mark, the police pushing at the crush of wondering peasants. It was on them now, legs beginning to grow heavy and stiffen, pain rocketing through muscle and sinew, blisters widening and burning.

Scott Reynolds willed himself into place behind Akbah and Hayes. His heart beat steady and calm. He had turned to measure himself against the others, saw the struggle in their faces and bodies, knew it to be true: he was different. Nature has favored G.P. Reynolds. The vaulting joy which broke inside him had to be disciplined. There would be a time of ordeal and he was impatient for it, because nature had given him the victory. The pace was set by the men ahead; he was drawn along by their undertow. Scott smiled, his breath bubbling on his lips.

"Liz, here I come."

He ran like that thinking about her, to move his mind from the boredom of this treadmill, saving his will for what would happen.

On the apron on the airport entrance, where the dual freeway joined, the refreshment station was set with soft drinks, fruit juices, Coca-Colas, sponges soaking in basins. The TV teams and still photographers jostled and set their cameras for close-ups, as the spent, dehydrated men would pause to gag and swallow.

On the long freeway, the white dot of Hayes and the black dot of Akbah loomed larger, beating an unchanged rhythm in the slanting sunlight.

The officials stood between the tables, paper cups held out, staring into the rigid mask as Harry Hayes came in, leaning slightly on the turn. A hand extended to offer a sponge slapped his chest. He grappled to dismiss the restraint, the sponge caught in his fingers. Harry Hayes was gone, without a halt, running the cruel white treadmill of concrete back toward the end of something.

Akbah had broken his stride at the refreshment station, his hand ready for his need. The bulbs flashed and pictured his anguish of uncertainty as Harry Hayes beat for home. Then Akbah wheeled and followed, the spilled orange sparkling on his dark arms. Scott Reynolds turned tight, gaining yards. Sunny Pintubi at his heels. The officials stood, holding the unused cups, their faces slack with unbelieving.

The pack jumbled and stopped. One man ran past, faltered, turned back to gag and heave at a table, trying to bolt a drink.

On the long road, Harry Hayes lifted the sponge to his mouth.

The great stadium scuffled and stared as the women's relay runners prepared for the victory ceremony. Shadows were crossing the field. Above the walls the Olympic flame peaked like a candle in a breathless room. The bulbs on the scoreboard lit, obliterating every other interest.

MARATHON 30 KMS—HAYES—G.B.—1 HOUR 25 MINUTES 28.7 SECONDS

Then the voice of the announcer trembled with excitement:

"Hayes of Great Britain, we have just learned, clocked 1 hour 8 minutes 22.8 seconds to pass the 15-mile mark."

As a storm first ruffles the leaves before the wind swells the trees, excitement grew in the stadium.

Liz clasped Harvey Tonkin's arm. "What does it mean, Harvey? Where's Scotty? Listen to them. What does it mean?"

A man on Harvey's other side leaned across. "It means, lady, that either Hayes is going to burst like a balloon or there won't be anyplace anywhere so goddamned lonely not to know his name by tomorrow."

Harvey fumbled again to unscrew his hip flask. "Take a pull, Liz. Before this thing's over I'm likely to burst like a balloon myself."

Harry Hayes came off the treadmill and hit the climb up the Avenida to the old city. He was running in a hot, white light of agony. There was no hurt in his body. The agony was in his mind. A casual voice that did not belong to him or anyone else he ever knew talked flatly on the white light.

"This is it, of course, just here. I would say that if you survive the climb, a two-hour Marathon is possible. Of course, death is the adversary. Dorandro Pietri displaced his heart by a half inch. It didn't seem to matter."

Harry's face worked ghastly patterns. He was trying to ask the voice to identify itself. The while light did not answer.

It was 26 miles 385 yards. It was the Marathon, and there was only one man there.

On the freeway and at the beginning of the Avenida climb, the wreckage mounted like the casualties of a bombing. Starved for oxygen, crushed by the heat, broken by the dreadful irrational pace, the Marathon men staggered and dropped in a screaming of police and ambulance sirens. The helicopter whacking and hovering above the route reported twenty-four out of the sixty-two starters still running. Some still moved, they were not running. They lurched and walked on rubber legs, dragging at the air with their bent fingers. Where the course crossed the overpass, a heavy wire screen protected pedestrians from traffic. The German champion broke there, walked quite steadily off the road, began to claw up the wire.

In the white light the flat voice sounded.

"This would appear to be it. I believe these are cobbles we are now running on. Goodbye. I'm going to have a milk shake."

Akbah almost fell on the cobbles, his eyes rolling, bulged from his head. He whimpered as he pitched every cell in his body toward the blurred, distant figure. It was no good. The boiling blood was draining from his heart. The awed watchers heard Akbah loudly shout one word: "No." Then he shambled sideways and went over, his head in the entrance of a bar.

The Ethiopian had been pulled off the cobbles, milk and brandy at his sobbing mouth, when Scott Reynolds dragged past, tongue protruded on his teeth. The watchers in their own silence, the heat awed out of them now, heard the shuffling before Sunny Pintubi appeared, followed by the Japanese. For a long time nobody else followed.

Big Jim Harcourt and Charlie Gilmour had scarcely spoken. Cigarette butts littered at their feet. They waited as many years ago they had waited for different things, hard lines at their mouths, eyes cold at the scoreboard, as though it were the first light before dawn and they waited for relief or attack.

390

The announcement system squealed a high note and set-tled.

"Here is an announcement concerning the Marathon. At the twenty-mile mark, Harry Hayes of Great Britain had increased his lead. His time, 1 hour 31 minutes 14.2 seconds. The time is not in doubt. It has been recorded electronically."

In another box the BBC reporter, relaying to Britain by satellite, said into his microphone, "God Almighty." He paused, "Sorry about that. If you were here today you would forgive me. Harry Hayes, our own Iron Man, is within reach of a two-hour Marathon. Is it humanly possible to keep up the pace which has put seven men in hospital? Today, in Santa Anna, athletic history could be made."

His vision was hot with blood. The leaning houses on the cobbled lanes were bloody with sunset, the sky which opened ahead fattened with bloody clouds. The sun balanced on the mountain and flamed a congested eye. The houses shimmered and bent toward him over the cobbles, as though they were leaning from the waist. Like Akbah he felt the blackened blood draining from his heart, leaving an awful cold, while demons shrieked inside his head to burst his eardrums. He was dying. In a few steps it would be over. It was too late to stop, had he known how. Perhaps he had stopped. Perhaps he was at rest somewhere. It did not matter. In that place it would be merciful. Harry Hayes stepped into the loving darkness, into the merciful peace. It folded and trapped him. He had no body, no lineaments. He was a single silver thread and from it music came.

She was hard to see, hard to hear, a tiny something in the blackness.

"Harry, it's Mary."

It was silly. There was no Harry. Just a single silver thead making music.

"Don't go. You've not seen your baby yet. Your son."

It was lighter about her. She held a child. He tried to smile. A single silver thread smiling.

"We love you."

He shook his head; he had one now.

"You've proved it, darling. You can be a god if you must. But don't leave us, don't leave us. We love you, love you, love you."

The black was lightening to gray, but he could not see her.

"Mary, don't go. Mary, come back. Where's the baby?"

He could not see her and terror rose. The gray lightened and lightened. Persons filled the void she had left.

"Lazaro ran himself to death at Stockholm. I told you, remember? Yes, you can, you can. When they can't remember the others, they'll remember us, us, us, us, us. Death is the adversary. You can do it if you are ready to run yourself to death."

Again like Akbah, they heard the stumbling man shout "No."

The light came back, the buildings straightened. He saw the cobbles clearly.

Scott Reynolds was jarring, as though one leg was wooden. Black waves had been lapping in him. Something was wrong. He was a machine of polished whirring parts, and something there kept jamming. He jarred all over when it happened. His head was clamped in a vise. He tried to scream, but could not. His brains were bubbling. He pushed himself off the wall, at the hands that touched and held him. The bubbling ceased. The pain flew away. Scott saw the sunset sky open ahead and moved slowly to meet it.

The electric scoreboard began to spell. All movement, all sound, ceased in the great stadium.

MARATHON 40 KMS—HAYES—G.B.—1 HR. 53 MIN. 48 SEC.

The announcer's voice was breaking.

"In the Marathon, Hayes of Great Britain is the only runner so far to pass the 40-kilometer mark. Reynolds, United States; Pintubi, Australia; Kenji, Japan, are behind, about to leave the old city. The rest, the survivors, are nowhere. Harry Hayes, this incredible athlete, who has shattered Abebe Bikila's historic Marathon at Tokyo, is now approaching the stadium. I would like to say . . . here, today, I would like to say . . ."

The announcer's voice choked off.

There was silence. Then the helicopter whacked over the stadium and hovered. They let out their breath in a gush like a moan. In the packed tiers, one hundred thousand spectators slowly pushed to their feet. Officials hurried out and formed up at the entrance tunnel to direct those who finished to the tape.

Persons had told him he would know revelation, a spiritual insight the nothing-men could never suspect. It had been on him ever since he had come away from the darkness. His whole life had been there, past, present and future. The past, the present, the future of everything that had ever lived, back to the first ameba, forward to the end of the universe. He knew now that the most and the best that could be known is the single comfort of love. Love for stones, flowers, animals, rats, ants, other men and the stars. Requited love, unrequited love, love without terms or conditions. Persons had it, he could see that. But something had addled Bill's love. He had wanted Harry to run himself to death. It wasn't enough for Bill to love. Bill wanted to make God better.

Harry had taken love, returned nothing. Now he would make a gift. He came off the cobbles to cross the Avenida to the packed hysteria waiting at the stadium entrance, rocking the world with their roars. He stopped on the last of the cobbles, weaving, one leg out to prop him. His head turned while the roar screamed on another note. He saw it all, fixed and forever. The black mouth of the tunnel, the floodlights that made a glowing bowl of light above the stadium, the crabbing helicopter, the Olympic flame peaked like a candle in a breathless room. He turned once to the alley that cut away beside him, once more to the crowd. Then he nodded, tried to smile on the awful, open-mouthed sawing of his struggle for breath, staggered into the alley and vanished.

It was minutes before anyone did anything. Alec McBride was out of the press box on the Avenida, as two officials sprinted from the stadium. He was into the alley well before them, held the reeling boy inside the wall of a courtyard as the shouting officials ran by.

"Do you know what you are doing?"

"Yes."

"Can you get back to the Village on your own?"

"Yes. Cable Mary, Alec, tell her—"

"You can tell her yourself," McBride said. He smiled into Harry's dawning face.

As the minutes passed, the disturbance in the stadium mounted. Several times the address system had rung, crackled, cut out. They were sitting again now, or standing to cup their mouths and shout. The helicopter rose suddenly, and whacked out of sight over the entrance tunnel. When the announcement came it was disordered, without preliminary, almost as though they eavesdropped.

"Oh, oh, this is terrible. Harry Hayes, Hayes of Great Britain, has taken the wrong route, almost at the stadium entrance. With the greatest Marathon ever run in his grasp, Hayes, tottering with exhaustion, lost himself in the old city. This is unbelievable. Nothing like it has happened since Jim Peters ran the wrong way at Rome. Hayes was running a two-hour Marathon. Now, incredibly, tragically, on the very threshold of glory . . ."

Other voices and sounds clamored for notice, a confused incoherent background. Then the announcer, shouting, his voice shrill:

"And now here comes Reynolds of the United States. He is crossing the Avenida. I don't have his time, but it could well be inside Abebe Bikila's record. Reynolds has crossed the Avenida. Here he comes, the winner of the 1968 Olympic Games Marathon. Reynolds, United States. Keep your eyes on the tunnel."

Harvey Tonkin caught Liz as she slumped against him. Tears streamed down her face. He struggled up, an arm about her, as once again the stands came to their feet and the helicopter whacked over the wall.

He was jarring again. The whirring polished machine parts were jamming, stiffening his leg, jarring every nerve and cell in his body. His brain was swelling, paining as if it were in a vise. Scott hit the wall in the tunnel, rolled on it, came off, as his momentum carried him down the incline. He came out of the track into the floodlit arena where the officials mouthed and pointed, their voices drowned in the crush of a hundred thousand shouting throats. He buckled and hit the cinders with one knee. He could see nothing, hear nothing; there was only the swelling, bursting torment in his head. As the stands gasped he pushed himself up. His hands scrabbling at his ears, and half bent, he trod in circles on the cinders. Then he stopped, took a few steps, straightened and began to run on their roared relief.

When the track bent and the tape waited on the straight opposite the official stand, Scott Reynolds straightened and drove for speed. He did not turn with the corner. Upright and driving, Scott angled across the cinders. He did not hear the great gasp of apprehension. Blind, lost in the effort, running from the agony that seared him, Scott Reynolds crashed face first, into the concrete wall. Above him they heard distinctly the breaking of bones, like the snapping of kindling wood. He was sprawled on his back in the cinders, one knee slowly flexing to draw the quivering leg up to his stomach. Under the fair curled hair the face was a pulped mask of jetting blood.

They hardly understood the meaning of it when Sunny Pintubi ran slowly out of the tunnel, the spinifex fire blazing and smoking in his brain, head up, blue eyes as glazed as jellies. The helicopter was settling as the crumpled body in the staining blanket was rushed to meet it. The helicopter was rising and turning when Sunny Pintubi broke the tape, head up, still running, one slow, trembling footfall upon another, unable to know—unable to make the decision—when to stop.

47

FIFTEEN DAYS AGO they had run the flame across the sugarcane flats from San Bernardino to where the sunset met the moonless night and had climbed the flame up the mountains. Now a half-grown moon was in the sky over the floodlights and searchlights that beamed and swung in the stadium. The young lieutenant of engineers, his hair blowing, peeped out from behind the great copper bowl high above the west wall and waited on his cue.

The teams had marched again for the closing ceremony, not divided by nations now. The young men and women walked together, their arms about each other, exchanging blazers, hats, flags, personal souvenirs. As they opened their throats on the tender Olympic hymn, the lieutenant slowly closed the oil cock on the torch. In the soft, symbolic glow of the dying flame the Olympic flag came down, the floodlights and searchlights dimmed. As the flame shortened in the bronze bowl, thousands of flaring, flickering newspaper torches lit up the dark walls of the arena. In the bronze bowl the Olympic flame continued to its death. The scoreboard lit.
FAREWELL SANTA ANNA.
GOOD-BY UNTIL MUNICH
The paper torches charred into black ash. The floodlights and searchlights beamed and swung. The press stand was almost empty, like a wedge cut from a cake in the stadium. The old man's throne in the official box was empty.

A few lights spotted in the restaurants and administration buildings on the darkened spread of the Village. Only the hospital was brightly lit. At the guarded gate, reinforced by riot police, reporters and photographers crowded. From the communications room at the press center the first priorities had flashed:

TRAGEDY STRIKES IN HORROR MARATHON.

Sam Clark's car hooted and edged its way through the newsmen. In the guardhouse and at the drop-gate barrier, police unslung their rifles. A sergeant hurried forward, his torch shining. Clark tried to open the door against the jam of bodies firing questions through the lowered window.

"How is Reynolds?"

"Make a statement, Clark."

"What does Kaverly say now?"

Shaking his head, Sam Clark pushed to the drop gate, cordoned by the police. He saw the small figure reel backwards, warded off by the flat of a rifle, and then reach toward him over the policeman's shoulder.

Harvey Tonkin's round, wrinkled little face implored him in the moonlight. "Sam, for God's sake, you have got to get us in. I have Liz here. Scotty will want to see her. You've got to get us in."

Clark could not see the girl. "Get her in the car."

The drop gate lifted to pass the car, slammed again into place.

Clark stood with his arms raised. "Listen," he shouted, waiting to be heard. "Quiet down. Listen."

The questioning broke out again as the newsmen pressed against the police. Clark kept his arms up, shaking his head, waiting.

"There's no good hanging about here. There is going to be no statement made about anything, here. Right now I don't know any more than you do. As soon as we have something official, you'll get it at the press center. Don't give me a hard time, Crissake."

They were still shouting as Clark bundled into the car.

They watched the car go, milling and talking among themselves, lit cigarettes and signaled waiting taxis. Others settled down, continuing the wait. They paused, heads tilted, listening and staring at each other.

"What's that?"

Away to the right and above them, the Olympic hymn had begun to swell. Silently, they watched and listened. The great bowl of reflected light illuminating the sky above the stadium dimmed and darkened. For a minute the Olympic flame was all there was, a flame suspended high against the night. Then it began to shorten. In a few minutes the dark put it out.

On the new bench in the new hospital they sat in the hurrying corridor. Harvey held Liz by the hand, squeezing her hand as he squeezed his eyes to press the tears back. She sat taller than Harvey, staring before her dumbly, her slanting eyes wide and dull and hot as fever. Her lips worked a little, making no sound. She sat very straight and very still, holding tightly to Harvey's sweated hand.

He saw Schultz and the army officer distant in the corridor, walking fast and soft on the rubber. Schultz was carefully putting on his hat. They were passing as Harvey jerked up, reaching out his free hand.

"Harvey." Schultz looked quickly at the girl. "Just a minute, Colonel."

"You've seen him? You've seen Scotty?"

Schultz turned his head, got composure. "It's all over."

"All over? What do you mean? What's all over?"

"Scott is dead."

Harvey held Schultz's sleeve. His face broke, his head shook, he stared up. "No, not Scotty. Scotty isn't dead."

"Not so loud," Schultz warned.

"He is dead?"

"They are doing a postmortem."

Tears rushed on the little man's face. He was turning to Liz when she sighed and slumped against him.

A nurse hurried over, called for assistance, lifted Liz to lay her on the bench. A doctor chafed her wrists, put his stethoscope to his ears.

"It's only a faint," he said, and sent the nurse scurrying for a stimulant.

Harvey Tonkin was backed against the wall. He pointed a shaking hand at Bob Schultz. "We did this, buddy. We fixed it in Bombay for old Scotty to die."

Bob Schultz blanched, glancing uneasily about the filling corridor.

Harvey's voice loudened. "We fixed it for Scotty to die here."

Schultz slammed Harvey against the wall. "Shut up. Do you hear? Shut up."

"We did it," Harvey sobbed. "We did it."

"Get a hold on yourself. Shut up."

Schultz said urgently to Colonel García, "Call the car. We've got to get them out of here."

Alec McBride crossed the lobby to the desk, collected his keys and a cheap envelope marked on the back with the crest and address of a hotel in the old city. At his room he kicked the door shut and went directly to the telephone.

"Addie? Mac. Anything new out there on Reynolds? No, nothing at the Village. Hayes is resting. He has been passed fit, but is too upset to see anybody. As you say, Addie, it's easy to imagine. Call me if anything breaks."

McBride sat back smiling. The envelope was bent in his hand. He turned it over. It was addressed: To Harry Hayes, care Alec McBride.

The handwriting was flourished, strong and looping. For a minute, McBride could not unblur his memory. He had received a note in this hand years ago from Bill Persons. McBride's curiosity raced. He had searched for Persons, sick and fearful for him. McBride smoothed the creased cover, held it up to the light. The letter was thin. He argued against his need to know, decided he had earned it. He had spun himself into this web long ago, tracking Persons to his past, the meaning of him. He had earned it by his involvement with Harry, with Mary Hayes and Gabby Charlton. McBride opened the envelope with a match.

The note was unheaded, unsigned.

> Perhaps, when he is old enough, you will teach him some of what we learned. I told you, didn't I, lad?

Alec McBride sighed heavily and leaned his head on the back of the chair, wondering at the ceiling. He got up and walked aimlessly, returning to stand over the table and read the note again. The mournful brown eyes were moist. He sniffed through the crooked nose and walked again. In the bathroom he ran the taps, leaning on the bowl, watching the splash of the water. He looked up into the mirror, inspected his image, and smiled widely and mockingly because the words were already there.

"They're not like us," McBride told his image. "You know that, don't you?"

In the house surgeon's office, Hans Stein stood at the small window, looking out, smoking in sharp agitation. Only the spotlight on the desk was lit. Outside its radiance shadows fell. The old man and the surgeon sat opposite each other, half lit, half shadowed in the angled beam. Stein's thin face was masked to the bone by the stretched, gray skin. He wore the Santa Anna seersucker suit which flapped on him with a scarecrow's absurdity. The old man's cluttered breathing rasped in the still room. The hand before him on the desk was knotted into a fist as the surgeon reported.

"A linear fracture of the skull was present with a thin, extradural hemorrhage and contusion of the brain substance together with a large recent brainstem hemorrhage and an associated basal—"

The old man banged his fist. "What does it mean?"

"In simple terms, you might say, death was caused by a brain hemorrhage."

"The wall, he ran into the wall."

"Most unlikely. He struck the wall with his face. The conditions described could be due to exaggerated demands on the oxygen-carrying capacity."

"The wall," the old man shouted. "The wall."

The surgeon glanced over his half-glasses and continued evenly. "There are also certain vascular indications. Changes in the structure of the arterial walls. These changes could have been present for some time, accelerated by stress."

"He wasn't fit." The old man's jowls were reddened in the light. "He wasn't fit. He ran into the wall."

Stein said, in a wispy voice, almost as though speaking to himself, "The altitude killed him. It was stress."

The old man banged his fist, shouting. "No. The wall, I tell you. He wasn't fit. He ran into the wall."

Stein said, "The wishful thinking is over, Mathew."

The surgeon kept his head down.

The old man's breathing loudened. "Put that on the paper: the wall. Not the altitude. The wall."

The surgeon said nothing, glanced at Stein and back to the autopsy report.

Stein's wispy voice sounded again from the shadow, almost dreamily. "Nothing can be changed. It's over. It can't be called back now to cancel half a line."

There was a knock, and a nurse put her head in. "The American officials are getting impatient, Doctor."

"You will have to excuse me," the surgeon said. "I can't keep them waiting any longer." He lifted his papers and hurried round the desk.

"The wall. You hear me?" the old man bellowed, swinging in his chair.

Stein dropped his cigarette and trod on it. He buttoned the jacket that hung dismally off his bony shoulders.

"There is nothing more we can do here, Mathew. I am leaving."

"You get out there," Kaverly said. "You're a doctor. You get out there and tell them about the wall."

"No, Mathew. I'm finished."

The old man lifted his head, his breath soaring.

"I'm finished, Mathew. I should have stopped all this years ago. I'm finished. Finished with you, finished with the movement."

The old man moved violently, scraping the chair, trying to push himself up. Stein had passed him on his way to the door.

"Go on, then, get out. I don't need you. I don't need anyone. Don't think I don't know. Don't think I don't know you've been one of the plotters."

The door clicked softly. The old man was alone in the shadowed room.

He had locked himself into his suite, unplugged the telephones, for he could no longer bear their shrilling. For hours he had lumbered through the rooms, going over it all in his head. He found it hard to hold his thoughts. One thought lapsed into another. It was the wall. The man had not been fit. They were goading him again, as they had goaded him before. It had not come to anything. It would not come to anything now. It was over and he had proved them wrong. The man had run into the wall. It was better this way. If it had to happen, he was glad of it. It had made Hans Stein show his hand. He had shown his true colors at last. Now, a fresh start could be made with a new chancellor. A man like himself, a man he could trust not to plot against him.

The old man was hungry. He wanted to order up food, but was reluctant. The press would be out there, waiting in the passage. He stood at the telephone table trying to make up his mind. The big brown envelope was marked MOST URGENT, MOST CONFIDENTIAL. The old man opened it, thinking about the food. A letter lay on the pages of the typescript.

Mathew C. Kaverly
Dear Sir,
Since these articles are so damaging, I feel it only fair that you should see them before publication. My editor has authorized me to offer you every facility to reply, either now or after the articles are published. I can assure you that as far as possible, every item has been checked for authenticity.
I await your comments with interest.
Sincerely,
ALEC McBBIDE

The old man sat down frowning and turned to the first page of typescript. It was headed "Santa Anna, the Crooked Olympics. As told by Conrad Carson, former Assistant to the International Olympics Committee Chancellor."

Big Jim Harcourt and Charlie Gilmour were still too stunned to celebrate. Now that it was over and belonged in some way to the world, the simple fact of it and their own part in it were difficult to grasp. They sat in the busy lounge, sipping their drinks, going over it all from the beginning. Gilmour had received a telephone call from Sunny. The chairman of the National Fitness Council of Australia had offered him a post as counselor with a franchise to encourage other aborigine athletes.

Harcourt had his bruised leg stretched out, balanced on the heel. When Sunny had held up his arms on the dais, Harcourt had lost his head and pushed out to the gangway. When the band impulsively struck up "Waltzing Matilda," following the national anthem, he had tried to storm the barriers.

Harcourt said, "That will be some party the team is giving him."

"Funny how it turned out. I mean with Reynolds. Sunny sounded pretty sick about it. That Yank was a good mate to Sunny."

"The Yank will be all right. You can't do much damage running into a wall. Can you imagine old Drewie when he gets the news?"

They thought about Drewie.

Gilmour shook his head. "You wouldn't read about it."

"That's for sure."

Harcourt banged his glass on the table. "You know what I'm going to do, Charlie?"

"What?"

"I am going to turn over my share of the winnings to Aboriginal Welfare." He paled. He had astonished himself.

Gilmour stared at him.

"You don't have to look at a man like that."

"You mean it?"

"I bloody well said so, didn't I?"

"You wouldn't read about it," Gilmour said, his voice awed.

After a silence, Harcourt coughed. "Of course, that's less the stake money and the cost of the trip and the few quid I'm down being away."

The old man had been weaving his head, moaning long before he turned the last page. He sat collapsed then, his head shrunken down in his shoulders. The migraine lashed at him, spinning black clouds in his mind. He tried to rise, fell back, sat with closed eyes, his chin weaving on his chest. Then he straightened. He stretched an arm and dashed the typed sheets off the table. Panting, dragging his feet, his corded neck stretched, the old man fumbled to unlock the door. In the lobby, bumping his way through the guests, he neither saw their surprise nor heard the desk clerk call his name. The heavy body leaned forward. The feet shuffled along the floor. He was out under the half-grown moon, bumping unheeding up the thronged pavement.

It was a long way and his feet did not direct him. He shuffled through a long dream which was all his life and sometimes the dream arched into nightmare. He heard the bird music and pursed his lips to whistle. He shuffled in the long dream, undirected by his feet, while the great stadium moved to intercept him. In the black tunnel he wondered at the mocking echoes which loudened and rasped his going. It was very black. He shuffled on toward the light.

A wind sighed in the empty arena, as though it was prisoner of the walls. The old man stood near the center of the field and thought he heard the bird music. He pursed his lips to whistle back. The black-painted steps that reached to the sky were opposite him. The old man shuffled forward, whistling.

It was a long climb. There were hundreds of steps. He failed often while the effort pounded his heart and curdled his belly with nausea. Once, he almost slept, sprawled on the steps, continuing to dream the dream. He could not remember where the steps were leading him. He thought it might be back to the desert, to the peace under Mount San Jacinto.

"Karl," the old man called. "Chocolate time, Miss Kaverly."

His heart was paining. He laid his hand on it, frowned at the pounding, swayed to his feet and climbed.

He was crawling, when the wind that topped the wall blew into his face and hair.

He closed his eyes and rested. The moon had shifted when he awoke. The bronze bowl was no longer in shadow. He reached out and pulled himself up.

The bronze was cold now. The old man stood, blown by the wind, his arms flung about the bowl, cooling his face on the polished metal. It was strange to be floating in the sky, looking down on the lights of the world. He raised his eyes and recognition came. Nightmare squealed in his head. The torch was out. They had put out the torch. At last, he had been beaten by evil.

"No," he whimpered, "no." And he weakly scrabbled a fist on the metal. When he opened his eyes, he saw the oil pipe in the bowl. And the box and the tapers and the matches.

It was hard to think over the pain and the nightmare. He shut his eyes and while they were shut it came to him as softly and swiftly as a bird alighting on a twig. It was so simple, so easy, that he smiled. They had put out the torch, because he had not been watching. He would light it again. That was all that was required. The old man shook his head, tears on his cheeks, wondering at the simplicity of it.

He had his strength now. High in the sky he chuckled as he moved. He turned the cock. Above him, slick oil spurted into the bowl.

Luba sat at Sardar's feet on the balcony, her head on his knee, his hand against her face. The stadium below was a monument of light and shadow in the moonbeams.

"Enough, now. One should not eat sorrow all at once."

"I am frightened, Sardar."

"Of what?"

"Of dying. Of being alone. He was so beautiful. Now, *pfft*, there is nothing, no?"

"It is the wheel, Princess."

"The wheel?"

"The wheel of life, the wheel of death. A Hindu concept."

"Sometimes I dream of babies," Luba said.

"That, too, is the wheel."

Luba lifted her face. "Sardar?"

"Yes?"

"I don't want to be alone anymore. Perhaps alone when some bad thing should happen."

"So?"

"I wish to marry someone. I think you would be best for me, no?"

Addie, the photographer, was used to being bored with McBride's moods. When McBride glowered over his glass and was rude to barmen and waiters, it was enough for Addie. He would finish his drink and leave. Addie had never seen McBride drunk this way, happily, optimistically, lifting his eyebrows to some interior monologue, smiling foolishly into the bar mirror.

"Anything on Reynolds yet, Mac?"

McBride shook his head.

"I'm off to the press center. Take it easy, can't you?" He walked away, looking back with a touch of worry.

When Addie had gone McBride went to the washroom and splashed his face under the cold tap. Then he took the elevator to Gabby Charlton's floor. Outside Mary's door he put his ear to the wood, oblivious of the curious stares of others walking the passage. Gabby's door was ajar. McBride pushed it open. She was on the telephone, her voice high and hard.

"I insist on an answer. Mrs. Hayes just happens to be my daughter. I insist you call again immediately." She cupped the receiver when she saw McBride. "Alec, Mary refuses to answer the telephone. Do you know who she's got in there with her? That wretched milkman. I've been half out of my mind." She uncupped the receiver. "I don't care what instructions have been given. I'm her mother. Connect me to my daughter at once."

Gabby gasped, stared unbelievingly at the instrument. "Mary won't take my call. Her own mother."

McBride took the telephone from her and put it on the cradle. "Why can't you leave them alone?" he asked sadly.

"Leave them alone? That wretched man? After everything he's done? He can sweep in here after everything and lock himself in with my daughter and grandson?"

"His son," McBride said. "His wife."

"No!" Gabby's voice was quite desperate. "They're not his. He deserted them. I won't have it. I won't have it, do you hear?"

There was sherry on the table. McBride poured two glasses. "Here," he said, giving one to Gabby. He tried his with distaste.

He rubbed his crumpled nose and inspected Gabby, who had risen to smooth her skirt and fumble agitatedly for a cigarette.

"What can they be doing?" she asked. "He's been in there for ages. What can they be doing?"

"For one thing, Mary will be showing him his son."

"It's not his son. He's got no right. I brought that child up. He's never had a father."

"He's got one now, Gabby."

"The man's mad. Quite mad. He even got lost in his wretched footrace."

McBride shook his head sadly. "You'll never learn, will you? From now until doomsday you'll never understand."

She took no notice. "He got lost, and his precious Persons won't have him. That's why he came here looking for comfort."

"He didn't get lost, Gabby. He found himself. He had it and he didn't need it. He gave it to Mary and the baby in the truest way that he could. Harry was as far above us as the gods today. He's a great man. There are only a few of him in the world. There'll be nothing in all the rest of his life that he won't be able to do if he wants it."

She wrinkled her forehead at him, tried to understand, and then abandoned the effort. "Stuff and nonsense. Sometimes I think you're as unbalanced as he is. What can they be doing in there?"

"Right now," McBride said deliberately, "they will be in bed in each other's arms."

Her face crumpled, her eyes closed; she even put out fingertips on the table to steady herself.

McBride went to the wall and tapped it. "Through there. Your precious daughter, Gabby. If you put your ear to the wall you might hear her."

"What a horrible thing." Gabby choked, staring at him. "What a horrible thing to say."

"Some of what you've missed, Gabby."

Gabby's lips trembled, blood filled her cheeks, a hand went to her throat.

McBride said, "I used to wonder about Mark Charlton. Mark and his women. You're a teaser, Gabby. You've been a teaser all your life. Mark didn't cheat you. You cheated Mark. At heart you're a stitched-up puritan. Just look at yourself. You're slavering, thinking about Mary."

"How horrible. How dare you!" She could hardly speak the words. "How can you bear to say such horrible things?"

McBride was ridiculously calm. "Do you remember what I told you the night they were married? What it is you need? I've been thinking about it. Now is the time, Gabby."

She shrank away. "Don't be silly."

McBride took off his jacket and slung it on a chair, finished his sherry and undid his tie.

"You've gone out of your mind. You wouldn't dare. Put that coat on at once."

McBride smiled cheerfully and unbuttoned his shirt. "Both sides of the wall, Gabby. It's symbolic."

"My God, you must be drunk. You wouldn't dare."

"You can always call the manager. You know, in some ways I'm a bit of an athlete myself."

She sagged, began to shake.

Calmly, fatefully, even amused, Alec McBride swept the stunned woman off her feet. Holding her, while she stared up helplessly and incredulously, McBride sought the bedroom. In passing he knocked on the wall between the suites.

"Here we go," he said.

The old man had spilled the matches. The wind blew them on the platform. He searched for them, crawling, feeling with his fingers against the ledges. He held his breath in concentration. The oil gushed into the bowl. He found the box. The matches flamed and blackened. Urgently, humping his shoulders for protection, he struck more sticks, touched flame to the taper. The taper hissed, flared yellow in the wind.

The old man climbed the tiny metal ladder, leaned into the bowl, touched the flame to the jet. The flame sickened on the spilling oil. The taper blackened where it touched. He leaned there in the wind, whimpering his disappointment.

Crouched, he pawed at the oil cock until the wheel opened no further. By the streaming flame of the taper he saw the smaller wheel that ran the gasoline for pre-ignition. The shaking fingers on the humped hand, spotted by age and the desert sun, were hard to manage. He scraped a knuckle turning the wheel. A tear of blood rose on the broken skin. The old man sat in the wind on the wall in the sky, his legs thrust around the bowl, resting his head on a metal leg.

He had forgotten what he must do. The dying taper reminded him, shaking in his hand. The blackened tip curled toward him in curiosity. He had great difficulty pulling himself up, treading the narrow metal steps again.

He leaned over and reached with the taper but his arm could not support its own wavering weakness. His head and belly were full of spinning dark clouds. The old man clutched at the sides of the bowl, stepped over the lip and sat there. He did not feel the slick black oil that rose above his ankles. He looked down once at the moon-whitened arena. Almost absently he touched the taper to the jet.

In the city of tears and laughter they saw the flame leap into the sky.